INQUIRY JOURNAL

UNITED STATES
HISTORY & GEOGRAPHY

GROWTH & CONFLICT

Joyce Appleby, Ph.D.
Alan Brinkley, Ph.D.
Albert S. Broussard, Ph.D.
James M. McPherson, Ph.D.
Donald A. Ritchie, Ph.D.

Mc Graw Hill Education

COVER: (t to b, l to r)NPS Photo; DNY59/Getty Images; luca amedei/Shutterstock; Michal Jastrzebski/Shutterstock; Comstock Images/Alamy

mheducation.com/prek-12

Send all queries to:
McGraw-Hill Education
8787 Orion Place
Columbus, OH 43240

ISBN: 978-0-07-906340-3
MHID: 0-07-906340-3

Printed in the United States of America.

9 10 11 12 13 QVS 23 22 21 20

Table of Contents

CHAPTER 5

A More Perfect Union 135

ESSENTIAL QUESTIONS

Why do people form governments? • How do new ideas change the way people live? • How do governments change?

CHAPTER 6

The Constitution 157

ESSENTIAL QUESTIONS

Why do people form governments? • How do new ideas change the way people live?

CHAPTER 7

The Federalist Era 173

ESSENTIAL QUESTIONS

What are the characteristics of a leader? • Why does conflict develop? • How do governments change?

CHAPTER 8

The Jefferson Era.......................................195

ESSENTIAL QUESTIONS

How do governments change? • How does geography influence the way people live? • Why does conflict develop?

CHAPTER 13

The Spirit of Reform 325

ESSENTIAL QUESTIONS

Why do societies change? • What motivates people to act? • How do new ideas change the way people live?

CHAPTER 14

Toward Civil War 351

ESSENTIAL QUESTION

Why does conflict develop?

CHAPTER 19

A Changing Society 497

ESSENTIAL QUESTIONS

Why do people move? • How do new ideas change the way people live? • Why do societies change? • What are the causes and consequences of prejudice and injustice?

Dear Student,

Most of us are curious, and we have questions about many things. We have the more personal questions, such as, “Will my favorite book be made into a movie?” or “Why does my former best friend not want to hang out with me anymore?” to questions of a larger nature about the world around us. These might include questions such as the following: What does being treated like an adult mean? Why can’t people share? Why do we have to go to war? How do I understand what I see or read about in history or online or in the news? Why is the peace process so difficult?

Asking good questions helps us take charge of our own learning. Learning to ask good questions is a process, as “yes” and “no” types of questions don’t get us very far in discovering why events happened or why people feel as they do. Once we master this process, however, we become better thinkers and researchers and can find out more about subjects that interest us. Asking good questions is also important if we want to understand and affect the world around us.

In this book, as in other parts of this program, there will be “Essential Questions” that you will research. These types of questions concern all people – those who have lived, those who are living now, and those who will live in the future. Examples of these questions include: “How do new ideas change the way people live?” and “What makes a culture unique?” and “What characteristics make a good leader?” and “Why does conflict develop?” You will choose some of your own supporting questions to help you answer the Essential Question.

As you move through the study of history, you will be reading primary and secondary sources about a specific time period. Primary sources – whether they are diaries, poetry, letters, or artwork – were created by people who saw or experienced the event they are describing. Secondary sources — whether they are biographies, or history books, or your student text — are created after an event, by people who were not part of the original event.

Once you have completed the readings and the text notes, there is a “Report Your Findings” project in which you answer the Essential Question. You will work on some parts of the project by yourself, and you will work on other parts of the project with your classmates. You will be given many opportunities to take informed action. This means that you will use what you have learned and apply it to a current issue in a way that interests you. You will share this information with other students or with people outside of the classroom.

Changing Ideas and a Changing World

ESSENTIAL QUESTION

How do new ideas change the way people live?

Think about how this question might relate to the people of Europe over a very long time period: from 1270 to 1770. Would you expect there to be a lot of new ideas and change over this 500-year period?

TALK ABOUT IT

Discuss with a partner what information you would need to know to answer the Essential Question: How do new ideas change the way people live? What questions would you ask to get this information? For example, you might ask, "What makes an idea powerful enough to change the way people live?"

DIRECTIONS: Now write down three additional questions that you need to answer to help you understand how new ideas change the way people live.

MY RESEARCH QUESTIONS

Supporting Question 1:

Supporting Question 2:

Supporting Question 3:

Europe Looks Out on the World

DIRECTIONS: Search for evidence in Chapter 1, Lesson 1 to help you answer the following questions.

ESSENTIAL QUESTION

How do new ideas change the way people live?

As you gather evidence to answer the Essential Question, think about

- what new ideas came to Europe.
- how these new ideas came to Europe.
- how these new ideas changed the way the people of Europe lived.

My Notes

1 **IDENTIFYING CAUSES** What new religion spread in the Middle East and Africa in the early 600s C.E.?

2A **EXPLAINING** What was the purpose of the Crusades?

2B How did the Crusades increase European interest in trade with Asia?

3 How did Marco Polo increase interest in trade between Europe and Asia?

4 **EXPLAINING** Complete the table.

The Renaissance	
Meaning of Word	
What It Was	

5A IDENTIFYING CAUSES AND EFFECTS Complete the table.

The Effects of New Technology	
Technology	**Effect**
printing press	
mapmaking	
astrolabe	
compass	
caravel	

5B What was the net, or overall, effect of these advances in technology?

ESSENTIAL QUESTION

How do new ideas change the way people live?

Isabella in Black

DIRECTIONS: Use the painting to answer the questions.

EXPLORE THE CONTEXT: The Renaissance produced master painters and masterpieces. Titian was a master painter in Italy. This is one of his masterpieces. His many paintings have influenced other artists to this day. This painting is of Isabella d'Este (1474–1539). She was a leading figure in Italy during the Renaissance. Her wealth enabled her to be a great patron of the arts. She was also a trendsetter: her fashion sense was widely copied.

VOCABULARY

masterpiece: an outstanding or best piece of work

patron: someone who supports an activity financially

PRIMARY SOURCE: PAINTING

Portrait of Isabella d'Este (or *Isabella in Black*) by Titian, c. 1534–1536

1. **INTERPRETING INFORMATION** What is your first impression of the painting?

2. **INFERRING** What can you infer about the economic status of Isabella d'Este from this painting?

3. **DRAWING CONCLUSIONS** What conclusions about Isabella d'Este might you draw from the expression on her face and from what she is wearing in this portrait, given what you were told about her on the previous page?

4. **ANALYZING SOURCES** Based on this painting, why do you think Titian was known for his masterful use of color?

5. **EXPLORING CULTURE** Does this image support the idea that new ideas change the way people live? Explain your answer.

ESSENTIAL QUESTION

How do new ideas change the way people live?

Da Vinci Explains the New Perspective

DIRECTIONS: Read the following excerpt. Then answer the accompanying questions.

EXPLORE THE CONTEXT: Painting is almost as old as humanity itself. It has changed over the centuries as people developed new ideas and the ideas traveled around the world. Perspective is a concept that radically changed painting in the early 1400s. Leonardo da Vinci (1452–1519), an Italian, is considered one of the greatest Renaissance painters. In this excerpt, he explores the idea of *perspective.*

VOCABULARY

plane: a level or flat surface

diminution: a diminishing or decrease

perspective: a technique in painting or drawing to make objects in a scene seem to have the right shape and to be the right distance apart

PRIMARY SOURCE: BOOK

"Natural perspective acts in a contrary way; for, at greater distances the object appears smaller, and at a smaller distance the object appears larger. ... But in artificial perspective when objects of unequal size are placed at various distances, the smallest is nearer to the eye than the largest and the greatest distance looks as though it were the least of all ...; and the cause of this is the plane on which the objects are represented. And this diminution of the plane is natural, but the perspective shown upon it is artificial since it nowhere agrees with the true diminution of the said plane."

—From The Notebooks of Leonardo da Vinci, By Leonardo Da Vinci

1 **ANALYZING SOURCES** Who wrote this passage?

2 **INTERPRETING** What can you infer about the author from this passage?

3 EXPLORING CULTURE Does this source support the idea that new ideas change the way people live? Explain your answer.

ESSENTIAL QUESTION

How do new ideas change the way people live?

As you gather evidence to answer the Essential Question, think about

- why Portugal sent sailors to explore.
- how the voyages of Christopher Columbus led to a great exchange.
- the impact Spain had on the native peoples of the Americas.

My Notes

Early Exploration

DIRECTIONS: Search for evidence in Chapter 1, Lesson 2 to help you answer the following questions.

1A EXPLAINING Why did Portugal search for new sea trading routes?

1B Complete the table.

Accomplishments of Prince Henry the Navigator

2 CITING TEXT EVIDENCE What was the overall effect of the voyages of Dias and da Gama?

3 IDENTIFYING STEPS Who were the first Europeans to settle in North America?

4A ECONOMIC DECISION MAKING Who supported Christopher Columbus's attempt to reach Asia by sailing west?

4B Why did they do so?

5A **IDENTIFYING** Which American empire did Hernán Cortés conquer in about 1521?

5B **IDENTIFYING** Which American empire did Francisco Pizarro conquer in about 1521?

5C **IDENTIFYING CAUSE AND EFFECT** What role did diseases play in these conquests?

---

6 **EXPLORING CULTURE** Complete the graphic organizer.

The Class System in Spanish America

peninsulares:

people born in the Americas whose parents were Spanish

mestizos

Enslaved Africans

ESSENTIAL QUESTION

How do new ideas change the way people live?

Coronado's Quest for Gold

DIRECTIONS: Read the passage below. Then answer the accompanying questions.

EXPLORE THE CONTEXT: In the wake of Columbus, many Spaniards sought fortunes in the "New World." Among these was Francisco Vásquez de Coronado. From 1540 to 1542, Coronado led an expedition through what is today Mexico and the American Southwest. His goal: to find the legendary "Seven Cities of Cíbola," the seven cities of gold. He sought them in a region the Native Americans called Quivira. It was located in what we now call Kansas.

VOCABULARY

province: region, area
league: a unit of distance of about three miles
rivulet: small stream
cows: buffalo

PRIMARY SOURCE: EXPLORER'S REPORT

"The province of Quivira is 950 leagues from Mexico. Where I reached it, it is in the fortieth degree [of latitude]. The country itself is the best I have ever seen for producing all the products of Spain, for besides the land itself being very fat and black and being very well watered by the rivulets and springs and rivers, I found prunes like those of Spain [or I found everything they have in Spain] & nuts and very good sweet grapes and mulberries. I have treated the natives of this province, and all the others whom I found wherever I went, as well as was possible, agreeably to what Your Majesty had commanded, and they have received no harm in any way from me or from those who went in my company. I remained twenty-five days in this province of Quivira, so as to see and explore the country and also to find out whether there was anything beyond which could be of service to Your Majesty, because the guides who had brought me had given me an account of other provinces beyond this. And what I am sure of is that there is not any gold nor any other metal in all that country, and the other things of which they had told me are nothing but little villages, and in many of these they do not plant anything and do not have any houses except of skins and sticks, and they wander around with the cows; so that the account they gave me was false,

. . . continued

because they wanted to persuade me to go there with the whole force, believing that as the way was through such uninhabited deserts, and from the lack of water, they would get us where we and our horses would die of hunger. And the guides confessed this, and said they had done it by the advice and orders of the natives of these provinces. ❞

—Francisco Vásquez de Coronado's report to the King of Spain, sent from Tiguex [what is now New Mexico], October 20, 1541

1A ANALYZING SOURCES What did Coronado hope to find in Quivira?

____

1B What did he find instead?

____

____

2 MAKING CONNECTIONS Today, what term would we use to refer to the people of Quivira?

____

____

3 DETERMINING CENTRAL IDEAS What does Coronado conclude is the reason he was led to Quivira?

____

____

____

4 EXPLORING CULTURE Does this source support the idea that new ideas change the way people live? Explain your answer.

____

____

____

____

ESSENTIAL QUESTION

How do new ideas change the way people live?

"Beyond ... Were Great Numbers of Pueblos"

DIRECTIONS: Read the excerpt from a report. Then answer the accompanying questions.

EXPLORE THE CONTEXT: About 40 years after Coronado's journey, in 1581, the Rodríguez-Sánchez expedition set out from Mexico to explore what is now New Mexico. The expedition consisted of three missionaries and eight soldiers led by Francisco Sánchez. Sánchez was also called "Chamuscado," which means "scorched," because of his red beard. In addition, the expedition included 19 Native American servants, almost 100 horses, and 600 head of cattle for food. Below is an excerpt from a report of the journey submitted by two of its soldiers to King Philip II of Spain.

VOCABULARY

pueblo: sun-dried clay brick, or adobe, house or apartments
maize: corn
whereat: at which
religious: priests
league: a unit of distance of about three miles
cacique: chief
veins: deposits
saline: saltwater
granulated: in grains

1A IDENTIFYING STEPS There were no people in the first pueblo. Why?

____

____

____

PRIMARY SOURCE: EXPLORERS' REPORT

❝"...[O]n August 21, we discovered a pueblo of forty-five houses of two and three stories. We also found great fields of maize, beans, and gourds, whereat we gave thanks to the Lord for having provided us with supplies. We all entered said pueblo, well-equipped, ready for war in case it should be necessary. That, however, was not our intention, for we were guided only by peace and love, and by a desire to bring the natives into the fold of our holy Catholic faith. In our midst we took three religious, bearing crosses in their hands and around their necks. Thus we entered into the pueblo, but we found no one there, for they had not dared to wait for us, not knowing what we were, as our entrance was made upon armored horses. Seeing this, we immediately left the pueblo, travelling through fields of maize for about half a league, when we discovered five more pueblos. In the open we pitched our camp and agreed not to go on until we had won over those natives and made friends of them. At the end of two days a cacique came with three Indians to see who we were, and by signs we saluted one another. They came near to us and we gave them iron hawk's bells, playing cards, and other trinkets, and thus made them friends. They went and summoned the rest of the people, who came in great numbers to see us, saying to each other that we

were children of the Sun. They gave us maize, beans, gourds, cotton mantas (blankets), and tanned cowhides. We remained four days in their midst, and in that space of time we learned from them, through signs, that beyond as well as to the sides were great numbers of pueblos. ...

We also discovered in the said country eleven mine prospects, all having great veins of silver. From three of them ore was brought to this city and given to his Excellency. ...

We also discovered in the said settlement a very rich saline containing a great quantity of granulated salt of good quality. Of it a sample was brought to his Excellency. ...

After stating the above I will add that we are ready and equipped, if his Majesty will give us permission, to go and settle and save so many souls ... by teaching and instructing them *berbo ad berbo* (word for word), as we say here. ”

—from Brief and True Account of the Exploration of New Mexico, 1583

1B What did the Spanish do when they found the pueblo abandoned?

______

1C Where did the explorers set up camp?

______

1D **ANALYZING** Why do you think the explorers mentioned finding "eleven mine prospects, all having great veins of silver"?

______

2 **INFERRING** The report states, "We learned from them, through signs, that beyond as well as to the sides were great numbers of pueblos." What does "through signs" mean?

______

3 **EXPLORING CULTURE** Does this source support the idea that new ideas change the way people live? Explain your answer.

______

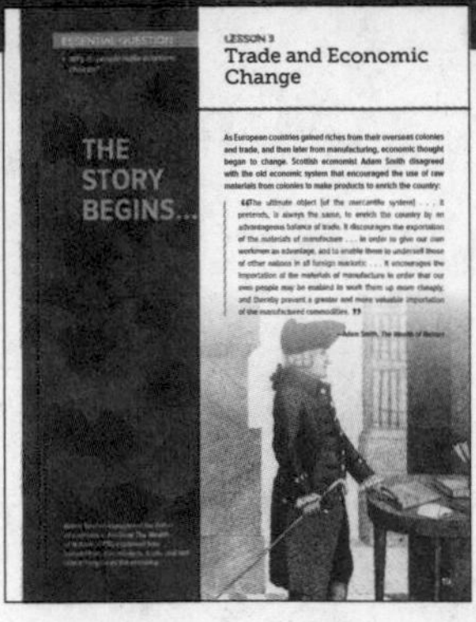

Trade and Economic Change

DIRECTIONS: Search for evidence in Chapter 1, Lesson 3 to help you answer the following questions.

ESSENTIAL QUESTION

How do new ideas change the way people live?

As you gather evidence to answer the Essential Question, think about

- how the growth of trade and money led to a new business class.
- why banks and banking developed.
- how competition for colonies changed the lives of millions of people.

My Notes

1 **EXCHANGE AND MARKETS** Complete the table.

Trade and Economic Change	
Concept	Explanation
Commercial Revolution	
capitalism	
financing ventures (include names of two families)	
joint-stock companies	
entrepreneurs	

2A **GLOBAL ECONOMY** What is mercantilism?

2B **DESCRIBING** What is bullion? Describe the role it played in mercantilism.

2C ANALYZING Why was trade important to mercantilism?

2D Describe the role a favorable balance of trade played in mercantilism.

2E IDENTIFYING MAIN IDEAS What role did colonies play in mercantilism?

3 PATTERNS AND MOVEMENT What types of things were exchanged in the Columbian Exchange?

4A IDENTIFYING EFFECTS How did European ideas influence foreign cultures during the Columbian Exchange?

4B IDENTIFYING EFFECTS How did foreign cultures influence Europeans during the Columbian Exchange?

ESSENTIAL QUESTION

How do new ideas change the way people live?

A Historian's View on the Columbian Exchange

DIRECTIONS: Read the excerpt below. Then answer the accompanying questions.

EXPLORE THE CONTEXT: The Columbian Exchange began after Christopher Columbus's voyage to America and continued through the 1500s. During this period, due to the frequent ocean voyages between Europe and the Americas, there were many transfers of ideas, culture, animals, technology, and plants between the Old World and the New World. Alfred W. Crosby, a historian, is credited with originating the term "Columbian Exchange." In the excerpt below from his book, he discusses what things were exchanged and their long-term effects.

VOCABULARY

hospitable: pleasant or welcoming

manioc: starchy tropical plant whose root is used for food

indispensable: absolutely necessary

demographic: relating to population or the study of population

Amerindians: Native Americans

SECONDARY SOURCE: BOOK

"Cattle and horses were brought ashore in the early 1600s and found hospitable climate and terrain in North America. Horses arrived in Virginia as early as 1620 and in Massachusetts in 1629. Many wandered free with little more evidence of their connection to humanity than collars with a hook at the bottom to catch on fences as they tried to leap over them to get at crops. Fences were not for keeping livestock in, but for keeping livestock out. . . .

The New World's great contribution to the Old is in crop plants. Maize, white potatoes, sweet potatoes, various squashes, chiles, and manioc have become essentials in the diets of hundreds of millions of Europeans, Africans, and Asians. Their influence on Old World peoples, like that of wheat and rice on New World peoples, goes far to explain the global population explosion of the past three centuries. The Columbian Exchange has been an indispensable factor in that demographic explosion.

All this had nothing to do with superiority or inferiority of biosystems in any absolute sense. It has to do with environmental contrasts.

. . . continued

Amerindians were accustomed to living in one particular kind of environment, Europeans and Africans in another. When the Old World peoples came to America, they brought with them all their plants, animals, and germs, creating a kind of environment to which they were already adapted, and so they increased in number. Amerindians had not adapted to European germs, and so initially their numbers plunged. That decline has reversed in our time as Amerindian populations have adapted to the Old World's environmental influence, but the demographic triumph of the invaders, which was the most spectacular feature of the Old World's invasion of the New, still stands.”

"The Columbian Exchange" by Alfred W. Crosby

1A ANALYZING SOURCES Name three foods new to Europe because of the Columbian Exchange.

1B IDENTIFYING CAUSE AND EFFECT How did foods from the New World affect population growth in the Old World?

1C IDENTIFYING What other influences were part of the Columbian Exchange?

2 INFERRING Why were fences "not for keeping livestock in, but for keeping livestock out" in 17th-century colonies?

3 EXPLORING CULTURE Does this source support the idea that new ideas change the way people live? Explain your answer.

ESSENTIAL QUESTION

How do new ideas change the way people live?

"The Raising of a Public Stock"

DIRECTIONS: Read the excerpt from the letter found below. Then answer the accompanying questions.

EXPLORE THE CONTEXT: European merchants who wanted to invest in exploration and colonization often created joint-stock companies. These companies sold stock, or shares, in a sea voyage or other venture, like creating a colony. People who owned the stock hoped to make a profit. Some joint-stock companies were created purely for private profit, but others were created for profit and the public good. The 16th-century geographer Richard Hakluyt (the younger) wrote this letter to the Queen of England to encourage her to back explorers' ventures with a public stock and make the country more competitive with other nations.

VOCABULARY

defects: missing things
cordage: ropes used for a ship's rigging
effected: brought about
exploit: a bold or daring adventure
public-weal: public well-being, the good of the people
industrious: hardworking
ignominious: disgraceful

1A ANALYZING SOURCES Why would England in particular rely on resources obtained through exploring other countries?

____

____

____

____

PRIMARY SOURCE: BOOK

"Reasons or motives: for the raising of a public stock to be employed for the peopling and discovering of such countries as may be found most convenient for the supply of those defects which this Realm of England most requires [the following]:

1. All kingdoms are maintained by rents or trade, but especially by the latter, which in maritime places flourishes the most by means of navigation.
2. The Realm of England is an island impossible to be otherwise fortified than by strong ships and able mariners, and is secluded from all corners with those of the main continent; therefore, fit abundance of vessels should be prepared to export and import merchandise.
3. The furniture of shipping consists in masts, cordage, pitch, tar, resin, and that of which England is by nature unprovided; at this present time it enjoys them only by the favor of a foreign country.
4. The life of shipping rests in the number of able mariners and worthy captains, which cannot be maintained without assurance of reward of honorable means to be employed for their adventures.
5. Private sources are cold comforts to adventurers and have ever been found fatal to all enterprises hitherto

undertaken by the English because of delays, jealousies, and unwillingness to back that project which did not succeed the first time.

6. The example of the Hollanders is very [relevant], for a main backing or stock has effected marvelous matters in trade and navigation in a few years.
7. It is honorable for a state to back an exploit by a public [corporation] rather than a private monopoly.
8. Where colonies are founded for a public-weal, they may continue in better obedience and become more Industrious than where private men are absolute backers of a voyage. Men of better behavior and quality will engage themselves in a public service, which carries more reputation with it, than a private, which is for the most part ignominious in the end, because it is presumed to aim at a profit and is subject to rivalry, fraud, and envy. . . . ”

—Richard Hakluyt (the younger), “Reasons for Raising a Fund to Settle America on the Value of Colonies to England,” a letter to Queen Elizabeth I, January 5, 1607

1B How will creating a public stock make trading crews and explorers more willing to venture out?

1C What is “public-weal”?

2 **INTERPRETING** What is the advantage of creating colonies for the public-weal rather than just for private profit?

3 EXPLORING CULTURE Does this source support the idea that new ideas change the way people live? Explain your answer.

ESSENTIAL QUESTION

How do new ideas change the way people live?

As you gather evidence to answer the Essential Question, think about

- how religion played a role in European exploration.
- the importance of a Northwest Passage.
- how exploration led to colonization in North America.

My Notes

Competing for Colonies

DIRECTIONS: Search for evidence in Chapter 1, Lesson 4 to help you answer the following questions.

1 EXPLANATORY WRITING What was the Reformation?

____

____

____

____

____

____

2 IDENTIFYING CAUSES AND EFFECTS Complete the diagram.

Religion, Royalty, War, and Colonization

England's Henry VIII leaves the __________ Church.

Elizabeth I establishes England as a __________ nation.

England's Protestantism angers its Catholic rival, __________.

King ______________ makes plans to invade England.

Spain creates a vast naval fleet called an __________.

English forces __________ the Spanish Armada.

Spain loses control of the sea to __________.

England can now start colonies in ______________

3 Complete the table.

Searching for the Northwest Passage	
Explorer	**Country Sailed For**
John Cabot	
Glovanni de Verrazano	
Jacques Cartier	
Henry Hudson	
Louis Jollet and Jacques Marquette	

4A **IDENTIFYING** Who followed the Mississippi River to the Gulf of Mexico and claimed the region for France?

4B What did he call the region? Why?

5 **EXPLANATORY WRITING** How did the French, as opposed to other European colonizers, treat Native Americans?

6 **MAKING CONNECTIONS** What was the significance of the Dutch West India Company?

ESSENTIAL QUESTION

How do new ideas change the way people live?

The Complaint of New Amsterdam

DIRECTIONS: Read the excerpts from the poem. Then answer the accompanying questions.

EXPLORE THE CONTEXT: In 1626, the Dutch established the colony of New Amsterdam. The colony was named after the Dutch city of Amsterdam. The colony stood where the famous skyscrapers of New York City stand today. In fact, the author of this poem lived in a house on what is now Pearl Street.

VOCABULARY

sponsors: people who support something
sustained: kept alive
feeble: weak
procured: obtained
bounteous: plentiful, abundant
nought: none
Supawn: corn mush
enumerate: count or list
fraught: filled
swine: pigs
dumb: silent
succour: relieve
disdain: look down on

1A ANALYZING CENTRAL IDEAS Reread the first stanza. What do you think it means?

____

____

____

PRIMARY SOURCE: POEM

The poem is written from the point of view of the colony. In other words, New Amsterdam is the speaker in the poem. Her "mother" is the Old World city in the Netherlands that she is named for: Amsterdam. The word "swine" in the eighth stanza, or group of four lines, refers to the English.

"From the moment I was born,
Indian neighbors made me mourn.
They pursued me night and day,
While my mother kept away.

But my sponsors did supply
Better my necessity;
They sustained my feeble life;
They procured a bounteous wife
....

True, both simple 'twas and scant,
What I had to feed my want.
Oft 't was nought except Supawn
And the flesh of buck or fawn.
....

For, I venture to proclaim
No one can a maiden name,
Who with richer land is blessed
Than th' estate by me possessed.

See! two streams my garden bind,
From the East and North they wind,
Rivers pouring in the sea,
Rich in fish, beyond degree.

Milk and butter; fruits to eat
No one can enumerate;
Ev'ry vegetable known;
Grain the best that e'er was grown.

All the blessings man e'er knew,
Here does our Great Giver strew,
(And a climate; ne'er more pure)
But for me,-yet immature,

Fraught with danger; for the Swine
Trample down these crops of mine;
Up-root, too, my choicest land;
Still and dumb, the while, I stand,

In the hope, my mother's arm
Will protect me from the harm.
She can succour my distress.
Now my wish, my sole request,

Is for men to till my land;
So I'll not in silence stand.
I have lab'rors almost none;
Let my household large become;

I'll my mother's kitchen furnish
With my knicknacks, with my surplus;
With tobacco, furs and grain;
So that Prussia she'll disdain. ”

from "The Complaint of New Amsterdam,
by Jacob Steendam (1615–1672)

1B What is the meaning of the third stanza ("True, both simple ...)?

1C **ANALYZING** In the last two stanzas, what does "my mother's kitchen" refer to?

2 Why does the poet refer to the English as "the Swine" in the eighth stanza?

ESSENTIAL QUESTION

How do new ideas change the way people live?

A Request: "To Speak out of the Book"

DIRECTIONS: Read the excerpt from the letter. Then answer the accompanying questions.

EXPLORE THE CONTEXT: The European settlement of North America took centuries. There were countless interactions between Europeans and Native Americans. This letter describes one. An English settler, Francis Yeardley, tells of one experience with local people in what is now North Carolina.

VOCABULARY

great man: probably a chief
province: region or area
civility: politeness
moons: months
appalled: horrified

PRIMARY SOURCE: LETTER

"After some days ... , the young man the interpreter prevailed with the great man, and his war-captains, and a great man of another province, and some other Indians, to come in and make their peace with the English; ... he brought them to me at my house, where they [stayed] a week, and [showed] much civility of [behavior].

In ... which time, hearing and seeing the children read and write, of his own free voluntary motion he asked me ... whether I would take his only son, ... and teach him to do as our children, namely, in his terms, to speak out of the book, and to make a writing; which motion I most heartily embraced; and with expressions of love, and many presents, ... dismissed him. At his departure he expressed himself desirous to serve that God the Englishmen served, and that his child might be so brought up; promising to bring him in to me in four moons ...

In [that time] my [business] calling me to Maryland, he came once himself, and sent twice to know, if I was returned, that he might bring his child.

[B]ut in my absence, some [English] people, supposing I had great gains by [business] with him, murmured, and carried themselves uncivilly towards [the Native Americans], forbidding their coming in any more; and by some over-busy justices of the peace, (my wife having brought him to

. . . *continued*

church in the congregation), after sermon, threatened to whip him, and send him away. The great man was very much afraid, and much appalled; but my wife kept him in her hand by her side, and confidently and constantly on my behalf resisted their threatenings. ... ”

—from "Francis Yeardley's Narrative of Excursions into Carolina, 1654"

1A ANALYZING Why did the Native Americans come into Yeardley's settlement?

1B CITING TEXT EVIDENCE Where did they stay, and for how long? How did they behave?

2A IDENTIFYING What did "the great man" want from Yeardley for his son?

2B DETERMINING POINT OF VIEW What was Yeardley's reaction to this?

3 NARRATIVE WRITING What happened when Yeardley was away on business?

4 EXPLORING CULTURE Does this source support the idea that new ideas change the way people live? Explain your answer.

ESSENTIAL QUESTION

How do new ideas change the way people live?

As you gather evidence to answer the Essential Question, think about

- what important ideas originated in Europe.
- how religions influenced European history.
- who were the major thinkers.

My Notes

The Enlightenment

DIRECTIONS: Search for evidence in Chapter 1, Lesson 5 to help you answer the following questions.

1 **IDENTIFYING CENTRAL IDEAS** What were the main ideas advanced by Thomas Aquinas?

2 **COMPARING AND CONTRASTING**

Differing Views: Hobbes and Locke		
Thomas Hobbes		**John Locke**
	Major Work	
	View of People	
	Major Idea About Government that Grew from This View	

3A **IDENTIFYING** Which European thinker suggested that evidence should be collected and analyzed in an orderly way?

3B What was this idea eventually known as?

3C Describe the scientific method.

4 **EXPLAINING IDEAS** Complete the table.

Enlightenment Thinkers	
Philosophe	**Major Ideas and Accomplishments**
Voltaire	
Denis Diderot	
Baron Charles de Montesquieu	

5 **EXPLAINING IDEAS** What were Jean-Jacques Rousseau's major ideas?

6 **ANALYZING INFORMATION** What was the significance of the Magna Carta?

7 **ANALYZING INFORMATION** What was the significance of the English Bill of Rights?

ESSENTIAL QUESTION

How do new ideas change the way people live?

The Spirit of Laws

DIRECTIONS: Read the excerpt below and answer the accompanying questions.

EXPLORE THE CONTEXT: Montesquieu (1689–1755) was one of the great thinkers of his time. His major work, *The Spirit of Laws*, was published in 1748. Its ideas deeply influenced the U.S. Constitution, which we live under every day. The book is still widely read today.

VOCABULARY

moderate: restrained
apt: likely
check: restrain
body: legislative unit
tyrannical: like a tyrant

PRIMARY SOURCE: BOOK

“Political liberty is to be found only in moderate governments; and even in these it is not always found. It is there only when there is no abuse of power: but constant experience shows us that every man invested with power is apt to abuse it, and to carry his authority as far is it will go.

To prevent this abuse, it is necessary, from the very nature of things, that power should be a check to power.

In every government there are three sorts of power; the legislative; the executive, in respect to things dependent on the law of nations; and the judicial, in regard to things that depend on the civil law. ...

When the legislative and executive powers are united in the same person, or in the same body of [legislators], there can be no liberty; because apprehensions may arise, lest the same monarch or senate should enact tyrannical laws, to execute them in a tyrannical manner... .

There would be an end of every thing were the same man, or the same body ... to exercise those three powers, that of enacting laws, that of executing the public resolutions, and that of judging the crimes or differences of individuals.”

—Charles-Louis de Secondat, Baron de Montesquieu, *The Spirit of Laws*

1A **ANALYZING SOURCES** According to this passage, what are the three sorts of power that government has?

1B How does Montesquieu think these powers can be checked, or contained?

1C **CITING TEXT EVIDENCE** Why does he say these powers need to be checked at all?

1D Does Montesquieu think the powers of government should be held by one person or group, or does he think the powers should be separated?

2 EXPLORING CULTURE Does this source support the idea that new ideas change the way people live? Explain your answer.

ESSENTIAL QUESTION

How do new ideas change the way people live?

Voltaire

DIRECTIONS: Read the excerpt below and then answer the questions that follow.

EXPLORE THE CONTEXT: Voltaire (1694–1778) was a French philosopher and writer. He is celebrated for his wit and his wisdom. Here, Voltaire writes about England in his book *Letters on the English*. It praised English customs and government. It was viewed as criticism of life in France. In this excerpt, Voltaire turns his attention to English taxes.

VOCABULARY

exempted: excused from
revenue: income or value
bill: proposed tax law
upon the same foot: at the same rate
apprehension: fear
livres: French unit of money

PRIMARY SOURCE: ESSAY

"No one is exempted in [England] from paying certain taxes because he is a nobleman or a priest. ...When the Bill has passed the Lords and is signed by the king, then the whole nation pays, every man in proportion to his revenue or estate, not according to his title. ...

The land-tax continues still upon the same foot, though the revenue of the lands is increased. Thus no one is tyrannised over, and every one is easy. The feet of the peasants are not bruised by wooden shoes; they eat white bread, are well clothed, and are not afraid of increasing their stock of cattle, nor of tiling their houses from any apprehension that their taxes will be raised the year following. The annual income of the estates of a great many commoners in England amounts to two hundred thousand livres, and yet these do not think it beneath them to plough the lands which enrich them, and on which they enjoy their liberty."

—Voltaire, from *Letters on the English*, 1778

1A **INFERRING** What does Voltaire imply about noblemen and priests being exempted from taxes in France?

1B **ANALYZING** In England, how is the amount an individual pays in taxes determined?

1C How does Voltaire explain that a consistent tax benefits people?

2 **CITING TEXT EVIDENCE** Does Voltaire approve or disapprove of the English tax system? How do you know?

3 EXPLORING CULTURE Does this source support the idea that new ideas change the way people live? Explain your answer.

ESSENTIAL QUESTION

How do new ideas change the way people live?

1 Think About It

Review the supporting questions that you developed at the beginning of the chapter. Review the evidence that you gathered in Chapter 1. Were you able to answer each supporting question? If there was not enough evidence to answer your supporting questions, what additional evidence do you think you need to include?

2 Organize Your Evidence

Use the graphic organizer below to list what you have learned about how new ideas change the way people live.

New Idea	How It Influenced the Way People Live
1.	
2.	
3.	
4.	
5.	
6.	
7.	
8.	
9.	
10.	

Review your list. Is there any way to organize your items into categories? Your categories might be based on geographic location, time period, or type of idea.

3 Write About It

Write a journal entry about a new idea that had an impact on your own life.

4 Connect to the Essential Question

Using your work from step 2 above, plan a visual essay that answers the Essential Question: How do new ideas change the way people live?

Your essay can be based on individual ideas, or categories, or both. Your visual essay should be in the form of a poster that has the Essential Question as its title and illustrations (that you draw or print or cut out) that provide an answer or multiple answers to the Essential Question. You may add captions to the images if you wish. Create your visual display for classroom presentation to your own class or the class of students one year younger.

CITIZENSHIP

TAKING ACTION

Much of what you learned about in this chapter forms the basis of your life today. How is that? Your local government was authorized, or chartered, by California. California's government must be in keeping with the U.S. Constitution. The U.S. Constitution is a result of many of the ideas you have been learning about. These ideas—the rule of law, binding agreements, limits on the power of government, the people having a greater say in representative government—were brand new centuries ago. Today, they are established as some of the greatest achievements in Western civilization.

Americans put these ideas into practice every time we hold an election. We elect representatives at the local, state, and national levels.

Think About It

Have you ever thought about participating in an election? Even if you are not old enough to vote, you are old enough to campaign for a candidate you support.

When will the next election in your community be held? What government offices will be at stake?

Research It

Using the Internet, conduct research to learn more about the next election in your community. Record the date here: ______________________

Choose one of the offices up for a vote. Again going online, research that office and find out what the officeholder's responsibilities are. Write down what you learn.

____

____

As the election approaches, decide who you want to support for that office and why.

Do It

Contact the campaign office of the candidate you support. Volunteer! Report your experiences in a narrative essay for your teacher.

Colonial America

ESSENTIAL QUESTION

How does geography influence the way people live?

Think about how this question relates to life in Colonial America.

TALK ABOUT IT

Discuss with a partner what type of information you would need to know to answer this question. For example, questions might be: Did the geography of the colonies help or hurt the colonists? Or: "How did the physical geography differ for each colony?"

DIRECTIONS Now write down three additional questions that you need to answer to be able to explain the impact of geography on Colonial America.

MY RESEARCH QUESTIONS

Supporting Question 1:

____

____

Supporting Question 2:

____

____

Supporting Question 3:

____

____

Roanoke and Jamestown

ESSENTIAL QUESTION

How does geography influence the way people live?

As you gather evidence to answer the Essential Question, think about:

- the difficulties that faced the settlers of Roanoke.
- the resources available to the settlers of Jamestown.

My Notes

1 **SPATIAL THINKING** Where is Roanoke Island located?

2 **DESCRIBING** Briefly describe each person's role in the Roanoke Colony.

Person	Role
Queen Elizabeth	
Sir Walter Raleigh	
John White	
Virginia Dare	

3A **IDENTIFYING CAUSE** Why did John White leave Roanoke?

3B What did White find when he returned?

4 **EXPLAINING** What is the significance of "Croatoan"?

5 ECONOMICS Investors in the Virginia Company hoped to make a profit in what two ways?

6 **IDENTIFYING CAUSE AND EFFECT** What was the "starving time"? What caused it?

Powhatan stopped providing food to the colonists of Jamestown.		They died.

7 **INFERRING** How did the weather play a role in the "starving time"?

8 **IDENTIFYING** Complete the table.

Colony	Date of First Settlement	Reason for Founding
Roanoke		
Jamestown		

9 **IDENTIFYING CAUSE AND EFFECT** Complete each item in the table to identify ways that Jamestown's physical geography affected the colony's economy.

Type of Thing	Name of Thing	How it Helped Jamestown
crop		
	head right	

ESSENTIAL QUESTION

How does geography influence the way people live?

Some Danger of Sinking

DIRECTIONS: Read the following excerpt and answer the accompanying questions.

EXPLORE THE CONTEXT: In August 1587, the leader of the Roanoke Colony, John White, returned to England for supplies. He hoped to be back within a few months. Unfortunately, war between England and Spain made it impossible for White to sail back to Roanoke for nearly three years. He was eager to see the colonists, including his daughter, son-in-law, and granddaughter, Virginia Dare. Just landing on Roanoke Island, however, proved challenging, as White relates in this report.

VOCABULARY

boat: small vessel
ship: large vessel
breach: break in the coast
victuals: food
rash: done without considering consequences
undiscreet: careless
thrise: three times
mischance: unlucky event

1 DETERMINING CENTRAL IDEAS What is the main event the passage is describing?

______

______

______

2 DESCRIBING What adjectives would you use to describe the event?

______

______

PRIMARY SOURCE: REPORT

"The next morning being the 17 of August, our boates and company were prepared againe to goe up to Roanoak, but Captaine Spicer had then sent his boat ashore for fresh water, by meanes whereof it was ten of the clocke afternoone before we put from our ships which were then come to an anker within two miles of the shore.

The Admiral's boat was halfe way toward the shore, when Captaine Spicer put off from his ship. The Admirals boat first passed the breach, but not without some danger of sinking, for we had a sea brake into our boat which filled us halfe full of water, but by the will of God and carefull styrage of Captaine Cooke we came safe ashore, saving onely that our furniture, victuals, match and powder were much wet and spoyled. For at this time the winde blue at Northeast and direct into the harbour so great a gale, that the Sea brake extremely on the barre, and the tide went very forcibly at the entrance.

By that time our Admirals boat was halled ashore, and most of our things taken out to dry, Captaine Spicer came to the entrance of the breach . . . , and was halfe passed over, but by the rash and undiscreet styrage of Ralph Skinner his Masters mate, a very dangerous Sea brake into their boate and overset them quite, the men kept the boat some in it, and some hanging on it, but the next sea set the boat on ground, where it beat so, that

some of them were forced to let goe their hold, hoping to wade ashore: but the Sea still beat them downe, so that they could neither stand nor swimme, and the boat twise or thrise was turned the keele upward, whereon Captaine Spicer and Skinner hung untill they sunke, and were seene no more.

But foure that could swimme a litle kept themselves in deeper water and were saved by Captaine Cookes meanes, who so soone as he saw their oversetting, stripped himselfe, and foure other that could swimme very well, and with all haste possible rowed unto them, and saved foure. There were 11 in all and 7 of the chiefest were drowned, whose names were Edward Spicer, Ralph Skinner, Edward Kelly, Thomas Bevis, Hance the Surgion, Edward Kelborne, Robert Coleman. This mischance did so much discomfort the saylers, that they were all of one mind not to goe any further to seeke the planters. But in the end by the commandement and perswasion of me and Captaine Cooke, they prepared the boates: and seeing the Captaine and me so resolute, they seemed much more willing. ”

—John White, *Early English and French Voyages Chiefly from Hakluyt 1534-1608*, 1590

3 **ANALYZING TEXT PRESENTATION** What tone is the writer using? Does this tone match your adjectives, or the event itself? Explain.

4 **EXPLAINING** Why does the report single out Ralph Skinner?

5 **IDENTIFYING PERSPECTIVES** How do you think the sailors viewed the coast of Roanoke Island? Why?

6 **HUMAN-ENVIRONMENT INTERACTION** Does this document support the idea that geography can influence the way people live? If so, is the influence positive, negative, or both? Explain your answer.

ESSENTIAL QUESTION

How does geography influence the way people live?

The Fort at Jamestown

DIRECTIONS Read the following excerpt and answer the accompanying questions.

EXPLORE THE CONTEXT William Strachey was an English writer. Shipwrecked in Bermuda, he eventually sailed to Virginia and later wrote about what he saw there. Here, he describes the fort at Jamestown as it was in 1609.

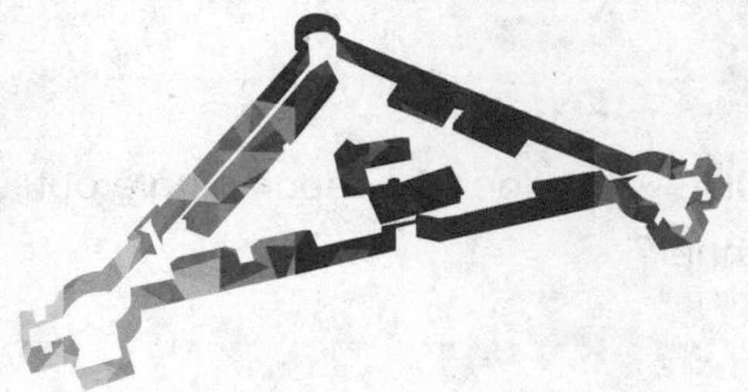

PRIMARY SOURCE: BOOK

❝[The] fort growing since to more perfection, is now... about half an acre... . [It] is cast almost into the form of a triangle and so palisaded. The south side next the river (howbeit extended in a line or curtain six score foot more in length than the other two, by reason the advantage of the ground doth require) contains 140 yards, the west and east sides a hundred only. At every angle or corner, where the lines meet, a bulwark or watchtower is raised and in each bulwark a piece or two well mounted... . And thus enclosed, as I said, round with a palisade of planks and strong posts, four feet deep in the ground, of young oaks, walnuts, etc. ... [T]he fort is called, in honor of His Majesty's name, Jamestown. The principal gate from the town, through the palisade, opens to the river, as at each bulwark there is a gate likewise to go forth and at every gate a demiculverin and so in the market-place.❞

—William Strachey, 1609

VOCABULARY

palisaded: surrounded by wooden stakes fixed in the ground to form a fence

score: twenty

bulwark: tower in the wall of a fort

piece: cannon

demiculverin: a type of cannon

His Majesty: King James of England

1 **HUMAN-ENVIRONMENT INTERACTION** Why do you think the builders of Jamestown chose the location that they did?

2 **ANALYZING SOURCES** Why is the south side of the fort longer than the other two sides?

3 **INFERRING** What do you think is also likely to be found near the fort? How do you think this affected the location of the fort?

4 **HUMAN-ENVIRONMENT INTERACTION** How does this document support the idea that geography can influence the way people live? Explain your answer.

The New England Colonies

1 IDENTIFYING CAUSE What motivated the Pilgrims to found a colony in North America?

2 EXPLAINING Why did they decide to stay at Plymouth instead of continuing on to Virginia?

3 DESCRIBING What did the Native Americans teach the Pilgrims about finding and storing food in a new land? List your answers.

ESSENTIAL QUESTION

How does geography influence the way people live?

As you gather evidence to answer the Essential Question, think about:

- how the Pilgrims learned to survive.
- how geography led to both cooperation and conflict between Native Americans and settlers.

My Notes

4 **IDENTIFYING** Complete the table.

Colony	Date of First Settlement	Reason for Founding
Massachusetts		
New Hampshire		
Connecticut		
Rhode Island		

5 **CONTRASTING** Give examples of how geography led to both cooperation and conflict between Native Americans and settlers.

Geography of New England: Cooperation	Geography of New England: Conflict

ESSENTIAL QUESTION

How does geography influence the way people live?

A Fondness for Agriculture

DIRECTIONS Read the following excerpt and answer the accompanying questions.

EXPLORE THE CONTEXT Samuel de Champlain was a French explorer who played a key role in the French settlement of Canada. In his explorations, he sailed the coast of New England. There, he took note of how the Native Americans grew and stored a variety of crops.

VOCABULARY

tillage: land prepared for growing crops
league: a unit of distance; about three miles
earth: topsoil
granaries: storehouses for grain

1 INFERRING Why do you think Champlain made a point of studying and recording how the Native Americans grew and stored corn?

PRIMARY SOURCE: BOOK

"The next day [July 9, 1605] Sieur de Monts and I landed to observe their tillage on the bank of the river [Saco River]. We saw their Indian corn, which they raise in gardens. Planting three or four kernels in one place, they then heap about it a quantity of earth with shells of the *signoc* [horseshoe crab] before mentioned. Then three feet distant they plant as much more, and thus in succession. With this corn they put in each hill three or four Brazilian beans [kidney bean], which are of different colors. When they grow up, they interlace with the corn, which reaches to the height of from five to six feet; and they keep the ground very free from weeds. We saw there many squashes, and pumpkins, and tobacco, which they likewise cultivate. The Indian corn which we saw was at that time about two feet high, some of it as high as three. The beans were beginning to flower, as also the pumpkins and squashes. They plant their corn in May, and gather it in September...

"On the east there is a bay extending back on the north some three leagues in which there is an island and two other little bays which adorn the landscape, where there is considerable quantity of land cleared up, and many little hills, where they cultivate corn and the various grains on which they live. There are, also, very fine vines, many walnut trees, oaks, cypresses, but only a

few pines. All the inhabitants of this place are very fond of agriculture, and provide themselves with Indian corn for the winter, which they store in the following manner.

"They make trenches in the sand on the slope of the hills, some five to six feet deep, more or less. Putting their corn and other grains into large grass sacks, they throw them into these trenches, and cover them with sand, three or foure feet above the surface of the earth, taking it out as their needs require. In this way it is preserved as well as it would be possible to do in our granaries."

—Samuel de Champlain, 1605

2 **DETERMINING CENTRAL IDEAS** Champlain states, "All the inhabitants of this place are very fond of agriculture." What do you think he means by this?

3 **ANALYZING POINT OF VIEW** In the last line of this excerpt, Champlain compares Native American methods to European ones. What is he comparing and why do you think he is doing so?

4 **HUMAN-ENVIRONMENT INTERACTION** What does this excerpt tell you about the importance of Native Americans to Europeans? Explain your answer.

ESSENTIAL QUESTION

How does geography influence the way people live?

Fishing the Grand Bank

DIRECTIONS: Study the following illustration and answer the accompanying questions.

EXPLORE THE CONTEXT: Fishing was an important activity in the New England colonies, as the map found in this lesson in your textbook shows. The earliest settlements were located near one of the richest fishing waters in the world: the Grand Banks of the Atlantic Ocean. A *bank* is a plateau, or higher area, of the seafloor. The water above a bank is relatively shallow. Sunlight penetrates into the ocean and attracts plankton, or tiny organisms. In turn, the plankton attract the fish that feed on them. Colonists set off in sailing ships made from local timber and voyaged to the Grand Banks. There, smaller boats full of fisherman were launched. They would use long lines to hook cod and other fish from the rich waters. To the colonists of New England, the Grand Banks were a source of food—and wealth. This engraving from 1683 shows fishing in the Grand Banks.

VOCABULARY

bank: elevation of the seafloor that makes the water above it shallower than the surrounding area

PRIMARY SOURCE: ILLUSTRATION

1 **INFERRING** These ships are fishing. Why do you think both larger ships and smaller boats are shown?

2 **EXPLANATORY WRITING** What does this illustration tell you about work and life in this region? Explain in a short paragraph, referring to the image in your answer.

3 **HUMAN-ENVIRONMENT INTERACTION** Does this engraving support the idea that geography influences the way people live? Explain your answer.

The Middle Colonies

ESSENTIAL QUESTION

How does geography influence the way people live?

As you gather evidence to answer the Essential Question, think about:

- why New Amsterdam thrived as a trading city.
- what role farmland played in the settlement of the Middle Colonies.

My Notes

1 **IDENTIFYING CAUSES** Identify two causes for New Amsterdam becoming a major shipping center.

Causes	Effect
	New Amsterdam became a major shipping center

2 **EXPLAINING** What was a patroon?

3A What was the purpose of the patroon system?

3B How did land play a role in the patroon system?

4 **EXPLAINING** How did New Netherland become New York?

5 **DESCRIBING** How was New Jersey created and named?

6 **DETERMINING MEANING** What does the word "Pennsylvania" mean? What does the name tell you about thls land?

7 **EXPLAINING** Explain the role religion played in the founding of Pennsylvania.

8 **IDENTIFYING** Complete the table.

Colony	Date of First Settlement	Cultural Influences
New York		
New Jersey		
Pennsylvania		
Delaware		

ESSENTIAL QUESTION

How does geography influence the way people live?

A View of New Amsterdam

DIRECTIONS Study the following illustration and answer the accompanying questions.

EXPLORE THE CONTEXT Today, Manhattan is an island and part of New York City. It is covered by human-made structures: skyscrapers, apartment buildings, and shops. On weekdays, the population of Manhattan swells to almost 4 million as people commute to the island for work. In colonial times, however, the island was home to a Native American population. Only the southern tip was settled by Europeans. That small settlement was called New Amsterdam. This illustration from 1626 is labeled "Fort Nieuw Amsterdam op de Manhatans," which means Fort New Amsterdam on the Manhattan.

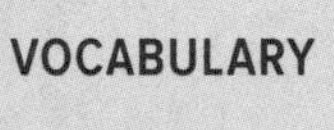

VOCABULARY

commute: travel

PRIMARY SOURCE: ILLUSTRATION

1 **DESCRIBING** New Amsterdam was settled on the tip of Manhattan Island. How does the illustration show this?

2 **INFERRING** What does the presence of Native Americans in a canoe tell you?

3 **ANALYZING SOURCES** Are all of the figures and other items in the illustration drawn to scale? Or do some of them seem too big or too small? Explain your answer.

4 **INFERRING** Why do you think the artist decided to show so many sailing ships?

5 **SUMMARIZING** How does this illustration show how the settlers used the following geographic features of the region:

Water	Land	Wind

6 **HUMAN-ENVIRONMENT INTERACTION** How does this image show that the Dutch used geography to their advantage? Explain your answer.

ESSENTIAL QUESTION

How does geography influence the way people live?

Robert's Gristmill

DIRECTIONS: Study the following illustration and answer the accompanying questions.

EXPLORE THE CONTEXT: The Middle Colonies enjoyed the advantage of good climate and good soil for growing grain, especially wheat. Farmers could grow enough to feed their own families and have a surplus to sell at the market. The grain could be sold for more money when it was milled, or ground into flour. Grinding was done at gristmills ("grist" means grain), usually located near water because water was used to power the mill using a waterwheel. The gristmill in this illustration was built in 1683.

VOCABULARY

gristmill: a mill that grinds grain into flour

PRIMARY SOURCE: ILLUSTRATION

1 **ANALYZING SOURCES** This gristmill was originally located along a stream. What part of the mill in this illustration might have been part of the way the mill used water?

2 **ANALYZING SOURCES** How could you estimate the size of the gristmill from this illustration?

3 **INFERRING** What do you think might be inside the mill building?

4 **HUMAN-ENVIRONMENT INTERACTION** What does this illustration tell you about the way people in the Middle Colonies interacted with natural resources?

The Southern Colonies

1 IDENTIFYING EFFECTS In what two ways was the demand for agricultural labor in the Virginia colony met?

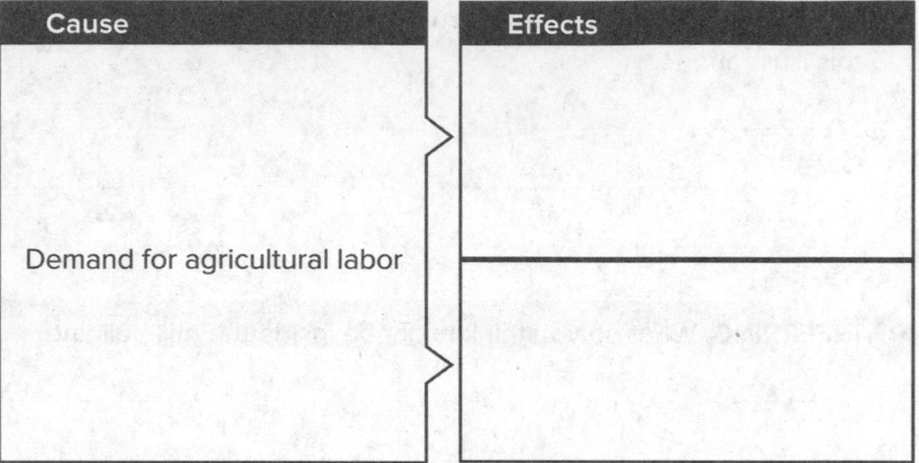

ESSENTIAL QUESTION

How does geography influence the way people live?

As you gather evidence to answer the Essential Question, think about:

- how farming the land affected the population of the southern colonies.
- how wanting more land to settle and farm led to Bacon's Rebellion.

2 DESCRIBING Describe the role religion played in the founding of Maryland.

My Notes

3 **DETERMINING CENTRAL IDEAS** What role did geography play in Nathaniel Bacon's Rebellion?

4 **IDENTIFYING** Complete the table.

Colony	Date of First Settlement	Reason for Founding
Virginia		
Maryland		
North Carolina		
South Carolina		
Georgia		

ESSENTIAL QUESTION

How does geography influence the way people live?

James Oglethorpe's Speech to the South Carolina Assembly

DIRECTIONS Study the following excerpt and answer the accompanying questions.

EXPLORE THE CONTEXT James Oglethorpe was one of the original founders of the Georgia colony, which was granted its charter in 1732. Oglethorpe and 114 colonists first landed in Georgia on February 12, 1733. The excerpt comes from a speech he gave to the Governor and Assembly of South Carolina on June 9, 1733.

VOCABULARY

signalized: witnessed
repulsed: drove back
advices: information
arms: weapons
endeavors: efforts
frontiers: boundaries

1 DETERMINING PURPOSE What is the main reason Oglethorpe gives this speech? What do you think he hopes for in the future?

______

______

______

______

______

______

2 IDENTIFYING DETAILS According to Oglethorpe, what were the main threats to the security of South Carolina?

______

______

PRIMARY SOURCE: SPEECH

"I should think myself very much wanting in justice and gratitude, if I should neglect thanking your Excellency, you Gentlemen of the Counsel, and you Gentlemen of the Assembly, for the assistance you have give to the Colony of Georgia....

"Your charitable and generous proceeding, besides the self-satisfaction which always attends such actions, will be of the greatest advantage to this Province. You, Gentlemen, are the best judges of this; since, most of you have been personal witnesses of the dangerous blows this country has escaped from French, Spanish, and Indian arms. Many of you know this by experience, having signalized yourselves personally; either, when this Province by its own strength, and unassisted by every thing but the courage of its inhabitants, and the providence of God, repulsed the formidable invasions of the French; or, when it defeated the whole body of the southern Indians, who were armed against it, and invaded the Spaniards, who assisted them. You, Gentlemen, know there was a time, when, every day brought fresh advices of murders, ravages, and burnings; when, no profession or calling was exempted from arms; when, every inhabitant of the Province was obliged to leave their wives, their families, their useful occupations, and undergo all the fatigues of war, for the

necessary defence of the country; and, all their endeavors scarcely sufficient to defend the western and southern frontiers against the Indians.

"It would be needless for me to tell you, who are much better judges, how the increasing settlements of the new Colony upon the Southern frontiers, will prevent the like danger for the future. Nor need I tell you, how much every plantation will increase in value, by the safety of the Province's being increased, since the Lands to the southward already sell for above double what they did when the new Colony first arrived."

—James Oglethorpe. Speech to the South Carolina Assembly, June 9, 1733

3 **CITING TEXT EVIDENCE** In what ways was the founding of Georgia supposed to be a benefit to South Carolina? What evidence in the excerpt supports this answer?

4 GEOGRAPHY How did geography play a role in the founding of Georgia?

5 **INFERRING** Why did the value of the land in the southern part of South Carolina more than double after the Georgia colony was founded?

ESSENTIAL QUESTION

How does geography influence the way people live?

Indigo from South Carolina

DIRECTIONS Read the following excerpt and answer the accompanying questions.

EXPLORE THE CONTEXT In colonial Carolina, indigo thrived. A blue flowering plant, indigo was used to dye cloth. James Glen, the governor of South Carolina, described this crop in 1761.

VOCABULARY

indifferent: any kind
Sugar Islands: Caribbean islands known for their sugar plantations
perennial: living several years
hitherto: until now
conversant: familiar
hogshead: a large cask or barrel of about 60 gallons
staves: boards used to make barrels

1 SUMMARIZING What does Glen say about soil and indigo?

____

____

____

____

____

2 ANALYZING TEXT PRESENTATION Why do you think he focuses so much discussion on the soil?

____

PRIMARY SOURCE: BOOK

"Indigo is of several sorts. What we have gone mostly upon is the sort generally cultivated in the Sugar Islands, which requires a high loose soil, tolerably rich, and is an annual plant; but the wild sort, which is common in this country, is much more hardy and luxuriant, and is perennial. Its stalk dies every year, but it shoots up again next spring. The indigo made from it is of as good a quality as the other [from the Sugar Islands], and it will grow on very indifferent land, provided it be dry and loose.

An acre of good land may produce about eighty pounds weight of good indigo, and one slave may manage two acres and upwards, and raise provisions besides, and have all the winter months to saw lumber and be otherwise employed in. But as much of the land hitherto used for indigo is improper, I am persuaded that not above thirty pounds weight of good indigo per acre can be expected from the land at present cultivated. Perhaps we are not conversant enough in this commodity, either in the culture of the plant or in the method of managing or manufacturing it, to write with certainty....

But I cannot leave this subject without observing how conveniently and profitably, as to the charge of labour, both indigo and rice may be managed by the same

persons; for the labour attending indigo being over in the summer months, those who were employed in it may afterwards manufacture rice in the ensuing part of the year, when it becomes most laborious; and after doing all this they will have some time to spare for sawing lumber, and making hogshead and other staves to supply the Sugar Colonies. ❞

—*A Description of South Carolina, Containing Many Curious and Interesting Particulars Relating to the Civil, Natural, and Commercial History of that Colony,* 1761

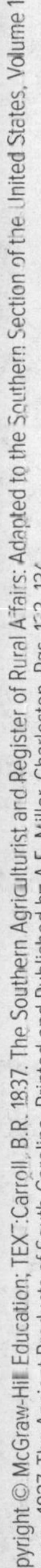

3 **ANALYZING POINT OF VIEW** Who are likely the "persons" Glen refers to?

4 **IDENTIFYING CENTRAL IDEAS** Why does Glen think that "conveniently and profitably... indigo and rice may be managed by the same persons"?

5 **HUMAN-ENVIRONMENT INTERACTION** Does this document support the idea that geography can influence the way people live? If so, is the influence positive, negative, or both? Explain your answer.

An American Identity Grows

1 SUMMARIZING Complete the table.

Colony	Major Economic Activities
New England	
Middle Colonies	
Southern Colonies	

2A IDENTIFYING CENTRAL IDEAS What role did slavery play in the American colonial economy?

2A How were enslaved Africans brought to the colonies?

3 IDENTIFYING CENTRAL IDEAS What two principles were at the heart of English and Colonial government?

ESSENTIAL QUESTION

How does geography influence the way people live?

As you gather evidence to answer the Essential Question, think about:

- how family life was the foundation of life in colonial America.
- how family life was based on American geography.

My Notes

4 **MAKING CONNECTIONS** Why do you think local governments grew in the colonies? How did they affect colonists' beliefs?

5 **SUMMARIZING** As you read the section titled Colonial Society, complete the table. The first row has been completed for you.

Task of Colonial Family Member(s)	Natural Resources Used
cooking	wood, water, animals, crops

6 **DESCRIBING** What was the Great Awakening?

ESSENTIAL QUESTION

How does geography influence the way people live?

A Massachusetts Meetinghouse

DIRECTIONS: Study the following photograph and answer the accompanying questions.

EXPLORE THE CONTEXT: As Americans settled villages throughout the colonies, they often built meetinghouses. As its name implies, it was a place for all of the villagers to meet. Meetinghouses were used for religious services as well as public meetings. They were some of the earliest government buildings in the colonies.

The meetinghouse shown in this photograph is in Lynnfield, Massachusetts. In 1713, the town was called Lynn. On November 22 of that year, 32 men and one woman voted to build a meetinghouse. They chose a convenient site, spent 130 pounds on construction, and built the meetinghouse where it still stands—and is used—today. In fact, the meetinghouse looks much the same as it did more than 300 years ago. One difference: the new settlers of Lynn could not afford to paint their meetinghouse, and so it stood as bare wood until the 1800s.

PRIMARY SOURCE: PHOTOGRAPH

1 **INFERRING** What material was used to build the meetinghouse in the photograph? What can you conclude from this?

2A **ANALYZING SOURCES** How many stories does the meetinghouse have?

2B **ANALYZING SOURCES** The roof of the meetinghouse is "pitched," meaning that it is steep. Why would New England colonists want a pitched roof?

4 **GEOGRAPHIC REASONING** The side of the meetinghouse with more windows is facing south to gather the maximum amount of sunlight. Why do you think the colonists oriented the meetinghouse this way?

5 **PREDICTING** Meetinghouses were places where the entire village could gather together to discuss important issues. What issues about geography can you imagine they might have discussed?

ESSENTIAL QUESTION

How does geography influence the way people live?

"To Make A Pen For To Catch Wolves"

DIRECTIONS Read the following excerpt and answer the accompanying questions.

EXPLORE THE CONTEXT Colonists often kept "town records" of the village meetings held at their meetinghouses. The record here is from a meeting held in the meetinghouse of Rowley, Massachusetts.

PRIMARY SOURCE: TOWN RECORD

"Leutenant Brockellbanke Henry Rily Thomas Wood and John Grant, Jachin Ranor and John Mighill, havinge ingaged for to make a pen for to catch wolves, had that priviledge granted that no boddy else should make any pen, any where upon the cow commons, duringe the space of three years, and were to have for every wolfe taken by there pen fifty shillings, payed by the towne."

—The Early Records of the Town of Rowley, Massachusets, 1639-1672

VOCABULARY

cow commons: piece of land shared by all for grazing cows

1 **SUMMARIZING** Why were these people given the right to catch the wolves?

2 **INFERRING** Why did the colonists want to catch wolves?

3A CIVICS For every wolf caught, the men were to be paid "by the towne." Where do you think the town would get its money?

3B What does this excerpt tell you about the town?

4 **HUMAN-ENVIRONMENT INTERACTION** How does this town record provide evidence of colonists altering their local geography?

ESSENTIAL QUESTION

How does geography influence the way people live?

1 Think About It

Review the supporting questions that you developed at the beginning of the chapter. Then review the evidence that you gathered in Chapter 2. Were you able to answer each Supporting Question?

If there was not enough evidence to answer your Supporting Questions, what additional evidence do you think you need to consider?

____

____

____

____

2 Organize Your Evidence

Use a chart like the one below to organize the evidence you will use to support your Position Statement.

Source of information	Specific evidence from the source to cite	How evidence helps support my Position Statement

3 Write About It

A position statement related to the Essential Question should reflect your conclusion about the evidence. Write a Position Statement for the ESSENTIAL QUESTION: ***How does geography influence the way people live?***

____

____

____

____

____

4 Talk About It

Work in small groups to present your position statement and evidence. Gather feedback from your classmates before you write your final conclusion. You may choose to refine your position statement after you have discussed it with your classmates. Group members should listen to one other's arguments, ask questions, and offer constructive advice about the statement.

5 Connect to the Essential Question

On a separate piece of paper, develop an essay using information from the three colonial regions to answer the ESSENTIAL QUESTION: ***How does geography influence the way people live?***

CITIZENSHIP
TAKING ACTION

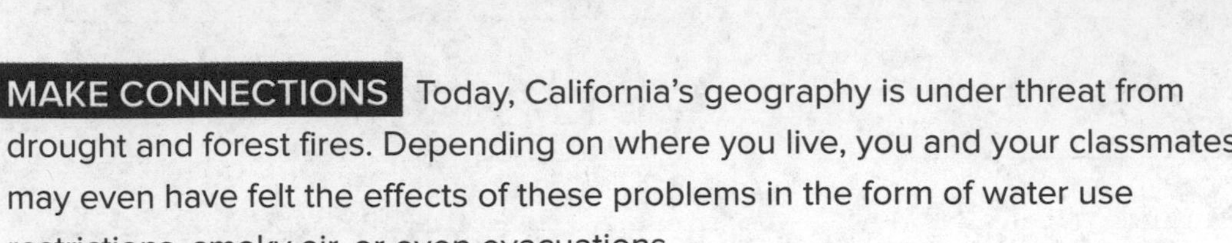

MAKE CONNECTIONS Today, California's geography is under threat from drought and forest fires. Depending on where you live, you and your classmates may even have felt the effects of these problems in the form of water use restrictions, smoky air, or even evacuations.

DIRECTIONS Research recent events in California having to do with forest fires and drought. Find one event to focus on and use the Internet to learn more about the causes and solutions to the problem, as well as what happened during the actual event. Then, write a social media feed—such as might be found on Twitter or Facebook—about these events. Use your creativity to show what most interested or concerned you about the events. Be sure to include at least 20 "posts" about the event in your mock social media feed.

The Spirit of Independence

ESSENTIAL QUESTION

Why does conflict develop between people and their government?

Think about how this question might relate to the American Revolution.

TALK ABOUT IT

Discuss with a partner what type of information you would need to know to answer this question. For example, one question might be: What events led up to the Revolution?

DIRECTIONS: Now write down three additional questions that you need to answer to be able to explain why the Revolution happened.

MY RESEARCH QUESTIONS

Supporting Question 1:

Supporting Question 2:

Supporting Question 3:

LESSON 1
Rivalry in North America

THE STORY BEGINS...

ESSENTIAL QUESTION

Why does conflict develop between people and their government?

As you gather evidence to answer the Essential Question, think about

- why the British initiated war against the French.
- where colonists' loyalties lay at this time.
- how Native Americans were caught between the interests of two European nations.

My Notes

Rivalry in North America

DIRECTIONS: Search for evidence in Chapter 3, Lesson 1 to help you answer the following questions.

1 IDENTIFYING CAUSE AND EFFECT In the graphic organizer below, describe the actions and reactions that began the French and Indian War, also known as the Seven Years' War. The first Action has been filled in for you.

Action	Reaction
British built a fort in Western Pennsylvania	

2 IDENTIFYING PERSPECTIVES Use the chart below to fill in the interests of the different parties involved in the French and Indian War. What was each group's reason for wanting control of the Ohio River Valley?

Group	Reason for Wanting Control
British	
French	
Colonists	
Native Americans	

3 **INFERRING** Look at the chart. How is each group's need in conflict with the needs of the other groups?

4 ECONOMICS When Prime Minister William Pitt told the colonists they would not have to pay for the French and Indian War, how did Pitt imply it would be paid for?

5 **IDENTIFYING CAUSE AND EFFECT** How did colonists feel about Pitt's plan?

6 **GEOGRAPHY** In addition to the Ohio River Valley, to what other region did Pitt expand his attacks on the French?

7 HISTORY What was the significance of the Treaty of Paris?

ESSENTIAL QUESTION

Why does conflict develop between people and their government?

French Officer's Account of the Battle of Fort Necessity

DIRECTIONS: Read the following journal entry about the Battle of Fort Necessity by French officer Louis Coulon de Villiers. Then answer the accompanying questions.

EXPLORE THE CONTEXT: The Battle of Fort Necessity was the only battle in which George Washington ever surrendered. At the time Washington was only a lieutenant colonel for the British, not yet an American general. On July 3, 1754, in Farmington, Pennsylvania, in one of the earliest battles of the French and Indian War, de Villier's forces successfully attacked Fort Necessity, and Washington and his troops were forced to surrender.

VOCABULARY

intrenchment: trench
sally: volley
vigour: strength
advantageous: helpful
consent: agree
obliged: required
capitulation: surrender

1 ANALYZING SOURCES How does this source relate to what you already know about the Battle of Fort Necessity?

____

____

____

PRIMARY SOURCE: JOURNAL

“As we had no Knowledge of the Place, we presented our Flank to the Fort, when they began to fire upon us; and almost at the same Time, I perceived the *English* on the Right, in order of Battle, and coming towards us. The *Indians,* as well as ourselves, set up a great Cry, and advanced towards them; but they did not give us Time to fire upon them, before they sheltered themselves in an Intrenchment, which was adjoining to their Fort: After which, we aimed to invest the Fort, which was advantageously enough situated in a Meadow, within a Musket Shot from the Woods. We drew as near them as possible, that we might not expose his Majesty's Subjects to no Purpose. The Fire was very brisk on both Sides, and I chose that Place which seemed to me the most proper, in Case we should be exposed to a Sally. We fired so smartly, as to put out...the Fire of their Cannon with our Musket-Shot. Towards Six at Night, the Fire of the Enemy increased with more Vigour than ever, and lasted until Eight....We took particular Care to secure our Posts, to keep the *English* fast up in their Fort all Night; and after having fixed ourselves in the best Position we could, we let the *English* know, that if they would speak to us, we would stop firing.

They accepted the Proposal. There came a Captain to the Place where I was: I sent M. *le Mercier* to receive him, and I went to the Meadow, where I told him, that as

we were not at War, we were very willing to save them from the Cruelties to which they exposed themselves... but if they were stubborn, we would take away from them all Hopes of escaping; that we consented to be favourable to them at present, *as we were come only to revenge my Brother's Assassination*, and to oblige them to quit the Lands of the King our Master; and we agreed to grant them the Capitulation. . . . We considered, that nothing could be more advantageous than this Capitulation, as it was not proper to make Prisoners in a Time of Peace. We made the *English* consent to sign, that they had assassinated my Brother in his own Camp. We had Hostages for the Security of the *French* who were in their Power; we made them abandon the King's Country; we obliged them to leave us their Cannon, consisting of nine Pieces; we destroyed all their Horses and Cattle, and made them to sign, that the Favour we granted them, was only to prove, how desirous we were to use them as Friends. That very Night the Articles of Capitulation were signed, and the two Hostages I had demanded, were brought to my Camp. ”

—Louis Coulon de Villiers,
from his journal describing the attack on Fort Necessity

2 **ANALYZING POINTS OF VIEW** What was de Villiers's only reason for fighting the British, besides being attacked?

3 **SUMMARIZING** What were the terms of the proposal de Villiers offered the British?

4 **ASKING QUESTIONS** Why do you think de Villiers offered George Washington a peaceful surrender, instead of taking the opportunity to destroy his forces?

ESSENTIAL QUESTION

Why does conflict develop between people and their government?

Settlers Disobey the Proclamation of 1763

DIRECTIONS: Read the following "official report" from colonial governor Lord Dunmore about American settlements beyond the Proclamation Line of 1763. Then answer the accompanying questions.

EXPLORE THE CONTEXT: With its victory in the French and Indian War, Great Britain gained the land between the Appalachian Mountains and the Mississippi River. The colonists looked at this newly acquired land as a great economic opportunity, but they were soon disappointed. In an effort to prevent further hostilities between the colonists and the Native Americans, King George III's Proclamation of 1763 forbade colonists from settling west of the Appalachian Mountains. The British would find themselves unable to stem the tide of western migration.

VOCABULARY

arbitrary: artificial
demarcation: border
proclamation: an announcement of policy
infringement: a violation
avidity: eagerness
emigrating: migrating, moving
engrafted: an acquired characteristic

1 DETERMINING CENTRAL IDEAS Is Lord Dunmore for or against expansion of colonial settlement to the west?

____

____

____

PRIMARY SOURCE: REPORT

Lord Dunmore's official report to the Secretary of State Lord Dartmouth, on the Tendency of Americans to Ignore Arbitrary Demarcation Lines

"The policy of government, respecting the back country... I cannot, as you rightly observe, be ignorant of, and I ...transmitted... a letter to Lord North, accompanied by a state of all the arguments, made use of by the people best acquainted with the back countries of America, against extending any settlements to the westward... I was then, as I am still, of opinion that it were best not to extend any settlement beyond the limits of the colonies as they stood then.

I have invariably taken every step which depended on me to prevent any infringement of it by the people of this colony; nor, with regard to grants, has any infringement been made, or settlement either that the power of this government could prevent.

But my lord I have learnt from experience that the established authority of any government in America, and the policy of government at home, are both insufficient to restrain the Americans; and that they do and will remove as their avidity and restlessness incite them. They acquire no attachment to place; but wandering about seems engrafted in their nature; and it is a weakness incident to it, that they should ever imagine

the lands further off, are still better than those upon which they are already settled.

I have had, My Lord, frequent opportunities to reflect upon the emigrating spirit of the Americans, since my arrival to this government. There are considerable bodies of inhabitants settled at greater and less distances from the regular frontiers of, I believe, all the colonies. In this colony proclamations have been published from time to time to restrain them; but impressed from their earliest infancy with sentiments and habits, very different from those acquired by persons of a similar condition in England, they do not conceive that government has any right to forbid their taking possession of a vast tract of country, either uninhabited, or which serves as a shelter to a few scattered tribes of Indians. Nor can they be easily brought to entertain any belief of the permanent obligation of Treaties made with those people...”

—Virginia governor Lord Dunmore, from his official report to Lord Dartmouth, Secretary of State for the colonies, December 24, 1774

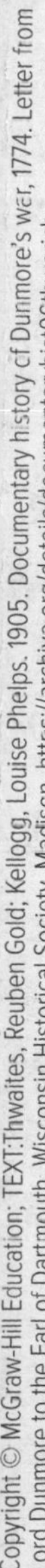

2 **IDENTIFYING CAUSES** How does Lord Dunmore think the Americans will respond to any government action restricting their settlement?

3 **ANALYZING POINTS OF VIEW** Can you tell what opinion Lord Dunmore has of Americans? How would you describe it?

4 **MAKING CONNECTIONS** How does this document demonstrate a conflict between people and their government?

ESSENTIAL QUESTION

Why does conflict develop between people and their government?

As you gather evidence to answer the Essential Question, think about:

- the new policies the British government established toward the colonists.
- the reactions of the American colonists to the British policies.

My Notes

No Taxation Without Representation

DIRECTIONS: Search for evidence in Chapter 3, Lesson 2 to help you answer the following questions.

1A IDENTIFYING CAUSE AND EFFECT How did the French and Indian War influence British policies in the American colonies?

1B How did this contribute to the development of conflict?

2A HISTORY Look at the chart called "A Growing Debt" found in the Student Edition textbook. How does the chart help explain why the British changed the way they governed the American colonies?

2B How would these changes have contributed to conflict with the colonies?

3 **IDENTIFYING CAUSE AND EFFECT** In the graphic organizer below, describe the Stamp and Townshend Acts. Then describe how the colonists reacted to them.

New Tax or Policy	Colonists' Reactions
Stamp Act	
Townshend Acts	

4 ECONOMICS Complete the following chart.

Individual or Group	How did their arguments or actions contribute to conflict between the colonists and the British government?
John Dickinson	
Sam Adams	
Patrick Henry	
Stamp Act Congress	

ESSENTIAL QUESTION

Why does conflict develop between people and their government?

John Adams on the Reaction to the Stamp Act

DIRECTIONS: Read the following excerpt and answer the accompanying questions.

EXPLORE THE CONTEXT: John Adams, who would become the second president of the United States, was an influential figure in the country's revolutionary and founding eras. A Boston lawyer, Adams became politically active in 1765 with Britain's introduction of the Stamp Act. The following excerpt is from Adams's diary from December 1765.

VOCABULARY

engine: machine
fabricated: created
thro: through
detestation: dislike
ignominy: disgrace
censure: punishment
discover: reveal

1 ANALYZING Does Adams believe the colonists' reaction to the Stamp Act will be important to the history of present and future citizens? Which of his words express his thoughts on the subject?

"I mean the stamp Act, has rasied and spread throught the whole spirit that will be recorded to our honor with all future genrations". John Adams reaction on the stamp Act is fine with him.

PRIMARY SOURCE: DIARY

"Braintree. December 18. [1765] Wednesday.

How great is my loss in neglecting to keep a regular journal through the last Spring, Summer, and Fall! ...The year 1765 has been the most remarkable year of my life. That enormous engine, fabricated by the British Parliament, for battering down all the rights and liberties of America, I mean the Stamp Act, has raised and spread through the whole continent a spirit that will be recorded to our honor with all future generations. In every colony, from Georgia to New Hampshire inclusively, the stamp distributors and inspectors have been compelled by the unconquerable rage of the people to renounce their offices. Such and so universal has been the resentment of the people, that every man who has dared to speak in favor of the stamps, or to soften the detestation in which they are held, how great soever his abilities and virtues had been esteemed before, or whatever his fortune, connections, and influence had been, has been seen to sink into universal contempt and ignominy.

The people, even to the lowest ranks, have become more attentive to their liberties, more inquisitive about them, and more determined to defend them, than they were ever before known or had occasion to be... Our presses have groaned, our pulpits have thundered, our legislatures have resolved, our towns have voted; the

crown officers have everywhere trembled, and all their little tools and creatures been afraid to speak and ashamed to be seen....

How long we are to remain in this languid condition, this passive obedience to the Stamp Act, is not certain. But such a pause cannot be lasting. Debtors grow insolent; creditors grow angry; and it is to be expected that the public offices will very soon be forced open, unless such favorable accounts should be received from England as to draw away the fears of the great, or unless a greater dread of the multitude should drive away the fear of censure from Great Britain.

It is my opinion that by this inactivity we discover cowardice, and too much respect to the Act. This rest appears to be, by implication at least, an acknowledgement of the authority of Parliament to tax us. And if this authority is once acknowledged and established, the ruin of America will become inevitable.”

—John Adams, from his diary, December 18, 1765

2 IDENTIFYING What does Adams say has happened to British officials and others who support the Stamp Act?

3 ANALYZING What does Adams mean when he says “Our Presses have groaned, our Pulpits have thundered, our Legislatures have resolved, our Towns have voted”?

The Presses are not liking the idea and people are angry towards the Stamp act and the ruler has changed the laws.

4 CIVICS How does Adams think the Stamp Act controversy has affected the colonists' view of freedom? Which words express his views?

ESSENTIAL QUESTION

Why does conflict develop between people and their government?

Consideration on the Trade and Finance of This Kingdom

DIRECTIONS: Read the following excerpt and answer the accompanying questions.

EXPLORE THE CONTEXT: While many American colonists strongly protested the taxes put in place by the Stamp and Townshend Acts, officials in the British government had a very different view. Thomas Whately, an official for the British treasury, wrote a book on British trade and economics in 1766. The following is an excerpt from his book.

VOCABULARY

Acquisitions: gains
publick: public
seasonable: suitable
Propriety: appropriateness

1 **DETERMING MEANING** Whately makes the analogy "the Darling Object of the Mother Country's Care." Who is the "Darling Object"? Who is the "Mother Country"? To what is he comparing the colonies?

____

____

____

____

____

____

PRIMARY SOURCE: BOOK

"Of all the Measures which were pursued for the Benefit of Trade, those were by far the most important which respected the Colonies, who have of late been the Darling Object of the Mother Country's Care: We are not yet recovered from a War undertaken solely for their Protection: Every Object for which it was begun, is accomplished; and still greater are obtained than at first were even thought of; but whatever may be the Value of the Acquisitions in America, the immediate Benefit of them is to the Colonies; ...

Were there no other Ground to require a Revenue from the Colonies, than as a Return for these Obligations, it would alone be a sufficient Foundation: Add to these the Advantages obtained for them by the Peace; add the Debt incurred by [Britain in] a War undertaken in their Defense only; the Distress thereby brought upon the [British] Finances, upon the Credit both publick and private, upon the Trade, and upon the people of this Country; and it must be acknowledged that no Time was ever so seasonable for claiming their Assistance. . . . [N]o more was desired than that they should contribute to the Preservation of the Advantages they have received, and take upon themselves a small Share of the [military] Establishment necessary for their own Protection: Upon these Principles several new Taxes

were laid upon the Colonies: Many were indeed . . . rather Regulations of Trade than Funds of Revenue: But some were intended to answer both Purposes. . . .

If from what has been said it appears, that no Principle of Finance or of Commerce forbids the Taxing of the Colonies for the Purposes of Revenue only; it must on the other Hand be admitted that the Circumstances of this Country [Britain] call for every Aid which any of its Subjects can give: And there is a peculiar Propriety in requiring it from the Americans, who have contributed so little and for whom so much has been done. . . . ”

—Thomas Whately, *Considerations on the Trade and Finances of This Kingdom*, 1766

2 **CITING TEXT EVIDENCE** Does Whately feel Britain is justified in asking for revenue from the colonies? What evidence can you cite from the excerpt?

____

____

____

____

____

3 **IDENTIFYING** What additional three reasons are listed for Britain to tax the colonies?

____

____

____

____

____

____

4 MULTIPLE PERSPECTIVES **DETERMINING POINT OF VIEW** How does Whately feel about what the colonies have contributed already?

____

____

____

____

____

____

Uniting the Colonists

DIRECTIONS: Search for evidence in Chapter 3, Lesson 3 to help you answer the following questions.

ESSENTIAL QUESTION

Why does conflict develop between people and their government?

As you gather evidence to answer the Essential Question, think about:

- the tensions that led up to the Boston Massacre.
- the causes and effects of the Boston Tea Party.

1 IDENTIFYING CAUSE AND EFFECT Use the chart to record important details surrounding the Boston Massacre.

Growing tensions prior to March 5, 1770

The Boston Massacre March 5, 1770

Actions by colonists to spread the news of the Boston Massacre

used Prop

2 INTERPRETING How did the Boston Massacre influence colonial opinion of Great Britain's rule?

The colonists Probably felt scared and Entimidated. They started to see the

My Notes

3 IDENTIFYING CAUSE AND EFFECT Fill in the chart with information surrounding the Boston Tea Party.

Cause: British policy on tea

The East India company shipped taxed tea.

Event: Boston Tea Party

The Sons of Liberty threw 342 chests (boxes) over board at midnight on December 16 th.

Effect: The Intolerable Acts

Pg. 109

Stamp Act & Tea Act.

ESSENTIAL QUESTION

Why does conflict develop between people and their government?

Engraving Showing the Boston Massacre

DIRECTIONS: Study the image and answer the accompanying questions.

EXPLORE THE CONTEXT: This engraving by Paul Revere first appeared in late March, 1770. The title above the picture reads: "The Bloody Massacre perpetrated in King Street BOSTON on March 5th 1770 by a party of the 29th Regt"

PRIMARY SOURCE: ENGRAVING

1 DESCRIBING Describe the scene shown in the image.

2 ANALYZING How is the crowd of colonists shown in the image? What do they appear to be doing? Does this depiction correspond with the description of the event in your text? Explain.

3 ANALYZING How are the British soldiers depicted in the image? Describe the action they are taking and their expressions.

4 DETERMINING POINT OF VIEW From whose viewpoint, the British or the American colonists, does this image appear to show the event? What emotions or response do you think the image was meant to draw from viewers? What evidence can you supply from the engraving to support your answer?

ESSENTIAL QUESTION

Why does conflict develop between people and their government?

The Glorious Seventy Four

DIRECTIONS: Read the following excerpt and answer the accompanying questions.

EXPLORE THE CONTEXT: "The Glorious Seventy Four" was one of many protests, or liberty, songs that appeared in the American colonies beginning in 1765. The anonymous song first appeared in Virginia in 1774. Like other liberty songs, "The Glorious Seventy Four" brought together and inspired colonists in their opposition to British rule.

NOTE: Bute and Mansfield and North were British political figures considered responsible for policies disliked in the colonies.

VOCABULARY

spurn: reject
sires: fathers
Neptune: god of the sea in Roman mythology
stores: supplies

PRIMARY SOURCE: SONG

" COME, come, my brave boys, from my song you shall hear,
That we'll crown seventy four a most glorious year;
We'll convince Bute and Mansfield, and North, though they rave,
Britons still, like themselves, spurn the chains of a slave.

CHORUS:

Hearts of oak were our sires,
Hearts of oak are their sons,
Like them we are ready, as firm and as steady,
To fight for our freedom with swords and with guns. . . .

Their tea still is driven away from our shores,
Or presented to Neptune, or rots in our stores;
But to awe, to divide, till we crouch to their sway,
On brave Boston their vengeance they fiercely display.

CHORUS: Hearts of oak, etc.

Now, unask'd we unite, we agree to a man,
See our stores flow to Boston from rear and from van;

Hark! the snows, how it flies, freedom's voice, how it sounds!
From each country, each clime, bark, the echo rebounds!

1 ANALYZING In the first stanza, how do you know the writer still considers Americans as British subjects?

____

____

____

2 IDENTIFYING Underline the phrase in the song that refers to the Boston Tea Party.

. . . *continued*

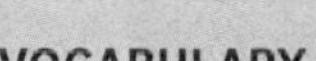

CHORUS: Hearts of oak, etc.

With sons, who I foster'd and cherish'd of yore,
Fair freedom shall flourish till time is no more;
No tyrant shall rule them, 'tis Heaven's decree,
They shall never be slaves while they dare to be free.

CHORUS: Hearts of oak, etc. ”

VOCABULARY

van: front
clime: climate (meaning region)
bark: angry voice
foster'd: raised
of yore: from times past

3 **CITING TEXT EVIDENCE** Which phrase in the song suggests that the cause of freedom is popular throughout the colonies?

4 **CITING TEXT EVIDENCE** Which phrases or lines in the song relate it to the specific time period and events from that period?

5 **DETERMINING POINT OF VIEW** Describe the tone of the song. What emotions or feelings are being expressed?

6 **DRAWING CONCLUSIONS** What does this song suggest about the growing conflict between the American colonies and Great Britain? In what way can such songs help or hurt the cause? Explain.

A Call to Arms

DIRECTIONS: Search for evidence in Chapter 3, Lesson 4 to help you answer the following questions.

ESSENTIAL QUESTION

Why does conflict develop between people and their government?

As you gather evidence to answer the Essential Question, think about:

- the events leading up to the battles of Lexington and Concord.
- the impact of actions by colonial supporters and opponents.

My Notes

1 **EXPLAINING** Why did the colonists come together to respond to acts of the British?

Toprotect the sons of Liberty - John Hancock & Samuel Adams. The British military was

2 GEOGRAPHY USING MAPS Study the map of the Battles of Lexington and Concord in your textbook. About how far did Dawes ride to Lexington? About how far did Prescott ride from Lexington to Concord?

Dawes - 8-10 miles
Prescott - 4miles

3 **ANALYZING** How did the work of colonial messengers like Paul Revere support the colonists in their confrontation with the British at the battles of Lexington and Concord?

Could prepare for battle

4 **EXPLAINING** How did Benedict Arnold's betrayal make conflict with the British more difficult for the colonists?

Benedict sold military information to the British.

5 SEQUENCING Use the chart below to describe the sequence of events that led to the Battles of Lexington and Concord.

Event 1

Britian increasing taxes and making laws (Coercive Act).

Event 2

Colonies except Georiga gathering together and discounting complaints against the British.

Event 3

Britian sending over 700 trops to fight the colonists.

Battles of Lexington and Concord

Lexington - Sam Adams & John Handcock

minute men. military was proding

men ready to fight in a minute military

April 18, 1775

ESSENTIAL QUESTION

Why does conflict develop between people and their government?

VOCABULARY

embattled: fighting

votive stone: monument

redeem: offset

sires: fathers

shaft: monument

Concord Hymn

DIRECTIONS: Read "Concord Hymn" by Ralph Waldo Emerson and answer the questions that follow.

EXPLORE THE CONTEXT: Ralph Waldo Emerson was a leading writer, speaker and thinker of the 1800s. He was a firm believer in the rights of the individual to freedom of thought and expression. He wrote "Concord Hymn" for the 1836 dedication of the Concord Monument, which marked the site of the Battle of Concord. It was first read at the Independence Day celebration for the city of Concord in 1837 and then sung by a choir as a hymn. Emerson felt a personal connection to the historic battle because his grandfather, William Emerson, witnessed it while he was living in the area.

PRIMARY SOURCE: SONG

"By the rude bridge that arched the flood,
Their flag to April's breeze unfurled,
Here once the embattled farmers stood
And fired the shot heard round the world.
The foe long since in silence slept;
Alike the conqueror silent sleeps;
And Time the ruined bridge has swept
Down the dark stream which seaward creeps.
On this green bank, by this soft stream,
We set today a votive stone;
That memory may their deed redeem,
When, like our sires, our sons are gone.
Spirit, that made those heroes dare
To die, and leave their children free,
Bid Time and Nature gently spare
The shaft we raise to them and thee."

1 **HISTORY** In the first stanza, where is the narrator standing, and what is he imagining or thinking about?

2 **INTERPRETING** What does Emerson mean by "And fired the shot heard round the world"?

3 **INTERPRETING** How is Emerson using the words "slept" and "sleeps"?

4 **INFERRING** What is Emerson's attitude toward the revolutionaries? What language reveals this?

ESSENTIAL QUESTION

Why does conflict develop between people and their government?

Before I Leave America

DIRECTIONS: Read the following excerpt and answer the accompanying questions.

EXPLORE THE CONTEXT: Isaac Wilkins was a representative in the New York General Assembly representing the town of Westchester. Facing the fury of Patriots because he was a Loyalist, Wilkins fled his home to take refuge in England. He published this open letter in a New York newspaper before he left.

VOCABULARY

proceeded: came from
endeavors: actions
inconsiderable: unimportant
maxim: principle
amity: friendship
conscientiously: virtuously

1 **DETERMINING POINT OF VIEW** Why does Wilkins publish this open letter?

____

____

____

____

PRIMARY SOURCE: NEWSPAPER

"My Countrymen,

Censured and harassed by New York Patriots, a Loyalist declares his sentiments before leaving his native country for Nova Scotia.

Before I leave America, the land I love, and in which is contained everything that is valuable and dear to me, my wife, my children, my friends and property; permit me to make a short and faithful declaration, which I am induced to do neither through fear nor a consciousness of having acted wrong. An honest man and a Christian hath nothing to apprehend [fear] from this world. God is my judge, and God is my witness, that all I have done, written or said in relation to the present unnatural dispute between Great Britain and her Colonies proceeded from an honest intention of serving my country. Her welfare and prosperity were the objects towards which all my endeavors have been directed. They still are the sacred objects which I shall ever steadily and invariably keep in view. And when in England, all the influence that so inconsiderable a man as I am can have, shall be exerted in her behalf.

It has been my constant maxim through life to do my duty conscientiously, and to trust the issue of my actions to the Almighty. May that God, in whose hands are all

events, speedily restore peace and liberty to my unhappy country. May Great Britain and America be soon united in the bands of everlasting amity; and when united, may they continue a free, a virtuous, and happy nation to the end of time.

I leave America, and every endearing connection, because I will not raise my hand against my Sovereign nor will I draw my sword against my Country. When I can conscientiously draw it in her favor, my life shall be cheerfully devoted to her service**”**.

—Isaac Wilkins, *Rivington's New York Gazetteer,* May 11, 1775

2 **CITING TEXT EVIDENCE** How does Wilkins feel about his decision? What evidence can you cite to support this answer?

3 **IDENTIFYING** What is Wilkins's position on the necessity of the Revolution?

4 **CITING TEXT EVIDENCE** What does Wilkins hope will happen in the near future? What evidence can you cite to support this answer?

ESSENTIAL QUESTION

Why does conflict develop between people and their government?

My Notes

Declaring Independence

DIRECTIONS: Search for evidence in Chapter 3, Lesson 5 to help you answer the following questions.

1 **SUMMARIZING** What reasons did colonists give in the "Causes and Necessity of Taking Up Arms" declaration for the conflict with the British? Use the chart below to summarize/list the reasons.

2 **COMPARING AND CONTRASTING** How did Benjamin Franklin, John Hancock and Thomas Jefferson contribute to the efforts that led to independence? Complete the graphic organizer below by describing what each delegate did to contribute to the efforts toward independence.

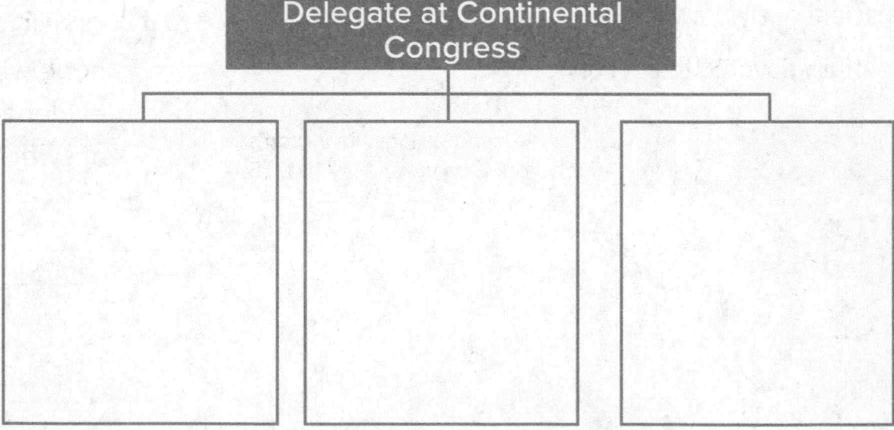

3 IDENTIFYING PROBLEM AND SOLUTION Although they were not yet ready to break away from their difficult relationship with Britain, what steps did the colonists take to start governing the colonies themselves?

Problem

Solutions

4 SEQUENCING How did General Washington prepare for his strike against the British?

____

____

____

____

5 EXPLAINING Why did Richard Henry Lee's June 1766 resolution lead to intense debate?

____

____

____

____

ESSENTIAL QUESTION

Why does conflict develop between people and their government?

A Woman's Opinion of the Boston Tea Party

DIRECTIONS: Read the following excerpt from a letter about the Boston Tea Party from Mercy Otis Warren to her friend Hannah Winthrop and answer the questions that follow.

EXPLORE THE CONTEXT: Mercy Otis Warren (1728–1814) was a political writer concerned with the American Revolution. She was highly educated for a woman of her time. Many of her writings were published anonymously and throughout her lifetime were wrongly thought to have been written by men. She published a collection of poems and plays under her own name, which was unheard of for women of the period. Her husband, Massachusetts politician James Warren, unlike most men of the time, viewed and treated his wife as an equal. He encouraged her writing and invited her to join political gatherings and discussions that were normally restricted to men.

VOCABULARY

speculate: theorize
commotions: clashes
acquiesce: give in
actuate: spur to action
benevolent: caring
laudable: admirable
designs: plans
apprehension: worry
expatiate: say more
perplexity: confusion
exhilarated: thrilled
Hemisphere: world

1 SUMMARIZING In the first paragraph, what is Warren saying she plans to do?

____

____

____

____

____

PRIMARY SOURCE: LETTER

"When I took up my pen I determined to leave the field of politicks to those whose proper business it is to speculate and to act at this important crisis; but the occurrences that have lately taken place are so alarming and the subject so interwoven with the enjoyments of social and domestic life as to command the attention of the mother and the wife who before the contest is decided may be called to weep over the manes of her beloved sons....

I tremble for the event of the present commotions;- there must be a noble struggle to recover the expiring liberties of our injured country; we must re-purchase them at the expence of blood, or tamely acquiesce, and embrace the hand that holds out the chain to us and our children.

Much interested in the success of the conflict — I feel myself unequal to the combat yet hope the women will never get the better of that disinterested regard to universal happiness which ought to actuate the benevolent mind. Heaven give us strength to sustain the shock, if this country should be compelled to the last appeal....

Whether the Patriots of the present day will be able to effect their laudable designs in our time is very uncertain, yet I trust they will lay the foundation deep and that future generations will not be wanting to

themselves, but will maintain and support the priviledges to which they are entitled both by nature and compact...

...the fears of a fatal interruption of private and social enjoyment often fill my mind with gloomy apprehensions...

But I expatiate no longer on the prospects of public distress nor dwell on the painful sensations of the human heart in this day of general perplexity, when the hero and the patriot are alternately exhilerated or depressed by the varying aspects of the political Hemisphere;- nor shall I make an apology for touching on a subject a little out of the line of female attention, as we are both happily united to such companions as think us capable of taking part in whatever affects themselves. As for that part of mankind who think every rational pursuit lies beyond the reach of a sex too generally devoted to folly, their censure or applause is equally indifferent to your sincere friend. ”

—Mercy Otis Warren, letter to Hannah Winthrop, after January 1, 1774

2 **INFERRING** The second paragraph reveals Warren's point of view regarding the struggle between the Patriots and the British. Does Warren support the rebels in their actions against the British government? Why or why not?

3 **HISTORY** What does Warren hope will be the outcome of the struggle?

4 **ANALYZING** In your own words, what does Warren say in her final paragraph about other people's attitudes about women and politics?

The Deceiver Unmasked

ESSENTIAL QUESTION

Why does conflict develop between people and their government?

DIRECTIONS: Read the following excerpt and answer the accompanying questions.

EXPLORE THE CONTEXT: After Thomas Paine's pamphlet *Common Sense* had been printed and distributed in January 1776, it immediately became a sensation. Loyalists were shocked by Paine's radical proposals to form a new nation and sever from Great Britain. The Reverend Charles Inglis was a Loyalist who led the large Trinity Church in New York City. It is believed that Inglis wrote "The Deceiver Unmasked," as a direct rebuttal to *Common Sense*.

VOCABULARY

availed: taken advantage for
calamitous: disastrous
infallibly: necessarily
Sensible: Realizing
insinuates: implies
insidious: sneaky
cants: using self-righteous speech
raillery: ridicule
malignant: evil, vengeful

PRIMARY SOURCE: PAMPHLET

"The author of COMMON SENSE has availed himself of all those advantages. Under the mask of friendship to America, in the present calamitous situation of affairs, he gives vent to his own private resentment and ambition, and recommends a scheme which must infallibly prove ruinous. He proposes that we should renounce our allegiance to our sovereign [king], break off all connection with Great Britain, and set up an independent empire of the republican kind. Sensible that such a proposal must, even at this time, be shocking to the ears of Americas, he insinuates that the novelty of his sentiments is the only obstacle to their success that "perhaps they are not yet sufficiently fashionable to procure them general favor . . .

I find no Common Sense in this pamphlet, but much uncommon frenzy. It is an outrageous insult on the common sense of Americans, an insidious attempt to poison their minds and seduce them from their loyalty and truest interest. The principles of government laid down in it are not only false but such as scarcely ever entered the head of a crazy politician . . .

... In the section before me [Section III, "Common Sense"], this Gentleman unfolds his grand scheme of a revolt from the crown of England and setting up an independent republic in America. He leaves no method untried, which the most experienced practitioner in the art of deceiving could invent to persuade any people to a measure which was against their inclinations and

1 DETERMINING POINT OF VIEW What seems to be Inglis's main purpose in writing "The Deceiver Unmasked"?

interest, that was both disagreeable and destructive. He unsays in one place what he had said in another if it happens to serve the present purpose. He cants and whines;, he tries wit, raillery, and declamation by turns. But his main attack is upon the passions of his readers, especially their pity and resentment — the latter of which is too apt to be predominant in mankind. As for himself, he seems to be everywhere transported with rage — a rage that knows no limits and hurries him along like an impetuous torrent. Everything that falls not in with his own scheme, or that he happens to dislike, is represented in the most aggravated light and with the most distorted features. Such a malignant spirit I have seldom met with in any composition. As often as I look into this section, I cannot forbear imaging to myself a guilty culprit, fresh reeking from the lashes of indignant justice, and raging against the hand that inflicted them. Yet I cannot persuade myself that such fire and fury are genuine marks of patriotism. On the contrary, they rather indicate that some mortifying disappointment is rankling at heart, that some tempting object of ambition is in view, or probably both. ”

—Rev. Charles Inglis, “The Deceiver Unmasked,” likely a rebuttal to *Common Sense*

2 CITING TEXT EVIDENCE What does Inglis think of Thomas Paine as a person? What evidence can you cite to support this answer?

3 IDENTIFYING What does Inglis believe most Americans will think of *Common Sense*?

4 CITING TEXT EVIDENCE In what way does Inglis question Paine's patriotism? What evidence can you cite to support this answer?

ESSENTIAL QUESTION

Why does conflict develop between people and their government?

1 Think About It

Review the supporting questions that you developed at the beginning of the chapter. Review the evidence that you gathered in Chapter 3. Were you able to answer each Supporting Question?

If there was not enough evidence to answer your Supporting Questions, what additional evidence do you think you need to consider?

____

____

____

____

2 Organize Your Evidence

Read the Essential Question and think about how you would answer it, or what position you would take, based on what you learned in this chapter. Use a chart like the one below to organize the evidence you will use to support your position.

Source of information	Specific evidence from the source to cite	How evidence helps support my Position Statement

3 Write About It

A position statement related to the Essential Question should reflect your conclusion about the evidence. Write a Position Statement for the ESSENTIAL QUESTION: ***Why does conflict develop between people and their government?***

4 Talk About It

Work in a small group to present your position statement and evidence. Gather feedback from your classmates before you write your final conclusion. You may choose to refine your position statement after you have discussed it with your classmates. Group members should listen to one other's arguments, ask questions, and offer constructive advice about the statement.

5 Connect to the Essential Question

On a separate piece of paper, develop an argumentative essay to answer the ESSENTIAL QUESTION: ***Why does conflict develop between people and their government?***

CITIZENSHIP

TAKING ACTION

MAKE CONNECTIONS You may have heard of a Pakistani woman named Malala Yousafzai. As a teenager, Malala came into conflict with her local government, which would not allow girls to attend school. Malala spoke out publicly about her view that all girls in Pakistan should be educated. The oppressive Taliban government tried to silence her, but she continued blogging and speaking out. The Taliban then sent someone to assassinate Malala as she rode home from school on the bus. She recovered from the gunshot wound, however, and continues to speak out. In 2014, Malala was awarded the Nobel Prize for Peace for her courage in promoting education for girls in Pakistan.

DIRECTIONS: What is an issue in the United States that you feel you should speak out about? Find a creative way to express your views. Write a song, speech, blog post, or other expression of the issue you want to highlight.

The American Revolution

ESSENTIAL QUESTION

Why does conflict develop?

Think about how conflicts expand to include other groups of people.

TALK ABOUT IT

Discuss with a partner what type of information you would need in order to understand the American Revolution from the viewpoint of groups that were outside the source of the conflict. For example, you might wonder: Who else lived in the regions where the American Revolution took place?

DIRECTIONS: Now write down three additional questions that will help you explain how the American Revolution expanded to include people who were neither Patriot nor Loyalist soldiers, and why these outside groups were involved.

MY RESEARCH QUESTIONS

Supporting Question 1:

____

____

Supporting Question 2:

____

____

Supporting Question 3:

____

____

ESSENTIAL QUESTION

Why does conflict develop?

As you gather evidence to answer the Essential Question, think about

- how the British and the Patriots responded to the outbreak of war.
- how the fighting impacted women and African Americans.
- why each side had certain advantages over the other.

My Notes

The War for Independence

DIRECTIONS: Search for evidence in Chapter 4, Lesson 1 to help you answer the following questions.

1 IDENTIFYING MAIN IDEAS In the graphic organizer below, describe the advantages and disadvantages of each side.

	British	Patriots
Advantages		
Disadvantages		

2 **CIVIC AND POLITICAL INSTITUTIONS** Explain why the Continental Congress faced obstacles organizing and paying for the war effort.

3 **DESCRIBING** Why was the Patriot cause near collapse at the beginning of the war?

4 **ANALYZING** Why were African Americans initially banned from serving in the Continental Army, but later allowed?

5 **GEOGRAPHY** How did geographic considerations play a role in the British strategy at the beginning of the war?

ESSENTIAL QUESTION

Why does conflict develop?

The Sentiments of an American Woman

DIRECTIONS: Read the following excerpt, and then answer the accompanying questions.

EXPLORE THE CONTEXT: In 1780, Esther De Berdt Reed, the wife of Pennsylvania's governor, launched a fundraising campaign with other influential Philadelphia women. They raised $300,000 to support the Continental Army. The broadside below, published anonymously but probably written by Reed, was issued during this campaign.

VOCABULARY

broadside: essay or pamphlet printed on a single page
commencement: beginning
manifested: acted on
sensible: aware
sex: gender
superfluities: unnecessary items
valor: bravery
mercenary: paid to fight

PRIMARY SOURCE: BROADSIDE

“On the commencement of actual war, the Women of America manifested a firm resolution to contribute as much as could depend on them to the deliverance of their country. Animated by the purest patriotism, they are sensible of sorrow at this day in not offering more than barren wishes for the success of so glorious a Revolution. They aspire to render themselves more really useful, and this sentiment is universal from the north to the south of the Thirteen United States. Our ambition is kindled by the fame of those heroines of antiquity, who have rendered their sex illustrious and have proved to the universe that if the weakness of our Constitution, if opinion and manners did not forbid us to march to glory by the same paths as the Men, we should at least equal and sometimes surpass them in our love for the public good.

The time is arrived to display the same sentiments which animated us at the beginning of the Revolution when we renounced the use of teas, however agreeable to our taste, rather than receive them from our persecutors, when we made it appear to them that we placed former necessaries in the rank of superfluities, when our liberty was interested, when our republican and laborious hands spun the flax, prepared the linen intended for the use of our soldiers, when exiles and fugitives we supported with courage all the evils which are the concomitants of war. Let us not lose a moment; let us be engaged to offer the homage of our gratitude at the altar of military valor, and you, our brave deliverers, while mercenary slaves combat to cause you to share with them the irons with which they are loaded, receive with a free hand our offering, the purest which can be presented to your virtue. ❞

—anonymous broadside, probably
written by Esther De Berdt Reed, 1780

1 **DETERMINING PURPOSE** What purpose was served by publishing this broadside?

2 **ANALYZING POINT OF VIEW** Why would the author prefer to remain anonymous?

3 **IDENTIFYING** According to the author, what kinds of support had American women given to the war effort?

4 **CITING TEXT EVIDENCE** What opposition does the author expect? How does she answer this opposition? What evidence can you cite from the excerpt?

ESSENTIAL QUESTION

Why does conflict develop?

Narrative of Boyrereau Brinch

DIRECTIONS: Read the following excerpt from the memoirs of Boyrereau Brinch, a formerly enslaved man who served in the Connecticut militia in the American Revolution. Then answer the accompanying questions.

EXPLORE THE CONTEXT: Boyrereau Brinch told an account of his life as an enslaved person to Benjamin Prentiss, who then published the tale as *The Blind African Slave* in 1810. Brinch was forced to fight for the British navy after being captured at age 16, then came to the colonies as an enslaved person in Connecticut. We know that he enlisted in the militia there in 1777 and fought for the Patriots. He was emancipated from slavery after the war in 1783, in honor of his service.

VOCABULARY

Esq.: Esquire, a land-owning gentleman

rod: distance of 16 1/2 feet *(8 rods is approximately 50 yards)*

arms: weapons

cutlass: sword

emancipated: freed

PRIMARY SOURCE: MEMOIR

“When this lady died I descended like real estate in fee simple to her son Benjamin Stiles, Esq. About four years after her death, her two sons, Benjamin and David, were drafted to fight in the revolution. I also entered the banners of freedom. Alas! Poor African Slave, to liberate freemen, my tyrants...

While I stood there anxiously waiting for their return, I suddenly discovered a man riding up to me not more than eight rods distant on full speed with a pistol in his hand and ordered me to lay down my arms. But not being so instructed by my officers you may well suppose that I did not. At first I thought he was a Jerseyman and was attempting to fool me, as they had played some such pranks before upon some of the soldiers belonging to our line—therefore in return I demanded to whom I was to surrender and by what authority he demanded it....

After we were disbanded, I returned to my old master at Woodbury, with whom I lived one year; my services in the American war, having emancipated me from further slavery, and from being bartered or sold. My master consented that I might go where I pleased and seek my fortune... I travelled to the town of Poltney in Vermont.... Here I enjoyed the pleasures of a freeman; my food was sweet, my labor pleasure: and one bright gleam of life seemed to shine upon me.”

—Boyrereau Brinch, formerly enslaved person, as told to Benjamin Prentiss, 1810

TEXT: Brinch, Boyrereau; Prentiss, Benjamin F. 1810. Boyrereau Brinch and Benjamin F. Prentiss, *The Blind African Slave, Or Memoirs of Boyrereau Brinch.* Printed by Harry Whitney, St. Albans, VT.

1. **IDENTIFYING CAUSE AND EFFECT** Describe the steps that took Brinch from slavery to freedom.

2. **ANALYZING POINT OF VIEW** Why does Brinch use the phrase "my tyrants"?

3. **IDENTIFYING** What are the two reasons Brinch does not immediately surrender his weapon when asked?

4. **ANALYZING** What can you infer about Brinch's reason for joining the Connecticut militia?

5. **CITING TEXT EVIDENCE** How does Brinch feel about his emancipation? What evidence can you cite from the excerpt?

LESSON 2
The War Continues

THE STORY BEGINS...

ESSENTIAL QUESTION

Why does conflict develop?

As you gather evidence to answer the Essential Question, think about

- why other countries became allies of the Americans.
- how individuals from other countries helped the Americans.
- how developments on the home front led to increased conflict.

My Notes

The War Continues

DIRECTIONS: Search for evidence in Chapter 4, Lesson 2 to help you answer the following questions.

1 **IDENTIFYING EFFECTS** Complete the table by identifying the effects of the Battle of Saratoga on each European country.

Effects of the Battle of Saratoga	
On France	
On Spain	

2 GEOGRAPHY What geographic factors made the Continental Army's stay at Valley Forge difficult?

3 **DETERMINING CENTRAL IDEAS** During the American Revolution, many individuals came from other countries to help the Americans. Complete the table. Be sure to fill in each blank.

Foreign Individuals Who Helped During the American Revolution		
Person	**Country**	**Contribution**
Marquis de Lafayette	France	
Thaddeus Kosciuszko		helped build important defenses
	Poland	won promotion to rank of General
	Prussia	trained troops at Valley Forge
Juan de Miralles		

3A GEOGRAPHY Consider the table you just completed. What do all of the entries in the second column have in common?

____

____

3B **EXPLAINING** What is the most likely reason for the answer in 3A?

____

____

____

4 **GEOGRAPHY** What conflict did each group of people have with most leaders and soldiers of the American Revolution? Or with the ideas of "liberty" and "freedom" that inspired them?

Group	Conflict with Liberty and Freedom
American Women	
Enslaved African Americans	
American Loyalists	

5 **HISTORY** List some ways that non-American individuals and other nations participated in the American Revolution.

____

____

____

____

ESSENTIAL QUESTION

Why does conflict develop?

Hill of Baton Rouge

DIRECTIONS: Read this excerpt from a poem about Don Bernardo Gálvez's capture of Báton Rouge.

EXPLORE THE CONTEXT: Bernardo de Gálvez y Madrid (1746-1786), Viscount of Gálveston and Count of Gálvez, was a Spanish military officer who served as governor of Louisiana and Cuba during the colonial period. He led Spanish troops against the British in the American Revolution. The city of Galveston, Texas, is named for him.

Julien de Lallande Poydras (1740-1824) was a French American businessman, teacher, poet, and politician who supported statehood for Louisiana. He wrote this poem in 1779, the same year that Spain declared war on Britain. The poem describes Bernardo de Gálvez as he leads his troops to victory over the British in Baton Rouge.

PRIMARY SOURCE: POEM

"I saw this Hero, who causes your alarms.
He resembled a God, clothed in his arms,
His superb plume, as the wind blew,
And his tossed hair were like ornaments.
A noble and proud bearing announced his courage,
The heroic virtue, shining on his face.
With one hand he held his dazzling saber,
With the other he held back his leaping horse.
He marched at the head of his brilliant procession,
who felt full of noble ardor and proud of the privilege
To run with him, the hazard of fighting.
They desired dangers to call them to arms.
The brave infantrymen followed them in rows,
All bubbling with the fire of Mars and Athena,
They walked in good order, with feet sure and bold,
And contemptuous of perils, they flew to the enemy.
Following them, one saw, walking without artifice,
Our proud inhabitants, the Intrepid Militia;

VOCABULARY

arms: weapons
saber: sword
ardor: passion
hazard: obstacles
artifice: tricks, schemes
intrepid: fearless

. . . *continued*

and their skillful hands, which once plowed furrows,
now raised bastions with the same ardor;
and made ditches, parapets, and trenches,
machines and canon mounts, invented for battle.
For the art of conquering they seem to be born.”

—Julien de Lallande Poydras, “The Capture of the Hill of Baton Rouge by Monseigneur de Galvez,” 1779

furrows: rows in soil in which seeds are planted
perils: dangers
parapets: walls
trenches: ditches

1 **ANALYZING POINTS OF VIEW** What does this excerpt demonstrate about the poet’s attitude toward war with the British?

____

____

2 **CITING TEXT EVIDENCE** What phrases does the poet use to describe Gálvez as a leader who should be followed?

____

____

3 **INTERPRETING** What effect does Gálvez have on the soldiers who have joined his militia? What language supports this?

____

____

4 **INFERRING** Why do you think the soldiers were eager to follow Gálvez into battle?

____

____

5 **DRAWING CONCLUSIONS** How might this poem have influenced other Spaniards to join the war against the British?

____

____

ESSENTIAL QUESTION

Why does conflict develop?

Lafayette on the American Revolution

DIRECTIONS: Read the following letters written by the Marquis de Lafayette.

EXPLORE THE CONTEXT: The Marquis de Lafayette of France came to the United States as a 19-year-old volunteer in June 1777. Lafayette was excited about the ideas expressed in the Declaration of Independence, and eager to join the battle for freedom. He believed the American cause represented the future of humanity.

1 ANALYZING POINTS OF VIEW How does Lafayette's love of liberty contrast with the way he felt in college?

____

____

____

____

2 INFERRING How does Lafayette's description of college help explain why he supports the colonists in their fight for freedom?

____

____

____

____

____

____

PRIMARY SOURCE: LETTER

“An irresistible passion that would induce me to believe in innate ideas and the truth of prophecy, has decided my career. I have always loved liberty with the enthusiasm which actuates the religious man... On leaving college, where nothing had displeased more than a state of dependence, I viewed the greatness and the littleness of the court with contempt, the frivolities of society with pity, the minute pedantry of the army with disgust, and oppression of every sort with indignation. The attraction of the American Revolution drew me suddenly to my proper place; I felt myself tranquil only when sailing between the continent whose powers I braved, and the place where, although our arrive and success were problematical, I could, at the age of nineteen, take refuge in the alternative of conquering or perishing in the cause to which I had devoted myself”.

--Marquis de Lafayette, from a letter explaining why he joined the American Revolution

"Be so good, Sir, as to present to Congress my plain and hearty thanks, with a frank assurance of a candid attachment, the only one worth being offered to the representatives of a free people. The moment I heard of America, I loved her; the moment I knew she was fighting for freedom, I burnt with a desire of bleeding for her; and the moment I shall be able to serve her, at any time, or in any part of the world, will be the happiest of my life".

—Marquis de Lafayette, letter to Henry Laurens, president of the Continental Congress, September 23, 1778

VOCABULARY

induce: cause
innate: natural
actuates: motivates
contempt: disrespect
frivolities: foolishness
pedantry: boring training
indignation: anger at unfair treatment
tranquil: peaceful
refuge: shelter

3 **INTERPRETING** What does Lafayette mean when he says that the "American Revolution drew me suddenly to my proper place"?

4 **ANALYZING** Why does Lafayette say that he "take[s] refuge in the alternative of conquering or perishing in the cause to which I had devoted myself"?

5 **CITING TEXT EVIDENCE** Which phrases in the second letter describe the "irresistible passion" Lafayette feels for the American Revolution?

ESSENTIAL QUESTION

Why does conflict develop?

As you gather evidence to answer the Essential Question, think about

- how Native Americans became involved in the war in the West.
- how the war at sea was fought and which side was better equipped.
- how early losses gave way to successes for the Americans.

My Notes

Battlegrounds Shift

1 **EXPLAINING** Why did more Native American groups side with the British than with the Patriots?

2 **IDENTIFYING CAUSE AND EFFECT** What was the attitude of mountain people in the Carolinas? Why did they decide to attack the British?

3 **EXPLAINING** How did the Spanish declaration of war on Britain aid the Patriots' cause?

4 SEQUENCING Why did General Cornwallis give up his campaign to conquer the Carolinas? Use the chart below to describe the sequence of events.

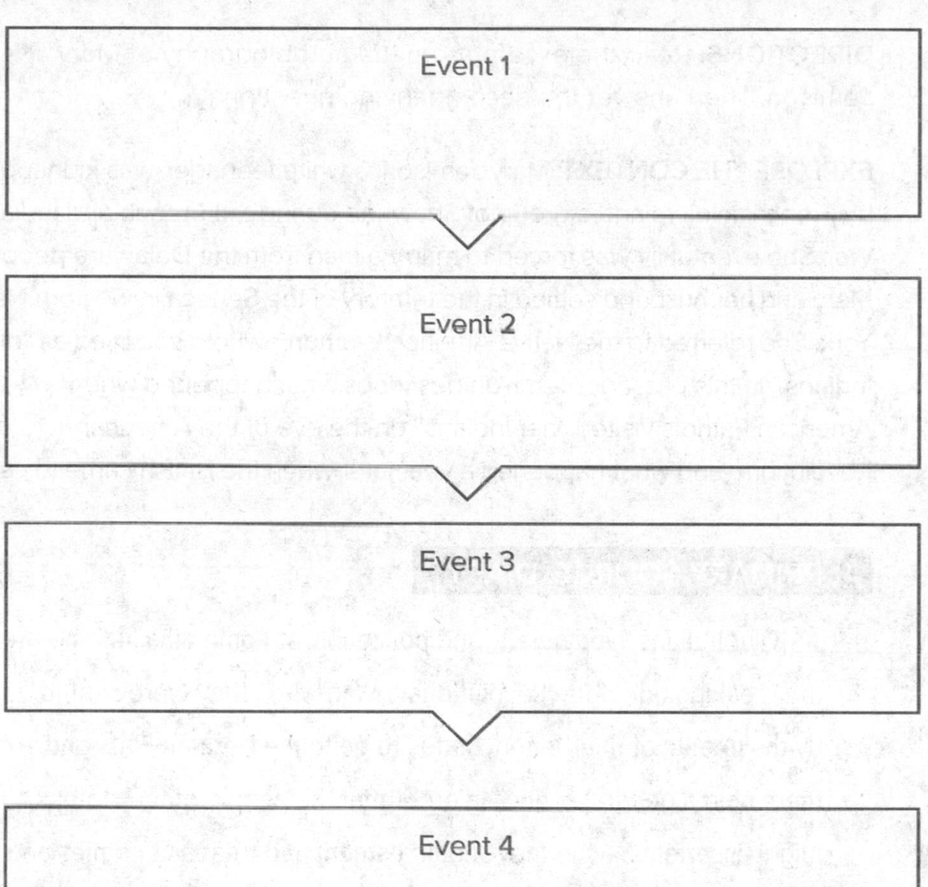

ESSENTIAL QUESTION

Why does conflict develop?

A Captive Recalls Meetings with the Americans and British

DIRECTIONS: Read the excerpt from the autobiography of Mary Jemison. Then answer the accompanying questions.

EXPLORE THE CONTEXT: Mary Jemison, a white teenager, was kidnapped by French soldiers and a group of Shawnee during the French and Indian War. She eventually was forced to marry a man from the Delaware people. Mary and her husband settled in the territory of the Seneca in western New York. She referred to the Native Americans among whom she lived as "our Indians." In this passage, Jemison describes what happened when American Patriots visited "her Indians" on the eve of the American Revolution—and what happened a year later when the British came to call.

VOCABULARY

council: meeting
ascertain: determine
neutrality: impartiality; not taking one side or the other
din: commotion; disturbance
subduing: conquering; defeating
entreaties: appeals; requests
avarice: greed
persevere: continue

1 EXPLAINING CAUSES
Why do you think the Native Americans agreed to meet with the Americans, and later the British?

____

____

____

____

____

____

____

PRIMARY SOURCE: DIARY

"[O]ur Indians lived quietly and peaceably at home till a little before the breaking out of the Revolutionary War, when they were sent for ... by the people of the [United] States to go to the German Flats and there hold a general council in order that the people of the states might ascertain ... who they should esteem and treat as enemies and who as friends in the great war which was then upon the point of breaking out between them and the King of England.

Our Indians obeyed the call and the council was held, at which ... a treaty [was] made in which the Six Nations [of the Iroquois Confederacy] solemnly agreed that if a war should eventually break out, they would not take up arms on either side, but that they would observe a strict neutrality. ...The Indians returned to their homes well pleased that they could live on neutral ground, surrounded by the din of war without being engaged in it.

About a year passed ... when a messenger arrived from the British Commissioners requesting all the Indians of our tribe to attend a general council which was soon to be held at Oswego.... [T]he British Commissioners informed the Chiefs that the object of calling a council of the Six Nations was to engage their assistance in subduing the rebels—the people of the [United] States—who had risen up against the good King, their master, and were about to rob him of a great part of his possessions and wealth, and added that they would amply reward them for all their services.

The Chiefs then arose and informed the Commissioners of the nature and extent of the treaty which they had entered into with the people of the states the year before, and that they should not violate it by taking up the hatchet against them.

The Commissioners continued their entreaties without success till they addressed their avarice by telling our people that the people of the states were few in number and easily subdued; ... and added that the King was rich and powerful, both in money and subjects: That ... his men were as numerous as the sands upon the lake shore —and that the Indians, if they would assist in the war and persevere in their friendship to the King till it was closed, should never want for money or goods.

Upon this the Chiefs concluded a treaty with the British Commissioners in which they agreed to take up arms against the rebels and continue in the service of his Majesty....

As soon as the treaty was finished, the Commissioners made a present to each Indian of a suit of clothes, a brass kettle, a gun and tomahawk, a scalping knife, a quantity of powder and lead, a piece of gold, and promised a bounty on every scalp that should be brought in. Thus richly clad and equipped, they returned home ... full of the fire of war and anxious to encounter their enemies. ”

—Mary Jemison, from her account of her life among Native Americans in the late 1700s

2 IDENTIFYING EFFECTS Who did the Native Americans meet at German Flats? What was the result of that council?

3 IDENTIFYING EFFECTS Who did the Native Americans meet at Oswego? What was the result of that council?

4 ECONOMIC DECISION MAKING What was the reason for the Native Americans' agreement with the British at the Oswego Council?

5 PREDICTING What can you predict might happen after the events described?

6 EXPLAINING ISSUES How does this reading help explain how conflict develops, or spreads?

ESSENTIAL QUESTION

Why does conflict develop?

A Revolutionary Patriot of South Carolina

DIRECTIONS: Read the excerpt below from Major Thomas Young's Memoirs on Joining the Carolina Patriot Cause and Kings Mountain and answer the questions that follow.

EXPLORE THE CONTEXT: When the British marched northward through South Carolina, they warned the people who lived in the mountains to join the Loyalist cause or else the British would "hang their leaders and lay their country waste." The fiercely independent people of Kings Mountain did not take kindly to such threats. Instead of joining the British, they formed a militia to expel them from their land. Thomas Young was sixteen when he joined the Little River Regiment in South Carolina. His brother had been killed by a Loyalist known as Bloody Bill Cunningham, and Thomas decided to fight in order to avenge his brother's death. He proved himself so capable that within a year he was promoted to the rank of major. He wrote a detailed memoir of his experiences at Kings Mountain, Cowpens, and other battles and skirmishes. Young died in 1848 and was buried in South Carolina.

THE BATTLE OF KING'S MOUNTAIN.

PRIMARY SOURCE: MEMOIR

"When our division came up to the northern base of the mountain, we dismounted, and Col. Roebuck drew us a little to the left and commenced the attack. I well remember how I behaved. Ben Hollingsworth and myself took right up the side of the mountain, and fought from tree to tree, our way to the summit. I recollect I stood behind one tree and fired until the bark was nearly all knocked off, and my eyes pretty well filled with it. One fellow shaved me pretty close, for his bullet took a piece out of my gunstock.

Before I was aware of it, I found myself apparently between my own regiment and the enemy, as I judged, from seeing the paper which the whigs wore in their hats, and the pine knots the tories wore in theirs, these being the badges of distinction.

VOCABULARY

galvanized: motivated
avenge: get revenge
memoir: autobiography
skirmishes: fights
commenced: began
summit: hilltop or mountaintop
whigs: Patriots
tories: Loyalists
ball: musket bullet

. . . continued

On the top of the mountain, in the thickest of the fight, I saw Col. Williams fall, and a braver or a better man never died upon the field of battle. I had seen him but once before that day; it was in the beginning of the action, as he charged by me at full speed around the mountain; toward the summit a ball struck his horse under the jaw, when he commenced stamping as if he were in a nest of yellow jackets. Col. W. threw the reins over the animal's neck -- sprang to the ground, and dashed onward.

The moment I heard the cry that Col. Williams was shot, I ran to his assistance, for I loved him as a father, he had ever been so kind to me, and almost always carried a cake in his pocket for me and his little son Joseph. They carried him into a tent, and sprinkled some water in his face. He revived, and his first words were, 'For God's sake, boys, don't give up the hill!'... Our loss at the battle of King's Mountain, was about twenty-five killed and wounded. The enemy lost above three hundred, who were left on the ground -- among them Major Ferguson. We took, moreover, seven or eight hundred prisoners.”

—Major Thomas Young, from his memoir of his experiences fighting against the British

1 **GEOGRAPHY** Describe how the Battle of Kings Mountain was fought: where were the Loyalists and the Patriots situated on the mountain and how did Major Young and the other mountain people move?

____

____

____

TEXT:Young, Major Thomas. 1843. The Orion: A Monthly Magazine of Literature and Art, Volume 3. Memoir of Major Thomas Young, A Revolutionary Patriot of South Carolina. Published by William Richards, Athens and Penfield, GA. Pgs. 86-87.

2 **INFERRING** Young says, "I recollect I stood behind one tree and fired until the bark was nearly all knocked off, and my eyes pretty well filled with it." How long is Young implying he was firing? Why does he use these details instead of telling the reader how many minutes he stood behind the tree and fired?

3 **EXPLAINING** Why was Young sad to see Col. Williams struck down by a bullet?

4 **RELATING EVENTS** What three things did Young do when he saw Col Williams fall?

5 Which side won the battle? Which details tell you this?

THE FINAL YEARS

DIRECTIONS: Search for evidence in Chapter 4, Lesson 4 to help you answer the following questions.

1 EXPLAINING Why did principles outlined in the Declaration of Independence inspire revolutions in other parts of the world?

2 IDENTIFYING CAUSE AND EFFECT What effect did the American Revolution have on France in the years shortly after the war?

3 COMPARING What ideals did the American colonists and French revolutionaries share?

ESSENTIAL QUESTION

Why does conflict develop?

As you gather evidence to answer the Essential Question, think about:

- how the Americans managed to defeat the British.
- what part Washington played in the war and in the peace.
- the effect the Revolution had on other countries.

My Notes

4 **IDENTIFYING CAUSE AND EFFECT** What ideals from the American Revolution inspired enslaved people in Haiti to take up arms against the French?

5 **DESCRIBING** Describe the events that led revolutionaries in Haiti to declare "We have asserted our rights. We swear never to yield them to any power on earth."

ESSENTIAL QUESTION

Why does conflict develop?

"The British Lion Engaging Four Powers"

DIRECTIONS: Study the cartoon. The text from it is reprinted in the chart on the following page. Then answer the accompanying questions.

INTRODUCTION: This cartoon was created in 1782. Great Britain had suffered humiliating defeats by the Americans and their allies. The country was forced into treaty negotiations. This cartoon captures a moment in time when Great Britain, long a dominant power, faced a new reality.

PRIMARY SOURCE: POLITICAL CARTOON

VOCABULARY

engaging: dealing with

drubbing: beating

Monsieur: mister, in French

curs: dogs

Gibraltar: southern tip of Spain

perfidious: untrustworthy

1. **INTEGRATING VISUAL INFORMATION** What is the relationship between the cartoon and the verse at the lower right that accompanies it?

____

____

2. **DETERMINING CENTRAL IDEAS** What is the main idea that the cartoonist is trying to express?

____

____

____

____

<table>
<tr><th>Animal</th><th>What the Animal Represents</th><th>What the Animal Is Saying</th><th>Verse at Bottom</th></tr>
<tr><td>Lion</td><td>Great Britain</td><td>“You shall all have an old English drubbing to make you quiet.”</td><td rowspan="6">Behold the Dutch and Spanish Currs, Perfidious Gallus [France] in his Spurs, And Rattlesnake with head upright
The British Lion join to fight;
He scorns the Bark, the Hiss, the Crow, That he’s a Lion soon they’ll know.</td></tr>
<tr><td>Fox (bottom right)</td><td>Charles Fox (British Foreign Secretary who supported independence of the American colonies)</td><td>“I counsel your Majesty to give Monsieur the first gripe.”</td></tr>
<tr><td>Spaniel (top)</td><td>Spain</td><td>“I will have Gibraltar, that I may be King of all Spain.”</td></tr>
<tr><td>Rooster</td><td>France</td><td>“I will have my Title from you and be call’d King of France.”</td></tr>
<tr><td>Rattlesnake</td><td>United States</td><td>“I will have America and be Independent.”</td></tr>
<tr><td>Pug Dog</td><td>Holland</td><td>“I will be Jack of all sides as I have always been.”</td></tr>
</table>

3 **RELATING EVENTS** How does this cartoon show that the American Revolution was more than a conflict between the American colonists and Great Britain?

4 **INFERRING** Why do you think the Spanish wanted to take possession of Gibraltar?

5 **EVALUATING MEDIA** Do you think a political cartoon was the best medium to use to communicate ideas about international events? Would another medium have been more effective? Explain.

ESSENTIAL QUESTION
Why does conflict develop?

Rochambeau Corresponds with Washington

DIRECTIONS: Read the letters from Comte de Rochambeau to George Washington about the Battle of Yorktown.

INTRODUCTION: In the first letter of April 26, 1781, Rochambeau writes to Washington about something he has just read that upset him. He refers to a private letter of Washington's that was printed in the *New-York Gazette*, a newspaper. Washington's private letter was written to one of his aides but was intercepted and printed. In the intercepted letter, Washington says he doubts the French navy will help the Patriots because Washington is sure that the French navy delayed departing after they received his request for help. He worries that they will not arrive on time to help the Patriot army on the ground. When Rochambeau, commander of the French navy and a friend of Washington's, read the intercepted letter, he wrote the letter below to Washington. In his letter, Rochambeau worries that Washington feels that the French navy took the easier of two assignments and that they are deliberately delaying. In his response, Rochambeau details his attempts to arrive as quickly as possible and begs Washington to believe that the French navy is doing everything it can to support the Patriots.

1 **INFERRING** How do you think Rochambeau felt after reading Washington's intercepted letter in the newspaper?

____

____

____

____

____

____

____

____

____

PRIMARY SOURCE: LETTER 1

"The New-york Gazette has published a Supposed intercepted Letter wrote, as it says by your Excellency... and in which is this Paragraph. "It is very unlikely, I say it to you in confidence that the French fleet and detachment did not undertake this present expedition at the time I proposed it. The destruction of Arnold's corps would have been unavoidable, and over before the British squadron could have put to sea: Instead of this, [the French navy] have sent the small squadron that took the [British ship] Romulus and some other vessels, But as I had foreseen it, [the French navy] could do nothing at Portsmouth, without the help of some Land Troops.

If really this Letter has been wrote by Your Excellency, I shall beg Leave to observe, that the result of this reflexion should seem to be, that We have had here the choice of two expeditions proposed, and that We

VOCABULARY

intercepted: captured
detachment: troops
vessels: ships
expedition: journey
undertaking: task
squadron: group of ships
Arnold: Benedict Arnold, a former Patriot officer who had recently been discovered working with the British; at this writing he is commanding British troops
Portsmouth: fort in Virginia, defended by Patriot troops, as well as French troops commanded by Lafayette

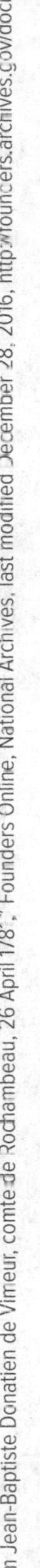

. . . continued

have preferred the Least to a more considerable undertaking which your Excellency desired. If this was the case, I should beg of your Excellency to call to mind that the [three ships] went out of Newport on the 9th February on a demand made by Congress and the State of Virginia to the Chevalier Destouches; that your Excellency's Letter with the plan for the going out of the Whole fleet with a detachment of [1000] Frenchmen abo[ard] which detachment was to act conjointly with that of The Marquis de La Fayette, bears date of the 15 Febr[uar]y, and that I only received it on the 19th; that having given an instant communication of it to the Chevalier Destouches, I had the honor on the 20th to send his answer to your Excellency: That [at the] end of January... I have offered of the Land forces all that could possibly be transported by the navy, and have not ceased to do it since. I shall not mention to your Excellency the reasons that have delayed the departure of the Chevalier Destouches's Squadron, because those he gave to your Excellency don't fall under my cognisance; I only have made mention of these facts to call to your Excellency's mind these epochas which I beg you'd verify in your Correspondence, that your Excellency may be entirely persuaded, that there will never be the least delay, in what concerns the Land and the small French corps which I command, for the possible execution of your Excellency's orders, as soon as I shall receive them. ❞

—Rochambeau in a letter to George Washington, April 26, 1781

VOCABULARY

Romulus: British ship
beg leave: beg your pardon
Chevalier Destouches: admiral in the French Navy
detachment: group
cognisance: control
epochas: events
Your Excellency: Washington

2 SPECULATING How might Rochambeau's reaction to the letter have reflected what the French felt when hearing about Washington's letter?

____
____
____
____
____
____
____

INTRODUCTION: Six months later, the Battle of Yorktown took place in October 1781, and the French navy was instrumental to the Patriots' success there. Rochambeau then wrote another letter to Washington to describe the battle after two nights of fighting.

PRIMARY SOURCE: LETTER 2

"We had resolved to attack as soon as dark, the two redoubts on the left of the Ennemy, that were detached from the rest of their works. The Marquis de La fayette undertook that on our right with the American troops; The Baron de Viomenil, that on our Left with the French troops. 400 Grenadiers opened the attack.... [Lafayette and Viomenil] made such a vigorous and strong disposition of their troops that they took the two redoubts, sword in hand, and killed wounded or took the greatest part of those who defended them. The number of prisoners amounts to 68.... The Batteries of the American troops are going to be erected there, which with those of the French will quite encompass Cornwallis and fire upon his town in a manner that will certainly be very hurtful to him. The troops, both American and French have shewn the most distinguished courage.... We have had 100 Men either killed or wounded."

VOCABULARY

redoubts: forts
Grenadiers: soldiers who launch grenades
encompass: surround
shewn: shown

1. **MAKING CONNECTIONS** How would people respond today to this controversy?

2. **INFERRING** What do Rochambeau's two letters suggest about French support for the Patriots?

3. **SPECULATING** How do you think the French people reacted to the news of so many French casualties at the battle?

ESSENTIAL QUESTION

Why does conflict develop?

1 Think About It

Review the supporting questions you developed in the chapter opener. Review the evidence you gathered in Chapter 4. Were you able to answer each Supporting Question? If there was not enough evidence to answer your Supporting Questions, what additional evidence do you think you need to consider?

____

____

____

____

2 Organize Your Evidence

Fill in the chart below with the information you learned about different people and groups who were drawn into the Revolution.

Person or Group	Who is the person or group?	Which side did they choose? (British/ Patriots)	How did they participate?	What were their reasons for getting involved?
Esther de Berdt Reed & her women's group				
Boyrereau Brinch				
Don Bernardo de Galvez				
Marquis de Lafayette				
the Seneca				
Major Thomas Young				
Spain				
France				
Comte de Rochambeau				

3 Talk About It

Talk with a partner about the evidence you included in your organization chart. Did you both include the same evidence, or were your partner's responses different? Discuss any differences in your charts, then make notes below about anything you'd like to add to yours or change.

____

____

____

____

4 Write About It

Using a computer, write a brief summary for each person or group listed in the left column, incorporating the evidence organized in your chart. Include a line or phrase from each primary source that you feel is significant in demonstrating the part the individual or group played for use in a visual display board. Each summary should be about a paragraph long.

5 Connect to the Essential Question

Create a stylish, clear and attractive informational project board. Imagine you are informing someone who hasn't read this chapter about the roles played by parties who were not directly involved in the American Revolution but who became involved or inspired by it. Be sure to include a map to show where each event took place and where each person or group lived, traveled, and fought. Be sure to include European nations on your map. Visually connect each of your written summaries to its place on the map. Use each primary source discussed in the four lessons of this chapter.

CITIZENSHIP

TAKING ACTION

MAKE CONNECTIONS Conflict is often caused by an imbalance in access to opportunities between groups of people. In the past, almost all American leaders were wealthy, land-owning men whose ancestors came to America from northern European countries. This imbalance led to many conflicts. The past 60 years of American history have seen enormous change. During this time, new groups have gained access to leadership roles in American government and society. Before, many groups of people were excluded from political and economic power: women, the poor, people of African, Hispanic, and Asian descent, and even other Europeans, such as Italians and those from Eastern Europe. Civil rights leaders, such as Martin Luther King Jr., Gloria Steinem, and many others, worked hard to expand access to opportunity for all Americans.

DIRECTIONS: Do you think access to equal opportunity causes conflict in your school? Does every person at your school feel that he or she has an equal chance to lead and be in power? Break into small groups and brainstorm ideas for increasing access to leadership opportunities for everyone at your school. Ask: how can every student be included and valued? In your small group, brainstorm ways to start a club, an event, or a campaign to improve inclusion and access to equal opportunity in your school. Record your group's ideas in the space below. Then, as a group, choose one idea and ask your teacher for help to make it happen.

A More Perfect Union

ESSENTIAL QUESTION

Why do people form governments?

Think about how government helps people avoid conflict by providing services to society.

TALK ABOUT IT

Discuss with a partner what type of information you would need in order to understand why the Founders needed more than just their own ideas to write the Constitution. For example, you might wonder: what other governments could the Constitution be based on?

DIRECTIONS: Now write down three additional questions that will help you explain why the Patriots chose to form a representative democracy with the separation of powers that is laid out in the Constitution.

MY RESEARCH QUESTIONS

Supporting Question 1:

Supporting Question 2:

Supporting Question 3:

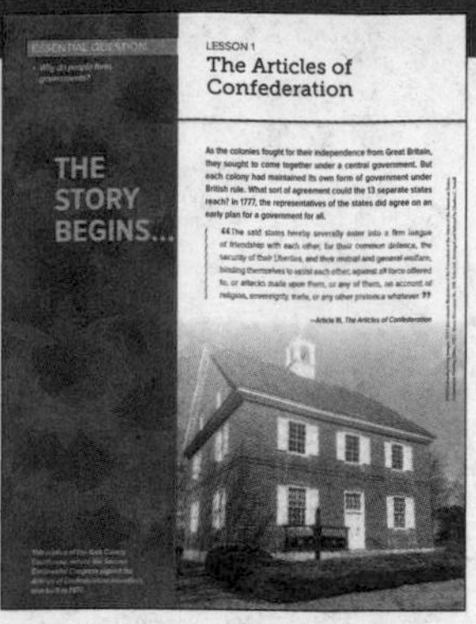

ESSENTIAL QUESTION

Why do people form governments?

As you gather evidence to answer the Essential Question, think about

- how do governments help secure the rights of citizens?
- what are the rights and responsibilities of citizens?
- why do people sometimes want to improve or change their governments?

My Notes

The Articles of Confederation

DIRECTIONS: Search for evidence in Chapter 5, Lesson 1 to help you answer the following questions.

1 **EXPLAINING** How did the first state constitutions address the concern that power should remain in the hands of the people?

2A **DRAWING CONCLUSIONS** What financial problems did the Confederation government face?

2B **INFERRING** What do the financial problems tell you about why a government needs to have the power to tax?

3A SEQUENCING What steps did the Confederation government take to ensure the peaceful expansion of the nation in Western lands? Use the graphic organizer to show the sequence.

Ordinance of 1785			
Congress passes an ordinance to survey and sell land north of the Ohio River			

Northwest Ordinance			
			The ordinance includes a bill of rights for settlers in the territory.

3B DRAWING CONCLUSIONS Why do you think the federal government was better suited than state governments to manage westward expansion?

4A IDENTIFYING PROBLEMS AND SOLUTIONS How did state governments cause trouble for the federal government in its relationships with Spain and Britain? What actions could a stronger federal government have taken to solve the problem? Use the graphic organizer below to show the answers.

Problem	Solution
Spain	Spain
Britain	Britain

ESSENTIAL QUESTION

Why do people form governments?

Letter from Alexander Hamilton to James Duane

DIRECTIONS: Read this letter from Alexander Hamilton to James Duane, 1780. Then respond to the questions.

INTRODUCTION: The Articles of Confederation established a weak central government. By the 1780s, the Confederation government had begun to cause problems for the United States at home and abroad. In this letter to James Duane, Alexander Hamilton describes his concerns.

VOCABULARY

subversive: disruptive
empire: group of states; kingdom
sovereign: supreme ruler; king
Grecian: ancient Greece
contempt: disrespect; scorn

PRIMARY SOURCE: LETTER

"The forms of our state constitutions must always give them great weight in our affairs and will make it too difficult to bend them to the persuit of a common interest, too easy to oppose whatever they do not like and to form partial combinations subversive of the general one. There is a wide difference between our situation and that of an empire under one simple form of government, distributed into counties provinces or districts, which have no legislatures but merely magistratical bodies to execute the laws of a common sovereign. Here the danger is that the sovereign will have too much power to oppress the parts of which it is composed. In our case, that of an empire composed of confederated states each with a government completely organised within itself, having all the means to draw its subjects to a close dependence on itself — the danger is directly the reverse. It is that the common sovereign will not have power sufficient to unite the different members together, and direct the common forces to the interest and happiness of the whole.

The leagues among the old Grecian republics are a proof of this. They were continually at war with each other, and for want of union fell a prey to their neighbours. They frequently held general councils, but their resolutions were no further observed than as they suited the interests and inclinations of all the parties and at length, they sunk intirely into contempt."

—Alexander Hamilton to James Duane, 3 Sept. 1780.

1 **INFERRING** Why do you think Hamilton argues that "the forms of our state constitutions" make it "too easy for states to oppose whatever they do not like?"

2 **INTERPRETING** According to Hamilton, how does the situation of the new republic differ from that of an empire? What dangers does each system pose?

3A **ANALYZING** How does Hamilton's example of Grecian republics support his argument for a strong central government?

3B **MAKING CONNECTIONS** Hamilton also uses the example of Grecian republics to talk about relations with Spain and Britain. What is the similarity between the two?

4 **DRAWING CONCLUSIONS** What advantages does the federal government have over state governments when it comes to dealing with other countries?

ESSENTIAL QUESTION
Why do people form governments?

The Northwest Ordinance

DIRECTIONS: Read these excerpts regarding the individuals rights guaranteed in the Northwest Ordinance.

INTRODUCTION: As the nation expanded into Western lands, the Confederation government played a key role. It passed a law (ordinance) so that settlement would be peaceful and orderly. The government also brought the ideas of universal rights to the new territories. The Northwest Ordinance included a bill of rights for settlers in the area.

VOCABULARY

ordained: ordered
compact: agreement
demeaning: behaving
peers: fellow citizens
exigencies: a need or demand
writ of habeas corpus: order to appear in court
fugitive: outlaw

1 DRAWING CONCLUSIONS Why do you think the federal government, rather than state governments, set policies for westward expansion?

____

____

____

____

____

____

PRIMARY SOURCE: LAW

"It is hereby ordained and declared by the authority aforesaid, That the following articles shall be considered as articles of compact between the original States and the people and States in the said territory and forever remain unalterable, unless by common consent, to wit:

Art. 1.

No person, demeaning himself in a peaceable and orderly manner, shall ever be molested on account of his mode of worship or religious sentiments, in the said territory.

Art. 2.

The inhabitants of the said territory shall always be entitled to the benefits of the writ of habeas corpus, and of the trial by jury; of a proportionate representation of the people in the legislature; and of judicial proceedings according to the course of the common law.... All fines shall be moderate; and no cruel or unusual punishments shall be inflicted. No man shall be deprived of his liberty or property, but by the judgment of his peers or the law of the land; and, should the public exigencies make it necessary, for the common preservation, to take any person's property, or to demand his particular services, full compensation shall be made for the same.

Art. 3

Religion, morality, and knowledge, being necessary to good government and the happiness of mankind, schools and the means of education shall forever be encouraged. The utmost good faith shall always be observed towards the Indians; their lands and property shall never be taken from them without their consent; and, in their property, rights, and liberty, they shall never be invaded or disturbed, unless in just and lawful wars authorized by Congress; but laws founded in justice and humanity, shall from time to time be made for preventing wrongs being done to them, and for preserving peace and friendship with them.

Art. 6.

There shall be neither slavery nor involuntary servitude in the said territory, otherwise than in the punishment of crimes whereof the party shall have been duly convicted: Provided, always, That any person escaping into the same, from whom labor or service is lawfully claimed in any one of the original States, such fugitive may be lawfully reclaimed and conveyed to the person claiming his or her labor or service as aforesaid.”

—An Ordinance for the government of the Territory of the United States northwest of the River Ohio, July 13, 1787

2 **CITING TEXT EVIDENCE** Which sentence shows that the federal government wanted to limit the westward expansion of slavery?

3 **EXPLAINING** What were the policies regarding Native Americans?

4 **DRAWING CONCLUSIONS** Why do you think the federal government agreed to create a bill of rights for the Northwest Territory?

ESSENTIAL QUESTION

Why do people form governments?

As you gather evidence to answer the Essential Question, think about

- how do governments help secure the rights of citizens?
- what are the rights and responsibilities of citizens?
- why do people sometimes want to improve or change their governments?

My Notes

Forging a New Constitution

DIRECTIONS: Search for evidence in Chapter 5, Lesson 2 to help you answer the following questions.

1 **IDENTIFYING CAUSE AND EFFECT** How did economic depression lead some farmers to regard the new government as another form of tyranny? Complete the graphic organizer to show the sequence.

1. Economic depression after the war affects markets and money supply.	2.	3.	4.

2 **INFERRING** Why do you think news of Shays's rebellion convinced George Washington to attend the Philadelphia Convention?

3 **EVALUATING** Do you think the Three-fifths Compromise was an effective solution to the problem? Why or why not?

3 **IDENTIFYING PROBLEM AND SOLUTION** Why did the question of slavery make discussions at the Convention more difficult? How did delegates solve the problem of representing states with enslaved populations? Use the graphic organizer below to answer these questions.

Problems	Solutions
	Delegates agreed to count every five enslaved persons as three persons in the state's population total.
Delegates from the South were concerned that Northerners wanted to ban slavery.	

5 **DRAWING CONCLUSIONS** Why do you think the issue of representation was so important in discussions about the new Constitution?

ESSENTIAL QUESTION

Why do people form governments?

Letter from George Washington

DIRECTIONS: Read this letter from George Washington to John Jay, 1786. Then respond to the questions that follow.

INTRODUCTION: George Washington was not enthusiastic about the plan to strengthen the national government. But news of Shays's Rebellion convinced him to attend the Convention. In this letter, Washington worries that fear may cause people to turn to tyranny.

VOCABULARY

suppliant: humble
nihility: nothingness; void
compliance: agreement
jest: joke
prerogatives: rights; privileges
despotism: tyranny
contingencies: unexpected events
fallacious: false

PRIMARY SOURCE: LETTER

"If you tell the Legislatures they have violated the Treaty of Peace, and invaded the prerogatives of the confederacy, they will laugh in your face. What then is to be done? Things cannot go on in the same train forever. It is much to be feared, as you observe, that the better kind of people, being disgusted with the circumstances, will have their minds prepared for any revolution whatever. We are apt to run from one extreme into another. To anticipate and prevent disastrous contingencies, would be the part of wisdom and patriotism.

What astonishing changes a few years are capable of producing. I am told that even respectable characters speak of a monarchical form of Government without horror. From thinking proceeds speaking, thence to acting is often but a single step. But how irrevocable and tremendous! what a triumph for our enemies to verify their predictions! what a triumph for the advocates of despotism to find that we are incapable of governing ourselves, and that systems founded on the basis of equal liberty are merely ideal and fallacious!"

—George Washington to John Jay, 1 Aug. 1786.

1 **CITING TEXT EVIDENCE** George Washington says that the state legislatures will "laugh in your face." What does this metaphor suggest about his views of the federal government?

When George Washington Says people will laugh in your face means that people will not take you seasorly.

2 **INTERPRETING** What does Washington mean when he says that in insecure times people "are apt to run from one extreme into another"?

When George Washington Says that in insecure times people "are apt to run frome one extreme into another". people all way make blind choichs that will lead them to one dangoure to another.

3 **ANALYZING** Washington warns Jay that "thinking proceeds speaking, thence to acting is often but a single step." What is Washington worried about?

Washington warns Jay because when you thinking you must caustion all the time because if you make a mistake it will lead to wrong speech, wrong action.

4 **EVALUATING** Do you think Washington's concern that people may want a return to tyranny is justified? Why or why not?

People want tranny to be Justified because trannys are twrinning agenist the people instead procitting the people.

5 **DRAWING CONCLUSIONS** Why do you think some people may welcome a tyrant during times of unrest?

The reason some people will welcom tranny because some people will want regune t roor to others.

ESSENTIAL QUESTION

Why do people form governments?

Bayard's Speech on Pennsylvania Abolition

DIRECTIONS: Read John Bayard's proposal for an Act for the Gradual Abolition of Slavery in Pennsylvania. Then respond to the questions that follow.

INTRODUCTION: Northern states banned slavery before the Constitutional Convention began. The decision to abolish slavery revealed how divided the nation had become.

VOCABULARY

abolition: end
contemplate: think about
abhorrence: hatred; strong dislike
wrought: made
manifold: many and different
thralldom: slavery
complexion: skin color
benevolence: kindness
imbibed: consumed; absorbed

1 ANALYZING Why does Bayard want his audience to look back on the dangers of the Revolutionary War if he is trying to talk about slavery?

____

____

____

____

____

____

PRIMARY SOURCE: SPEECH

"When we contemplate our abhorrence of that condition to which the arms and tyranny of Great Britain were exerted to reduce us; when we look back on the variety of dangers to which we have been exposed, and how miraculously our wants in many instances have been supplied, and our deliverances wrought, when even hope and human fortitude have become unequal to the conflict; we are unavoidably led to a serious and grateful sense of the manifold blessings which we have undeservedly received.... Impressed with these ideas, we conceive that it is our duty, and we rejoice that it is in our power to extend a portion of that freedom to others, which hath been extended to us; and a release from that state of thralldom to which we ourselves were tyrannically doomed, and from which we have now every prospect of being delivered. It is not for us to enquire why, in the creation of mankind, the inhabitants of the several parts of the earth were distinguished by a difference in feature or complexion....We find in the distribution of the human species, that the most fertile as well as the most barren parts of the earth are inhabited by men of complexions different from ours, and from each other; from whence we may reasonably, as well as religiously, infer, that He who placed them in their various situations, hath extended equally his care and protection to all, and that it becometh not us to

counteract his mercies. We esteem it a peculiar blessing granted to us, that we are enabled this day to add one more step to universal civilization, by removing as much as possible the sorrows of those who have lived in undeserved bondage, and from which, by the assumed authority of the kings of Great Britain, no effectual, legal relief could be obtained. Weaned by a long course of experience from those narrower prejudices and partialities we had imbibed, we find our hearts enlarged with kindness and benevolence towards men of all conditions and nations; and we conceive ourselves at this particular period extraordinarily called upon, by the blessings which we have received, to manifest the sincerity of our profession, and to give a Substantial proof of our gratitude. ”

—John Bayard, Speaker, Enabled into a law at Philadelphia, on Wednesday, the first day of March, A.D. 1780

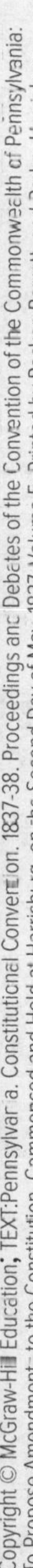

2 **INFERRING** What do the phrases "human species" and "universal civilization" suggest about Bayard's view of liberty?

3 **DRAWING CONCLUSIONS** What conclusions might an audience member from the South have drawn after hearing Bayard speak of "universal civilization"?

4 **SPECULATING** How do you think Bayard would have responded to the Three-fifths Compromise reached at the Constitutional Convention?

A New Plan of Government

DIRECTIONS: Search for evidence in Chapter 5, Lesson 3 to help you answer the following questions.

1A IDENTIFYING POINTS OF VIEW How did John Locke's views on natural rights influence the Framers of the Constitution?

1B EXPLAINING Why did the Framers create a system of government that divided powers between the federal government and the states?

2A CATEGORIZING Use the graphic organizer below to show how federalism works. Which powers belong to the federal government? Which powers belong to the states? Which powers do they share?

Federalism

Federal Government	State Governments

ESSENTIAL QUESTION

Why do people form governments?

As you gather evidence to answer the Essential Question, think about

- how do governments help secure the rights of citizens?
- what are the rights and responsibilities of citizens?
- why do people sometimes want to improve or change their governments?

My Notes

2B CATEGORIZING Use the graphic organizer to show how the Constitution further divides powers among the three branches of government.

Legislative	Executive	Judicial
		The Supreme Court and federal courts hear cases involving the Constitution, federal laws, and disputes between states.

3 DRAWING CONCLUSIONS Why do you think the power to declare war is a federal power? Why do states have the power to establish schools?

4 IDENTIFYING POINTS OF VIEW Why did the Anti-Federalists oppose the principle of federalism?

5 EVALUATING Do you think a strong federal government or strong state governments best protect individual liberty? Why or why not?

ESSENTIAL QUESTION

Why do people form governments?

John Locke's *Two Treatises*

DIRECTIONS: Read this excerpt from John Locke's *Two Treatises of Civil Government*. Then respond to the questions that follow.

INTRODUCTION: The Framers of the Constitution borrowed their ideas about government from European political institutions and writers. The English philosopher John Locke influenced the way the Framers thought about the proper role of government.

VOCABULARY

treatise: essay
obliges: shapes, causes
omnipotent: all powerful
infinitely: without end
furnished: given
faculties: senses
subordination: being lower in rank
impair: make worse; prevent

PRIMARY SOURCE: TREATISE

"The state of nature has a law of nature to govern it, which obliges every one: and reason, which is that law, teaches all mankind, who will but consult it, that being all equal and independent, no one ought to harm another in his life, health, liberty, or possessions: for men being all the workmanship of one omnipotent, and infinitely wise maker; all the servants of one sovereign master, sent into the world by his order, and about his business; they are his property, whose workmanship they are, made to last during his, not one another's pleasure: and being furnished with like faculties, sharing all in one community of nature, there cannot be supposed any such subordination among us, that may authorize us to destroy one another, as if we were made for one another's uses, as the inferior ranks of creatures are for our's. Every one, as he is bound to preserve himself, and not to quit his station willfully, so by the like reason, when his own preservation comes not in competition, ought he, as much as he can, to preserve the rest of mankind, and may not, unless it be to do justice on an offender, take away, or impair the life, or what tends to the preservation of the life, the liberty, health, limb, or goods of another."

Source: John Locke, *The Two Treatises of Civil Government* [(Hollis ed.) [1689], section 6

1 **EXPLAINING** What does Locke mean when he says that people are "furnished with like faculties, sharing all in one community of nature?" Why does he make this claim?

2 **INTERPRETING** How does Locke's claim that people are "sharing all in one communlty of nature" support his argument that "no one ought to harm another in his life, health, liberty, or possessions?"

3 **EXPLAINING** According to Locke, what duties and responsibilities do people have to others when they feel safe and secure?

4 **MAKING CONNECTIONS** How might the principles Locke describes have also been used to oppose a strong central government?

ESSENTIAL QUESTION

Why do people form governments?

Patrick Henry's Speech

DIRECTIONS: Read this excerpt from a speech given by Patrick Henry. Then respond to the questions that follow.

INTRODUCTION: Federalists supported the new Constitution because they believed a strong central government, as outlined in the document, would protect liberty. Others took the opposite point of view. In this speech Patrick Henry strongly rejects the Federalist position.

VOCABULARY

resolution: proposal
radical: extreme
sovereignty: independence; self-rule
relinquishment: given up
fortitude: strength
indignation: contempt; scorn
defective: imperfect; broken
perpetrate: commit an offense or crime

1 **SUMMARIZING** What does Patrick Henry think will happen to the rights of Americans if the new Constitution passes?

____

____

____

____

____

____

____

PRIMARY SOURCE: SPEECH

“Here is a resolution as radical as that which separated us from Great Britain. It is radical in this transition; our rights and privileges are endangered, and the sovereignty of the states will be relinquished: and cannot we plainly see that this is actually the case? The rights of conscience, trial by jury, liberty of the press, all your immunities and franchises, all pretensions to human rights and privileges, are rendered insecure, if not lost, by this change, so loudly talked of by some, and inconsiderately by others. Is this tame relinquishment of rights worthy of freemen? Is it worthy of that manly fortitude that ought to characterize republicans? It is said eight states have adopted this plan. I declare that if twelve states and a half had adopted it, I would, with manly firmness, and in spite of an erring world, reject it.

This Constitution is said to have beautiful features; but when I come to examine these features, sir, they appear to me horribly frightful. Among other deformities, it has an awful squinting; it squints towards monarchy; and does not this raise indignation in the breast of every true American?

Your President may easily become king. Your Senate is so imperfectly constructed that your dearest rights may be sacrificed by what may be a small minority; and a very small minority may continue forever unchangeably

this government, although horridly defective. Where are your checks in this government? Your strongholds will be in the hands of your enemies. It is on a supposition that your American governors shall be honest, that all the good qualities of this government are founded; but its defective and imperfect construction puts it in their power to perpetrate the worst of mischiefs, should they be bad men; and, sir, would not all the world, from the eastern to the western hemisphere, blame our distracted folly in resting our rights upon the contingency of our rulers being good or bad?"

—Patrick Henry, Speech Before Virginia Ratifying Convention, June 5, 1788

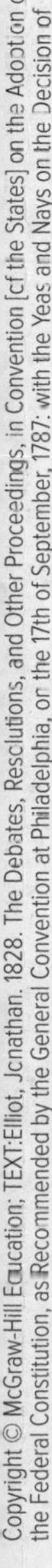

2A **EXPLAINING** Why does Henry say that the new Constitution "squints toward monarchy?"

____

____

____

____

____

2B **CITING TEXT EVIDENCE** Which sentence best explains why he makes this claim?

____

____

____

3 **EXPLAINING** What argument does Henry make against giving too much power to the President?

____

____

____

4 **MAKING CONNECTIONS** At one point Henry asks, "Where are your checks in this government?" What checks would the Federalists have placed on the President to prevent tyranny?

____

____

____

____

ESSENTIAL QUESTION

Why do people form governments?

1 Think About It

Review the supporting questions you developed at the beginning of the chapter. Review the evidence you gathered in Chapter 5. Were you able to answer each Supporting Question? If there was not enough evidence to answer your Supporting Questions, what additional evidence do you think you need to consider?

2 Organize Your Evidence

Complete the chart below with the information you learned about the ideas that influenced the Framers of the Constitution. The first source has been provided for you.

Source	Description of Ideas
Magna Carta	

3 Talk About It

Work in small groups. Talk with your group about the evidence you included in the chart in question 2. Did you include the same evidence, or were your classmates' responses different from your responses? Discuss any differences in your charts, then take notes so that you can create one new chart that includes the responses of everyone in the group.

4 Write About It

Write about the reasons you think people form governments. Be sure to incorporate the evidence you and your group organized in questions 2 and 3 and excerpt a line or phrase from a primary source that you think is important in order to support your argument.

5 Connect to the Essential Question

Create an informational podcast for someone who is not familiar with the United States Constitution in which you introduce the important thinkers and ideas that influenced the writers of the Constitution. Include the chart that you created in question 2 and your ideas in questions 3 and 4. Explain that borrowing from other sources is an example of how the United States values diversity of people, values, traditions, and ideas.

CITIZENSHIP

TAKING ACTION

Organize into small groups. Brainstorm to create a list of ideas that would be included in a Bill of Rights and Responsibilities for your classroom. Consider and be open to all ideas. Record your group's suggestions in the space below. Make a visual representation of your Bill of Rights and Responsibilities. Create a blog or video of your Bill of Rights and Responsibilities so that you can present it to your teacher and to others in your school. Post the visual version of your Bill of Rights and Responsibilities project in your classroom.

The Constitution

ESSENTIAL QUESTION

How do new ideas change the way people live?

Think about the effect of ideas on people's lives, including your own. Think also about how new ideas influence what the government does.

TALK ABOUT IT

Discuss with a partner what type of information you would need to know to answer this question. For example, one question might be: how do people react when they face new ideas that challenge their traditions?

DIRECTIONS: Now write down three additional questions that you need to answer to be able to explain how new ideas change the way people live and what the government does.

MY RESEARCH QUESTIONS

Supporting Question 1:

____

____

Supporting Question 2:

____

____

Supporting Question 3:

____

____

ESSENTIAL QUESTION

How do new ideas change the way people live?

As you gather evidence to answer the Essential Question, think about

- which ideas had an influence over the Founders.
- how those ideas affect our lives today.
- why the Constitution includes a process for adding amendments.

My Notes

Principles of the Constitution

DIRECTIONS: Search for evidence in Chapter 6, Lesson 1 to help you answer the following questions.

1 CIVICS Complete the blank spaces in the chart below by defining each of the key principles built into the U.S. Constitution and giving an example of that principle in action.

Key Principles of the U.S. Constitution		
Principle	Definition	Example
Popular Sovereignty		
Republicanism		
Limited Government		
Federalism		
Separation of Powers		

2 **ANALYZING** How are the principles of limited government, checks and balances, and individual rights related to each other?

3 **DETERMINING POINT OF VIEW** Why do you think the Founders made the Constitution difficult to amend?

4 **IDENTIFYING** What are the two ways the meaning of the U.S. Constitution can change?

ESSENTIAL QUESTION

How do new ideas change the way people live?

Vices of the Political System of the United States

DIRECTIONS: Read the following excerpt and then answer the accompanying questions.

INTRODUCTION: James Madison was one of the delegates at the Constitutional Convention. He wanted to start the convention with an agenda prepared so that the delegates would be able to get to work without unnecessary delays. To prepare for the convention, he wrote this essay examining the problems a democratic society faces.

VOCABULARY

prevalent: widespread
industrious: busy
Constituents: people a member of the legislature represents
perfidious: disloyal
displace: remove
pretexts: excuses
expediency: usefulness
unwary: unsuspecting
dupe: fool or victim
sophistical: hard to follow

PRIMARY SOURCE: ESSAY

"Representative appointments are sought from 3 motives. 1. ambition. 2. personal interest. 3. public good. Unhappily the two first are proved by experience to be most prevalent. Hence the candidates who feel them, particularly, the second, are most industrious, and most successful in pursuing their object: and forming often a majority in the legislative Councils, with interested views, contrary to the interest, and views, of their Constituents, join in a perfidious sacrifice of the latter to the former. A succeeding election it might be supposed, would displace the offenders, and repair the mischief. But how easily are base and selfish measures, masked by pretexts of public good and apparent expediency? How frequently will a repetition of the same arts and industry which succeeded in the first instance, again prevail on the unwary to misplace their confidence?

How frequently too will the honest but unenligh[t]ened representative be the dupe of a favorite leader, veiling his selfish views under the professions of public good, and varnishing his sophistical arguments with the glowing colours of popular eloquence?"

—James Madison, "Vices of the Political System of the United States," 1787

1 **IDENTIFYING MAIN IDEAS** What is the problem Madison is most concerned about in this excerpt?

2 **CITING TEXT EVIDENCE** Why does Madison worry that elections will not solve the problem he identifies? What evidence can you cite from the excerpt to support your answer?

3 **ANALYZING** How does Madison think an honest representative will act?

4 **CIVICS** Which of the seven key principles is/are directed at solving the problem Madison discusses in this excerpt?

ESSENTIAL QUESTION

How do new ideas change the way people live?

Patrick Henry Speaking Against Ratification of the Constitution

DIRECTIONS: Read the following excerpt, then answer the accompanying questions.

INTRODUCTION: In June, 1788, the Virginia ratifying convention met to debate ratifying the U.S. Constitution. Patrick Henry, a prominent Anti-Federalist, gave this speech urging the delegates to vote against ratification.

VOCABULARY

contemplate: think about
mad: crazy
supposable: realistic
relinquish: give up
concur: agree
salutary: beneficial
grievous: terrible
accede: agree
trifling: tiny or trivial
contemptible: shameful

PRIMARY SOURCE: SPEECH

"To encourage us to adopt it, they tell us that there is a plain, easy way of getting amendments: When I come to contemplate this part, I suppose that I am mad, or that my countrymen are so... it appears that three-fourths of the States must ultimately agree to any amendments that may be necessary. Let us consider the consequence of this... Let us suppose (for the case is supposable, possible, and probable) that you happen to deal those powers to unworthy hands; will they relinquish powers already in their possession, or agree to amendments? Two-thirds of the Congress, or, of the State Legislatures, are necessary even to propose amendments: If one-third of these be unworthy men, they may prevent the application for amendments; but what is destructive and mischievous, is, that three-fourths of the State Legislatures, or of the State Conventions, must concur in the amendments when proposed: In such numerous bodies, there must necessarily be some designing bad men: To suppose that so large a number as three-fourths of the States will concur, is to suppose that they will

1 **IDENTIFYING MAIN IDEAS** What part of the Constitution does Henry attack in this portion of his speech? What is his concern about it?

possess genius, intelligence, and integrity, approaching to miraculous. It would indeed be miraculous that they should concur in the same amendments... For four of the smallest States, that do not collectively contain one-tenth part of the population of the United States, may obstruct the most salutary and necessary amendments... A bare majority in these four small States may hinder the adoption of amendments; so that we may fairly and justly conclude, that one-twentieth part of the American people, may prevent the removal of the most grievous inconveniences and oppression, by refusing to accede to amendments. A trifling minority may reject the most salutary amendments. Is this an easy mode of securing the public liberty? It is, Sir, a most fearful situation, when the most contemptible minority can prevent the alteration of the most oppressive Government; for it may, in many respects, prove to be such. Is this the spirit of republicanism?”

—Patrick Henry. 1836. The Debates in the Several State Conventions on the Adoption of the Federal Constitution

2 DETERMINING POINT OF VIEW Which key principles built into the U.S. Constitution does Henry seem to think are most important? What phrases does he use that express his view?

____

____

____

____

____

____

____

____

3 DESCRIBING What kind of example does Henry use to demonstrate the problem he is discussing? How does this example support his main point?

____

____

____

____

____

____

____

____

____

ESSENTIAL QUESTION

How do new ideas change the way people live?

As you gather evidence to answer the Essential Question, think about

- how the design of the government reflects the key principles of the Constitution.
- why the three branches are designed the way they are.
- the rights and responsibilities of U.S. citizenship.

My Notes

Government and the People

DIRECTIONS: Search for evidence in Chapter 6, Lesson 2 to help you answer the following questions.

1. **IDENTIFYING** Complete the chart below by describing the main powers and responsibilities of each branch of government as well as the way it checks the other branches. You may need to check in Lesson 1 to review the checks and balances.

Main Powers and Responsibilities of the Branches of Government		
Branch	Main Powers and Responsibilities	Checks on Other Branches
Legislative		
Executive		
Judicial		

2 **ANALYZING** How do the three branches work together to protect society?

3 **CIVICS** What role does the power of judicial review play in the system of checks and balances? Which key principles are protected by judicial review?

4 **CIVICS** What are the differences between the duties and responsibilities of citizenship in the United States? Use specific examples.

ESSENTIAL QUESTION

How do new ideas change the way people live?

The Original First Amendment

DIRECTIONS: Read the following excerpt and then answer the accompanying questions.

INTRODUCTION: After the 1st Congress met in 1789, both houses passed twelve amendments for the states to consider. The excerpt below is the first amendment on the list, but it was never passed by the required three-fourths of the states, so it did not become part of the Constitution. If it had been passed, the House of Representatives would now have over 6,000 members instead of the 435 that it currently has.

VOCABULARY

misconstruction: misunderstanding
declaratory: stating
restrictive: limiting
beneficent: beneficial
concurring: agreeing
pursuant: according to
enumeration: count of the population

1 DETERMINING PURPOSE Why did Congress propose a set of amendments for the states to consider? What evidence does the text provide to support your answer?

PRIMARY SOURCE: GOVERNMENT DOCUMENT

"**THE** Conventions of a number of the States, having at the time of their adopting the Constitution, expressed a desire, in order to prevent misconstruction or abuse of its powers, that further declaratory and restrictive clauses should be added: And as extending the ground of public confidence in the Government, will best ensure the beneficent ends of its institution.

RESOLVED by the Senate and House of Representatives of the United States of America, in Congress assembled, two thirds of both Houses concurring, that the following Articles be proposed to the Legislatures of the several States, as amendments to the Constitution of the United States, all, or any of which Articles, when ratified by three fourths of the said Legislatures, to be valid to all intents and purposes, as part of the said Constitution...

Article the first... After the first enumeration required by the first article of the Constitution, there shall be one Representative for every thirty thousand, until the number shall amount to one hundred, after which the proportion shall be so regulated by Congress, that there shall be not less than one hundred Representatives, nor less than one Representative for every forty thousand persons, until the number of Representatives shall amount to two hundred; after which the

. . . *continued*

proportion shall be so regulated by Congress, that there shall not be less than two hundred Representatives, nor more than one Representative for every fifty thousand persons. ”

Source: Transcription of the 1789 Joint Resolution of Congress Proposing 12 Amendments to the U.S. Constitution. https://www.archives.gov/founding-docs/bill-of-rights-transcript

2 **ANALYZING POINT OF VIEW** Why is the second paragraph of this excerpt an unnecessary addition to this document? Why do you think the men who wrote this resolution felt it was important to include it nonetheless?

3 **CIVICS** Which key principle of the Constitution does the original First Amendment reflect? How do the requirements of this amendment respect that principle?

4 **HISTORY** During the debate to ratify the Constitution, the Federalists promised the Anti-Federalists that they would add protections for individual rights once the new government was set up. How did that promise influence the writing of this proposal?

ESSENTIAL QUESTION

How do new ideas change the way people live?

"Remember the Ladies"

DIRECTIONS: Read the following excerpt and then answer the accompanying questions.

INTRODUCTION: This letter was written at the beginning of the Revolutionary War by Abigail Adams, wife of John Adams, a Founder who would later become the second President of the United States. At the time this letter was written, Adams was in Philadelphia attending the Second Continental Congress. He and his wife wrote numerous letters to each other as the Continental Congress wrote and signed the Declaration of Independence.

VOCABULARY

independancy: independence

favourable: beneficial

foment: start

sex: gender

endearing: attractive

PRIMARY SOURCE: LETTER

"I have sometimes been ready to think that the passion for Liberty cannot be Equelly Strong in the Breasts of those who have been accustomed to deprive their fellow Creatures of theirs. Of this I am certain that it is not founded upon that generous and christian principal of doing to others as we would that others should do unto us. . . .

I long to hear that you have declared an independancy—and by the way in the new Code of Laws which I suppose it will be necessary for you to make I desire you would Remember the Ladies, and be more generous and favourable to them than your ancestors. Do not put such unlimited power into the hands of the Husbands. Remember all Men would be tyrants if they could. If perticuliar care and attention is not paid to the Ladies we are determined to foment a Rebelion, and will not hold ourselves bound by any Laws in which we have no voice, or Representation.

That your Sex are Naturally Tyrannical is a Truth so thoroughly established as to admit of no dispute, but such of you as wish to be happy willingly give up the harsh title of Master for the more tender and endearing one of Friend."

—Abigail Adams.

1 **DETERMINING PURPOSE** Why do you think Abigail Adams wrote this letter?

2 **ANALYZING** How does Adams argue for her position?

3 **ANALYZING** Why does Adams bring up the "christian principal of doing to others as we would that others should do unto us"?

4 **DETERMINING POINT OF VIEW** In his reply to his wife's letter, John Adams wrote, "We have been told that our struggle has loosened the bonds of government everywhere, that children and apprentices were disobedient; that schools and colleges were grown turbulent; that Indians slighted their guardians, and negroes grew insolent to their masters. But your letter was the first intimation [hint] that another tribe, more numerous than all the rest, were grown discontented." Why do you think Adams responded this way?

ESSENTIAL QUESTION

How do new ideas change the way people live?

1 Think About It

Review the Supporting Questions you developed in the chapter opener and look over the evidence you gathered in Chapter 6. Were you able to answer each Supporting Question? If there was not enough evidence to answer your Supporting Questions, what additional evidence do you think you need to consider?

____

____

____

____

2 Organize Your Evidence

Complete a table similar to the one below with answers to your Supporting Questions.

Supporting Questions	Answers from Inquiry Journal	Answers from Textbook

❸ Talk About It

Share your table with one or more other students. Review their tables. Discuss everybody's ideas and decide on the best way to answer the ESSENTIAL QUESTION: *How do new ideas change the way people live?* Be sure to focus on today's world. What ideas are powerful enough to change society? Use the answers to your Supporting Questions to help you come up with as many ideas as possible. Talk about them, and agree on one answer. Write the idea below.

____

____

____

____

____

❹ Write About It

Now that you have identified the idea, list the ways you think it would change the way people live.

____

____

____

____

____

____

____

❺ Connect to the Essential Question

You and the other group members will create a Web page to present your answer to the ESSENTIAL QUESTION: *How do new ideas change the way people live?* If you do not have access to the necessary technology, you can create a mockup of the Web page on paper. Your page should have a heading that presents the Essential Question. Below this heading, present the name of the new idea you find powerful. Then, using words and images, convince someone who is visiting your Web page that the new idea will truly change the way people live.

CITIZENSHIP

TAKING ACTION

The Constitution is based on the principle of popular sovereignty. As the text says, "Exercising the right to vote is probably the most important responsibility of a citizen," but U.S. citizens do not get to vote directly on either laws or Constitutional amendments; these are both done through their elected representatives at the local, state, and national levels. Despite this, citizen engagement can and does have an impact on the lawmaking and Constitutional amendment process. Have students find out about a proposed Constitutional amendment, or devise their own proposal for a new amendment, and instruct them to devise a plan for citizens to take action to get that amendment passed by Congress and the states.

The Federalist Era

ESSENTIAL QUESTION

What are the characteristics of a leader?

Think about how this question might relate to the creators of the new United States government.

TALK ABOUT IT

Discuss with a partner what information you would need to know to answer the Essential Question by considering the leaders of the young American nation. For example, you might ask, "Who were the leaders or the creators of the new American government?"

DIRECTIONS: Now, write down three additional questions that you need to answer to be able to describe the characteristics of a leader.

MY RESEARCH QUESTIONS

Supporting Question 1:

____

____

Supporting Question 2:

____

____

Supporting Question 3:

____

____

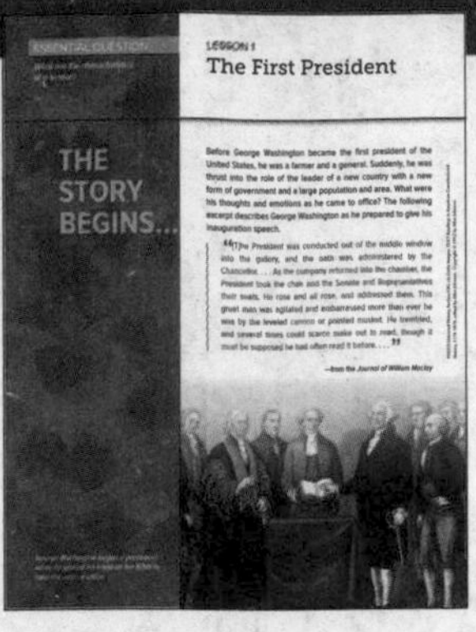

ESSENTIAL QUESTION

What are the characteristics of a leader?

As you gather evidence to answer the Essential Question, think about

- who the leaders were who led the American government in its early days.
- the challenges they faced.
- the decisions they made.
- conflicts that developed around their decisions.

My Notes

The First President

DIRECTIONS: Search for evidence in Chapter 7, Lesson 1 to help you answer the following questions.

1A **INFERRING** When choosing the members of his cabinet, what qualities might President Washington have sought in his advisors?

1B Why does a leader such as a president need advisors?

1C What leadership qualities must a president have in order to make the best use of his cabinet of advisors?

1D In the Lesson Opener, William Maclay observes that President Washington felt nervous and uncomfortable delivering his inauguration speech. Were you surprised at this observation? What did this passage reveal about the president's leadership qualities?

2 **CIVICS** Why did the Founders feel it was necessary and important to create the Bill of Rights?

____

____

____

____

____

3 **ECONOMICS** Use the graphic organizer below to examine Alexander Hamilton's monetary policies and the opposition he encountered. If there was opposition, explain who opposed the policy and why. If a solution was required, indicate how Hamilton responded to the controversy.

Hamilton's Monetary Policies			
POLICY	REASON FOR POLICY	WHO OPPOSED & WHY (where applicable)	HAMILTON'S SOLUTION
pay off war debts to other nations			
pay off war debts owed to states			
create a national bank with a common currency			
tariffs placed on imported goods			
taxes			

ESSENTIAL QUESTION

What are the characteristics of a leader?

A Communication to the *Pennsylvania Gazette*

DIRECTIONS: Read the following letter to the editor of a newspaper and then answer the accompanying questions.

INTRODUCTION: Alexander Hamilton took the lead on national financial challenges as Secretary of the Treasury under George Washington. Hamilton had bold plans. Among them was a plan to pay off the debts of the country and the states in order to establish firm credit for future borrowing needs. The plan met bitter opposition. Much of the debt was held by speculators. Why, Americans wondered, should *they* profit from public money? There were other arguments against the plan as well, as this letter to the editor from a Pennsylvania farmer makes clear.

PRIMARY SOURCE: LETTER TO THE EDITOR

"The following consequences will follow the adoption of the proposed funding system.

It will draw all the cash from the country to our cities, from whence it will be exported to England and Holland, to pay the annual interest of greatly oppressive debt.

It will rend it impossible for the farmers to borrow money to improve their lands, for who will lend money to an individual for 6 percent when government securities will yield 8 and 12 percent?

It will check trade and manufactures.

It will fill our country with brokers and idle speculators.

It will produce a principal of $200,000 to a few Nabobs in each of the states, who will sell this principal after a while to foreigners, and lay it out in buying townships and counties, to be cultivated by tenants who will administer to the ambition and power of these nabobs, and thereby enable them to establish titles, et cetera and to overthrow the liberties of our country.

VOCABULARY

oppressive: burdensome
rend: make
check: stop
idle: nonworking
speculators: investment risk-takers
nabobs: privileged, wealthy people
remonstrate: complain
duped: tricked
defrauded: cheated

1 ANALYZING POINTS OF VIEW How does the farmer who wrote this letter feel about the government's monetary policies?

____

____

. . . continued

Would it not be proper for the farmers to unite immediately, and remonstrate against these evils. They were never in half the danger of being ruined by the British government, that they now are by their own.

Had any person told them in the beginning of the war, that, after paying yearly rent of their farms for seven years to carry on this war, at the close of it their farms should not be worth more than one fourth of their original cost and value, in consequence of a funding system – is there a farmer that would have embarked in the war? No, there is not. Why then should we be deceived, duped, defrauded and ruined by our new rulers?”

—a Pennsylvania farmer, in a letter to the *Pennsylvania Gazette,* February 3, 1790

2 **SUMMARIZING** What does the farmer say will happen as a result of Hamilton's policies?

3 **DETERMINING POINT OF VIEW** How does he feel about the war, now that it is over and he can see the effects on farmers?

4 **DETERMINING PURPOSE** Why might the farmer have written this letter?

ESSENTIAL QUESTION

What are the characteristics of a leader?

1 DETERMINING POINT OF VIEW What is the writer's view of the Federalists and Anti-Federalists' attitudes regarding the adoption of the constitution put forth by the Federalists? Where do his sympathies lie?

VOCABULARY

moderate: reasonable
obstinate: stubborn
sentiment: feeling
swayed: persuaded
hazard: risk
arrogance: attitude of superiority

Letter to the *Hampshire Chronicle*

DIRECTIONS: Read the following letter to the editor of the *Hampshire Chronicle*, a newspaper in Springfield, Massachusetts. Then answer the accompanying questions.

INTRODUCTION: The great debate over the ratification of the Constitution pitted the Federalists, who supported it, against the Antifederalists, who opposed it. The Federalists were led by Alexander Hamilton, James Madison, and John Jay. As you read the letter to the editor, consider what the writer might have thought about these men and their leadership roles.

PRIMARY SOURCE: SONG

"I find that all are clearly agreed in the truth of this position — that an energetic Federal Government is essential to our happiness and existence as a nation. . . . The only thing, therefore, remaining to be decided is whether under this constitution our essential freedom can be maintained?

A hot brained Federalist will tell you that it must be adopted without limitations or reserve, and I have known some to go so far as to call in the assistance of tar and feathers against such as were of different sentiment.

The Antifederalists in general are more moderate but equally obstinate. Some of them would reject the whole, purely because some few parts of it do not meet with the approbation [approval].

Persons of the above description are swayed by passions, not by reason, and should not be regarded by the honest and sensible part of the community.

I really think that if a bill of rights had accompanied our new constitution, little or no opposition would have been made to it. It may be true that it is defective, but none have yet been able to maintain that it is materially so. We have, however, much reason to expect amendments, if necessary, from our representatives who act under it in the first instance [first session of Congress]. In short, we cannot hazard much, provided we are previously secured by a bill of rights. This with the antifederalist seems to be the thread on which hangs suspended all their hopes and wishes.

. . . continued

Let those, therefore, who call themselves Federalists lay aside a little of their arrogance and instead of abusing, endeavor to convince their fellow citizens of the necessity of embracing the constitution as it stands, the impracticability of securing a better one, and that anarchy will be the consequence of its rejection. Let them unite with their brethren in recommending a bill of rights which is, in fact, the best security we can have against the encroachments of despotism, and I flatter myself that our state will not be the last that shall accede to it.”

—Letter to the *Hampshire Chronicle*, Springfield, Massachusetts, December 25, 1787

VOCABULARY

endeavor: try
impracticability: lack of practicality
anarchy: chaos, lack of government
encroachments: trespass
despotism: control by a tyrant
accede: agree

2 DETERMINING MEANING What is the writer's advice to both groups?

3 CIVICS What is the writer's opinion regarding a bill of rights, and what words in his letter reveal it?

4 DETERMINING PURPOSE What might be the author's purpose in writing this letter to the editor?

5 INFERRING How might the author's advice be applied to good leadership?

ESSENTIAL QUESTION

What are the characteristics of a leader?

As you gather evidence to answer the Essential Question, think about:

- how Washington responded to challenges the new nation faced at home and abroad
- what factors a leader must consider before deciding upon a course of action

My Notes

Early Challenges

DIRECTIONS: Search for evidence in Chapter 7, Lesson 2 to help you answer the following questions.

1 IDENTIFYING CAUSE AND EFFECT President Washington faced challenges during his presidency. Use the graphic organizer to organize the events and his responses to them.

President Washington Faces Challenges		
Challenge	Description	Washington's Response
Whiskey Rebellion		
American settlers ignore treaties with Native Americans		
Washington asks for help from the French, and the British become angry.		
French Revolution		

Britain/France go to war		
Spanish leaders concerned about Jay's Treaty		

2A INTERPRETING What are the positive and negative effects of sending in troops as a response to difficulties?

2B What are the positive and negative effects of negotiating treaties to solve difficulties?

3 INFERRING Why might it be hard for a president to determine a course of action in response to a challenge?

ESSENTIAL QUESTION

What are the characteristics of a leader?

The Failure of the Expedition of 1791

DIRECTIONS: Read the following excerpt. Then answer the accompanying questions.

INTRODUCTION: November 4, 1791: It is cold. The sun won't rise for another half hour. About 1,400 American soldiers wake up in their camp along the Wabash River in Ohio. Suddenly, Native Americans surround the camp. Their numbers grow rapidly. A group of about 250 American volunteer soldiers panic and run through the professional army ranks, causing confusion. Soon, more than 1,000 Native American warriors under the command of Miami Chief Little Turtle have the Americans surrounded. Major General Arthur St. Clair, the American leader, decides to retreat with some of the military forces. He breaks through the Native Americans' defenses and escapes to the safety of a fort 20 miles away. Left behind are more than 900 dead and wounded soldiers, as well as women and children. Survivors are mistreated and some die. The U.S. Congress hears of these shocking events and forms the first Congressional Special Committee investigation.

1 **ANALYZING** Who wrote this report?

____

____

____

____

____

____

____

____

VOCABULARY

furnish: provide
consequent: as a result of
gross: complete
Quartermaster: army officer responsible for supplies
forage: grass for horses
procured: obtained
manifested: acted on
want: lack, absence
imputed: attributed to, caused by
peculiar: unique
intrepidity: courage
zeal: enthusiasm

PRIMARY SOURCE: CONGRESSIONAL SPECIAL COMMITTEE REPORT

"[T]he committee suggest the following as the principal causes, in their opinion, of the failure of the late expedition under Major General St. Clair.

The delay in furnishing that materials for, and in passing the act for the protection of the frontiers; at the time, after the passing of which, was hardly sufficient to complete and discipline an army for such an expedition during the summer months of the same year.

The delays consequent upon the gross and various mismanagements and neglects in the Quartermaster's and contractors' departments; the lateness of the season at which the expedition was undertaken, the green forage having been previously destroyed by the frost, so that a sufficiency of substance for the horses necessary for the army could not be procured.

The want of discipline and experience in the troops.

. . . continued

The committee conceive it but justice to the commander in chief, to say, that, in their opinion, the failure of the late expedition can, in no respect, be imputed to [St. Clair's] conduct, either at any time before or during the action; but that as his conduct in all the preparatory arrangements was marked with peculiar ability and zeal, so his conduct during the action furnished strong testimonies of his coolness and intrepidity. ❞

—*Causes of the Failure of the Expedition Against the Indians in 1791, Under the Command of Major General St. Clair,* Special Committee Report, U.S. House of Representatives, May 8, 1792

2 DETERMINING PURPOSE What was the purpose of this report?

3 DETERMINING CENTRAL IDEAS To what factors does the committee attribute St. Clair's defeat?

4 DETERMINING POINT OF VIEW What is the committee's opinion of Major General St. Clair? Which words tell you their opinion?

5 CITING TEXT EVIDENCE How much of the blame does the committee place on St. Clair for his defeat? Cite evidence from the excerpt.

6 MAKING CONNECTIONS How might the committee have answered the question, "What are the characteristics of a leader?"

Jefferson and Hamilton on the French Revolution

DIRECTIONS: Read the following excerpts. Then answer the accompanying questions.

INTRODUCTION: The American Revolution inspired the French Revolution. An eyewitness to the early part of the French Revolution was the American minister there: Thomas Jefferson, whose Declaration of Independence had thrilled the French revolutionaries. Jefferson refers to Robespierre, the leader of the French Revolution who created a "reign of terror," killing thousands of fellow revolutionaries who did not agree with him.

VOCABULARY

consequent: as a result of
iniquities: injustices
piously: sincerely
zeal: passion, enthusiasm
pervading: spreading to
unanimity: agreement by all
animating: stirring feeling in
exemplary: as an example
persevere: continue
partiality: in favor of
annihilates: destroys
beneficent: kindly and beneficial
persecuting: cruel
desolating: depressing, not inspirational
atheism: lack of belief in God

1 **COMPARING** What do Jefferson and Hamilton agree on about the early stages of the French Revolution?

____

____

____

____

____

____

PRIMARY SOURCE: LETTER

"[T]here is a god in heaven, and that he will not slumber without end on the iniquities of tyrants, or would-be tyrants..... this ball of liberty, I believe most piously, is now so well in motion that it will roll round the globe, at least the enlightened part of it, for light & liberty go together. it is our glory that we first put it into motion, & our happiness that being foremost we had no bad examples to follow. [W]hat a tremendous obstacle to the future attempts at liberty will be the atrocities of Robespierre!"

—Thomas Jefferson, Letter to Tench Coxe, June 1, 1795

PRIMARY SOURCE: PRIVATE PAPER

Another American statesman who took an interest in the French Revolution was Alexander Hamilton. Hamilton was Secretary of the Treasury at the time.

"In the early periods of the French Revolution, a warm zeal for its success was in this Country a sentiment truly universal. The love of Liberty is here the ruling passion of the Citizens of the United States pervading every class animating every bosom. As long therefore as the Revolution of France bore the marks of being the cause of liberty it united all hearts.... But this unanimity...has been for a considerable time decreasing. ... [T]hat a people like that of the United States—exemplary for humanity and ... a just reverence for Religion should so long persevere in partiality for a state of things... which annihilates the foundations of social order and true liberty....and substitutes to the mild & beneficent religion of the Gospel a gloomy, persecuting and desolating atheism....If there be anything solid in virtue—the time must come when it will have been a disgrace to have advocated the Revolution of France in its late stages."

—Alexander Hamilton, 1794

2 **COMPARING** What do Jefferson and Hamilton agree on about the later stages of the French Revolution?

3 **CONTRASTING** In these excerpts, how do Jefferson's and Hamilton's criticisms of the later stages of the French Revolution differ?

4 **CIVICS** What might each American have said about the leadership of the French Revolution?

The First Political Parties

DIRECTIONS: Search for evidence in Chapter 7, Lesson 3 to help you answer the following questions.

1A HISTORY Why did President Washington oppose the formation of political parties?

1B Do you agree with President Washington's opinion? Use the text to help you explain why you do or do not agree with his opposition to political parties.

2 ANALYZING POINTS OF VIEW Use the graphic organizer below to identify the benefits and drawbacks of each view of the Constitution.

Two Views of the Constitution

Party	Leaders	Benefits of This View	Drawbacks of This View
Federalists: "Implied Powers"			
Democratic-Republicans: No Implied Powers (Strict Reading)			

ESSENTIAL QUESTION

What are the characteristics of a leader?

As you gather evidence to answer the Essential Question, think about:

- how differing opinions of the first American leaders led to the first political parties.
- how the new nation and its leaders had to learn to deal with foreign countries.

My Notes

3 **CIVICS** Use the chart below to examine the leadership qualities of President John Adams in meeting the challenges of his presidency.

John Adams: Leadership Qualities			
Event	President Adams's Response	Quality of Leadership: Good/Bad/ Unsure	Reason for your answer
French seize American ships			
Federalists call for war with France			
Populace becomes wary of French immigrants			

ESSENTIAL QUESTION

What are the characteristics of a leader?

1 **INFERRING** In the first paragraph, what does Smith imply about the value of Jefferson's writings and his motives for "composing essays on civil rights"?

VOCABULARY

merit: value
composing: writing
tranquility: peace
accrued: resulted
vouchers: receipts
conspicuously: obviously

The Character of Mr. Jefferson

DIRECTIONS: Read the following excerpt. Then answer the accompanying questions.

INTRODUCTION: In 1781, during Thomas Jefferson's term as governor of Virginia, the state was invaded by British forces under American traitor Benedict Arnold. Jefferson fled the state capital, Richmond, which the British burned behind him. Later, General Cornwallis attempted to capture Jefferson at his home, Monticello, but, tipped off to their plans, Jefferson fled to his other plantation, Poplar Forest, evading capture. While the General Assembly later determined that Jefferson had acted with honor, not everyone agreed. In the following essay, William Loughton Smith, a Federalist Congressman from South Carolina, states his opinion of Jefferson and contrasts his behavior with that of Jefferson's rival, Alexander Hamilton.

PRIMARY SOURCE: ESSAY

"There is no great merit in composing, in the cabinet, [in] seasons of tranquility, essays on civil rights, which are frequently done to obtain popularity, and without any risk of personal inconvenience.

It appears, however, that Mr. Jefferson has generally sacrificed the civil rights of his countrymen to his own personal safety. We are told, in a public address, by Mr. Charles Simms, of Virginia, who must have been well acquainted with the circumstance, 'that Mr. Jefferson, when governor of Virginia, abandoned the trust with which he was charged, at the moment of an invasion by the enemy, by which great confusion, loss, and distress, [accrued] to the state, in the destruction of public records and vouchers for general expenditures.

Now here was a period of public danger, when Mr. Jefferson's attachment to the civil rights of his countrymen might have shown very conspicuously, by facing and averting the danger; here would have been a fine opportunity for him to have displayed his public spirit, in bravely rallying around the standard of liberty and civil rights; but, though in times of safety, he could rally around the standard of his friend, Tom

. . . continued

Paine, yet when real danger appeared, the governor of the dominion dwindled into the poor, timid philosopher, and instead of rallying his brave countrymen, he fled for the safety from a few light horsemen, and shamefully abandoned his trust!!

How different was the conduct of the spirited and truly patriotic Hamilton? He wished to retire as much as the philosopher of Montecello; he had a large family, and his little fortune was fast melting away in the expensive metropolis, but with a Roman spirit he declared 'that much as he wished for retirement, yet he would remain at his post, as long as there was any danger of his country being involved in war.' ❞

—William Loughton Smith, South Carolina Congressman, *Letters of Phocion*

VOCABULARY

averting: avoiding
standard: symbolic flag
dominion: governed area
metropolis: large city

2A DETERMINING MEANING What is meant by, "It appears, however, that Mr. Jefferson has generally sacrificed the civil rights of his countrymen to his own personal safety"?

2B Why does Smith feel Jefferson "abandoned the trust with which he was charged"?

3 CONTRASTING How does Smith use Alexander Hamilton as a point of contrast for Jefferson?

4 ANALYZING POINTS OF VIEW In your opinion, is William Loughton Smith a reliable source of information about Thomas Jefferson? Explain your answer.

ESSENTIAL QUESTION

What are the characteristics of a leader?

Virginia Resolution of 1798

DIRECTIONS: Read the following excerpt. Then answer the accompanying questions.

INTRODUCTION: In December 1798 the Virginia Senate adopted a five-point resolution written by James Madison protesting Congress's passage of the Alien and Sedition Acts. Thomas Jefferson collaborated with Madison on the resolution and penned his own version for the state of Kentucky.

PRIMARY SOURCE: STATE SENATE RESOLUTION

"That the General Assembly doth particularly protest against the palpable and alarming infractions of the Constitution, in the two late cases of the "alien and sedition acts," passed at the last session of Congress, the first of which exercises a power nowhere delegated to the Federal Government; and which by uniting legislative and judicial powers to those of executive, subverts the general principles of free government, as well as the particular organization and positive provisions of the federal Constitution; and the other of which acts exercises in like manner a power not delegated by the Constitution, but on the contrary expressly and positively forbidden by one of the amendments thereto; a power which more than any other ought to produce universal alarm, because it is levelled against that right of freely examining public characters and measures, and of free communication among the people thereon, which has ever been justly deemed the only effectual guardian of every other right."

—James Madison, *Virginia Resolutions of 1798*

VOCABULARY

doth: does
palpable: easily seen
infractions: violations
alien: a resident of a country who is not a citizen
sedition: writing that encourages rebellion
subvert: undermine
levelled: directed
effectual: valid and impactful

1A DETERMINING MEANING To what does "the first of which" refer?

1B What power is meant by "...exercises a power nowhere delegated to the Federal Government"?

2 CITING TEXT EVIDENCE Where does the Virginia Senate express concern about violating the right to free speech guaranteed in the Constitution?

3 INFERRING What can you infer about the Virginia Senate's view of President John Adams's leadership?

ESSENTIAL QUESTION

What are the characteristics of a leader?

1 Think About It

Review the supporting questions that you developed at the beginning of the chapter. Review the evidence that you gathered in Chapter 7. Were you able to answer each supporting question? If there was not enough evidence to answer your supporting questions, what additional evidence do you think you need to include?

2 Organize Your Evidence and Draw Conclusions

Use the graphic organizer below to compare and contrast the leadership qualities of Washington, Hamilton, Jefferson, Madison, and Adams and give your evaluation of each.

Leadership Qualities of Early Leaders		
Leader	Most Significant Achievements and Mistakes	My Evaluation of Leadership: Great, Good, Fair or Poor?
George Washington (President)		
Alexander Hamilton (Secretary of Treasury)		
Thomas Jefferson (Secretary of State)		
James Madison (Congressman)		
John Adams (as President)		

3 Write About It

What qualities do you value in a leader? How difficult do you think it might be to be a leader of a new nation?

4 Talk About It

Get together with a partner or small group and discuss the qualities of the leaders explored in this chapter. Do you and the other group members have differing opinions in favoring the leadership of one of the Founders over the others? What evidence are you using to draw your conclusions?

5 Connect to the Essential Question

Choose one or more of the leaders in your chart in question 2 and write an argumentative essay about the characteristics of leadership and how the leader or leaders you have chosen demonstrate those characteristics.

CITIZENSHIP

TAKING ACTION

MAKE CONNECTIONS Although American political parties are different today than they were in the 1700s, the U.S. government continues to work as a mostly two-party political system. During the elections held today, Americans have to make choices about the leadership qualities of various candidates, just as Americans in the late 1700s had to examine those same qualities in the early leaders.

Strong, effective leadership comes in many forms. A leader might be a quiet person who is able to get difficult things done by working diligently with a team. Other effective leaders might be great public speakers or have good ideas. What kind of leader are you? What opportunities for leadership exist in your school?

TALK ABOUT IT

Work in small groups and talk about your individual leadership style. What skills, interests, and personality traits would be assets to you as a leader? List them below.

WRITE ABOUT IT

Write a journal entry about your leadership qualities and how you would like to get involved in your school in a leadership role (athletic team, student government, theater program, etc.).

CHAPTER 8

The Jefferson Era

ESSENTIAL QUESTION

Why does conflict develop?

Think about the reasons conflict develops among individuals and groups of people.

TALK ABOUT IT

Discuss with a partner the type of information you would need to understand why conflicts occurred in the years following American independence. You may want to consider the following: What were some of the issues that divided Americans? Why did the United States go to war with Britain and Native American nations? How did these conflicts affect the lives of individuals? How might these conflicts have been resolved?

DIRECTIONS: Now write down three additional questions that will help you explain why conflicts developed in the early years of American Independence.

MY RESEARCH QUESTIONS

Supporting Question 1:

____

____

Supporting Question 2:

____

____

Supporting Question 3:

____

____

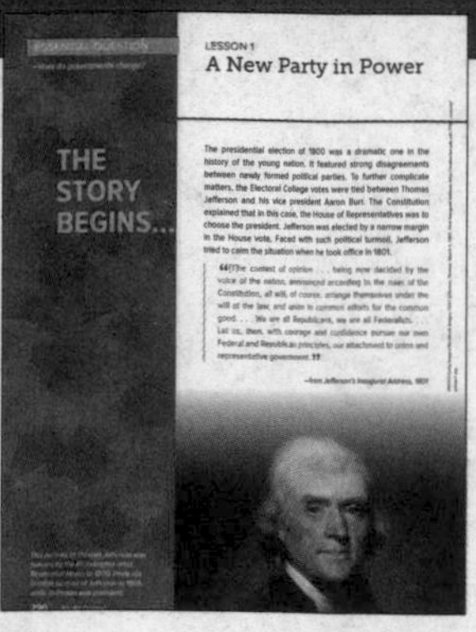

ESSENTIAL QUESTION

Why does conflict develop?

As you gather evidence to answer the Essential Question, think about

- how Americans were divided.
- how conflict leads groups of people to form alliances with one another.
- why people respond to conflict in different ways.

My Notes

A New Party in Power

DIRECTIONS: Search for evidence in Chapter 8, Lesson 1 to help you answer the following questions.

1 SEQUENCING How did conflict in the election of 1800 lead Congress to pass the Twelfth Amendment to the Constitution? Complete the chart to show the sequence of events.

				Congress passes the Twelfth Amendment to the Constitution.

2 IDENTIFYING MAIN IDEAS Why did Jefferson pledge to limit the size of the federal government?

3A SPECULATING One way Jefferson limited the size of the federal government was by cutting federal jobs. How do you think citizens responded to this proposal?

3B SPECULATING Jefferson also reduced the power of the federal government by cutting federal taxes. How do you think citizens responded?

4 EXPLAINING How did Chief Justice Marshall's ruling in *Marbury* v. *Madison* provide an important check on the power of the executive and legislative branches of government?

ESSENTIAL QUESTION

Why does conflict develop?

Jefferson Makes the Case for National Unity in his Inaugural Address

DIRECTIONS: Read the following excerpt from Jefferson's Inaugural Address. Then answer the accompanying questions.

INTRODUCTION: Federalists and Republicans squared off against one another in the presidential election of 1800. After a bitter campaign season, Republicans won the election, and Thomas Jefferson took office as the third president of the United States.

VOCABULARY

animation: moving excitedly
exertions: efforts
prevail: win
intercourse: communication
dreary: gloomy
full tide: surge
abandon: give up
visionary: person who looks to the future

1 **INFERRING** What can you infer about the campaign for President based on Jefferson's call to return to communication "that harmony and affection without which liberty and even life itself are but dreary things?"

Jefferson feared that the voices of the minority woulb be not heard. Although Jebberson said that the "minority shoud privial", he says the they be rightful and also be reasonable.

PRIMARY SOURCE: INAUGURAL ADDRESS

"During the contest of opinion through which we have passed the animation of discussions and of exertions has sometimes worn an aspect which might impose on strangers unused to think freely and to speak and to write what they think; but this being now decided by the voice of the nation, announced according to the rules of the Constitution, all will, of course, arrange themselves under the will of the law, and unite in common efforts for the common good. All, too, will bear in mind this sacred principle, that though the will of the majority is in all cases to prevail, that will to be rightful must be reasonable; that the minority possess their equal rights, which equal law must protect, and to violate would be oppression. Let us, then, fellow-citizens, unite with one heart and one mind. Let us restore to social intercourse that harmony and affection without which liberty and even life itself are but dreary things.

We are all Republicans, we are all Federalists. If there be any among us who would wish to dissolve this Union or to change its republican form, let them stand undisturbed as monuments of the safety with which error of opinion may be tolerated where reason is left free to combat it. I know, indeed, that some honest men

fear that a republican government can not be strong, that this Government is not strong enough; but would the honest patriot, in the full tide of successful experiment, abandon a government which has so far kept us free and firm on the theoretic and visionary fear that this Government, the world's best hope, may by possibility want energy to preserve itself? I trust not. I believe this, on the contrary, the strongest Government on earth. I believe it the only one where every man, at the call of the law, would fly to the standard of the law, and would meet invasions of the public order as his own personal concern. Sometimes it is said that man can not be trusted with the government of himself. Can he, then, be trusted with the government of others? Or have we found angels in the forms of kings to govern him? Let history answer this question. ”

—Thomas Jefferson Inaugural Address, March 4, 1801

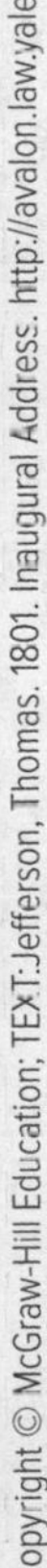

2 **CITING TEXT EVIDENCE** Which phrases from the excerpt best summarize the concerns of the Federalists?

3 **ANALYZING POINT OF VIEW** What does Jefferson predict will happen to the country now that the election is over?

4 **DRAWING CONCLUSIONS** Why does Jefferson argue that those who "wish to dissolve this Union" should be "left undisturbed?"

ESSENTIAL QUESTION

Why does conflict develop?

A Newspaper Editor Argues Against Electing Thomas Jefferson President

DIRECTIONS: Read this excerpt from a newspaper editorial and then answer the accompanying questions.

INTRODUCTION: The presidential election of 1800 took place shortly after Napoleon came to power in France. Jefferson had close ties with the French. Some Federalists worried that France would have too much influence on the United States if Jefferson won the election.

VOCABULARY

agitated: troubled; nervous
deviate: stray from
conciliation: resolving a problem
tri-consulate: government body under Napoleon
Jacobin: radical political group known for its cruelty during the French Revolution
colossi: very large and important things
reviling: criticizing; insulting
vilifying: denouncing; speaking badly about
opulence: luxury; splendid
pious: devoted; sacred

PRIMARY SOURCE: EDITORIAL

"The approaching election for President, and the situation of our mission to France are the two most important political subjects on which the public mind is now agitated.... France, like almost every other nation, will not deviate from what she deems her interest, and it is not her interest to adjust with us our respective differences. All the effect which, it is probable, this last attempt at conciliation will have, will only be to discover the hollowness of the professions of the tri-consulate.

To effect the election of Mr. Jefferson to the head of the government is the favourite wish of every Jacobin from Georgia to New Hampshire. No stone is left unturned to accomplish the object. ... We cannot, however, believe that such men as Giles, Gallatin, and others of the Jacobin colossi, to whom Mr. Jefferson will be indebted for his elevation, will remain unnoticed by him. These it is probable, will be his prime favourites. ... The real and native patriot who has done his country service for years in public employment, must then yield his place to some favourite foreigner, some graceless [man], whose whole merit consists in reviling and vilifying the acts of an administration which has raised this country to its present state of prosperity, opulence, and respectability. These observations are made that our present, pious and able President may still continue to fill the chair of

1 IDENTIFYING Why does the author think that negotiations with France are a waste of time?

____

____

____

____

____

state. It is hardly possible that one material benefit can accrue to America by a change. The affairs of the nation have progressed and prospered as when our beloved Washington was our pilot. Why then should we not continue to support the man who has proved himself in the most difficult situations, the able and active friend of his country, rather than by electing another, to rush on evils that we know not of. ”

Source *Farmers Museum* (Walpole, New Hampshire), October 13, 1800

2 **ANALYZING** What connection does the author make between France and the Presidential election?

3 **EXPLAINING** Why does the author think that Americans will lose their jobs under a Jefferson administration?

4 **CITING TEXT EVIDENCE** What phrase does the author use to describe Americans who will lose their jobs? What does he mean by this phrase?

ESSENTIAL QUESTION

Why does conflict develop?

As you gather evidence to answer the Essential Question, think about

- how Americans were divided
- how conflict leads groups of people to form alliances with one another
- why people respond to conflict in different ways

My Notes

The Louisiana Purchase

DIRECTIONS: Search for evidence in Chapter 8, Lesson 2 to help you answer the following questions.

1 **IDENTIFYING EFFECTS** Complete the table by identifying the effects of Haitian independence on each country.

Effects of Haitian Independence	
On France	
On the United States	

2 **MAKING CONNECTIONS** How did the Louisiana Purchase benefit the United States economy?

3 **EXPLAINING** Why was finding the Northwest Passage a key goal of the Lewis and Clarke expedition?

4 **IDENTIFYING CAUSES** Why did some Federalists respond to the Louisiana Purchase by plotting to secede from the Union?

ESSENTIAL QUESTION

Why does conflict develop?

Eyewitnesses Describe the Duel Between Aaron Burr and Alexander Hamilton

DIRECTIONS: Read this excerpt from an eyewitness account of the duel between Alexander Hamilton and Aaron Burr, 1804. Then answer the accompanying questions.

INTRODUCTION: After the Louisiana Purchase, some Federalists in the Northeast worried that power would shift westward. They plotted to secede from the Union, and enlisted the support of Aaron Burr. When Alexander Hamilton learned of the plot, he accused Burr of treason. Burr responded by challenging Hamilton to a duel. Although Hamilton accepted the challenge, he believed that dueling was wrong. Hamilton promised that he would not fire at Burr during the duel.

VOCABULARY

duel: a prearranged fight, combat

discharged: fired

subsequently: later

principals: participants

conceive: think

barge: flat-bottomed boat

PRIMARY SOURCE: EYEWITNESS ACCOUNT

"The pistols were discharged within a few seconds of each other and the fire of Col: Burr took effect; Genl Hamilton almost instantly fell. Col: Burr then advanced toward Genl H——n with a manner and gesture that appeared to Genl Hamilton's friend to be expressive of regret, but without Speaking turned about & withdrew. Being urged from the field by his friend as has been subsequently stated, with a view to prevent his being recognised by the Surgeon and Bargemen who were then approaching. No farther communications took place between the principals and the Barge that carried Col: Burr immediately returned to the City. We conceive it proper to add that the conduct of the parties in that interview was perfectly proper as suited the occasion."

—Joint Statement by William P. Van Ness and Nathaniel Pendleton on the Duel between Alexander Hamilton and Aaron Burr, 17 July 1804.

1 **INFERRING** What can you infer about dueling based on the observation that "the conduct of the parties ... was perfectly proper as suited the occasion?"

2 **SPECULATING** Why do you think Hamilton opposed dueling as a way to resolve conflict?

3 **DRAWING CONCLUSIONS** Why do you think Hamilton agreed to the duel even though he had promised not to shoot at Burr?

4 **CITING TEXT EVIDENCE** What evidence from the text shows that dueling was illegal?

4 **ANALYZING POINTS OF VIEW** Why do you think that Burr appeared to be "expressive of regret" after he shot Hamilton?

ESSENTIAL QUESTION

Why does conflict develop?

Haiti Declares Independence from France

DIRECTIONS: Read this excerpt from the Haitian Declaration of Independence, 1804. Then answer the accompanying questions.

INTRODUCTION: Inspired by the principles of the French and American Revolutions, enslaved people in Saint-Domingue rebelled against French colonial rule. Forces sent by Napoleon were finally defeated in 1804. On declaring independence, Haiti became the first nation in the Western Hemisphere to make slavery illegal.

VOCABULARY

torpor: inactivity; apathy
specter: ghost; shadow
firebrands: radicals
drenched: soaked
absurdity: ridiculousness; unreasonableness
posterity: future generations
dreading: fearing
vengeance: revenge

1 DRAWING CONCLUSIONS Why does the author insist that "it is not enough" to have achieved independence?

____

____

____

____

PRIMARY SOURCE: DECLARATION OF INDEPENDENCE

"Citizens:

It is not enough to have expelled the barbarians who have bloodied our land for two centuries; it is not enough to have restrained those ever-evolving factions that one after another mocked the specter of liberty that France dangled before you. We must, with one last act of national authority, forever assure the empire of liberty in the country of our birth; we must take any hope of re-enslaving us away from the inhuman government that for so long kept us in the most humiliating torpor. In the end we must live independent or die...

We have dared to be free, let us be thus by ourselves and for ourselves. Let us imitate the grown child: his own weight breaks the boundary that has become an obstacle to him. What people fought for us? What people wanted to gather the fruits of our labor? And what dishonorable absurdity to conquer in order to be enslaved. Enslaved? ... Let us leave this description for the French; they have conquered but are no longer free.

Let us walk down another path; let us imitate those people who, extending their concern into the future, and dreading to leave an example of cowardice for posterity,

preferred to be exterminated rather than lose their place as one of the world's free peoples.

Let us ensure, however, that a missionary spirit does not destroy our work; let us allow our neighbors to breathe in peace; may they live quietly under the laws that they have made for themselves, and let us not, as revolutionary firebrands, declare ourselves the lawgivers of the Caribbean, nor let our glory consist in troubling the peace of the neighboring islands. Unlike that which we inhabit, theirs has not been drenched in the innocent blood of its inhabitants; they have no vengeance to claim from the authority that protects them. ”

—The Haitian Declaration of Independence, 1804.

2 **ANALYZING** What comparison does the Declaration make in the second paragraph? Why does the author make this comparison?

3 **CITING TEXT EVIDENCE** What phrases show that liberty and freedom are the most important principles?

4 **INTERPRETING** According to the Declaration, how should Haiti behave toward its neighbors in the Caribbean?

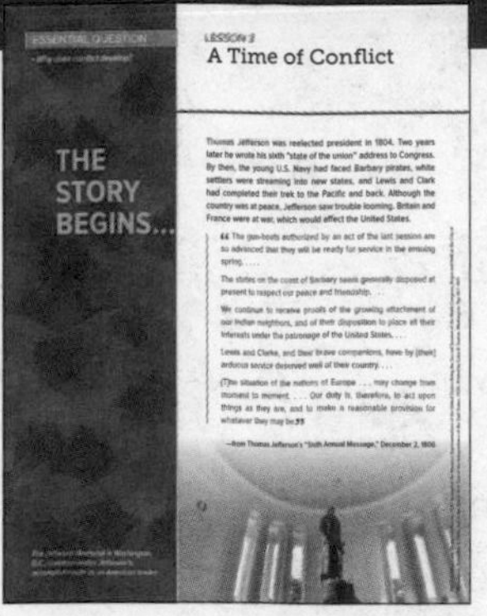

ESSENTIAL QUESTION

Why does conflict develop?

As you gather evidence to answer the Essential Question, think about

- how Americans were divided.
- how conflict leads groups of people to form alliances with one another.
- why people respond to conflict in different ways.

A Time of Conflict

DIRECTIONS: Search for evidence in Chapter 8, Lesson 3 to help you answer the following questions.

1. **SEQUENCING** What events led Stephen Decatur to burn the U.S. warship *Philadelphia*? Complete the graphic organizer to show the sequence of events.

1	2	3	4	5	6

2. **EXPLAINING** Why did American merchants initially prosper from the war between Britain and France? What happened to disrupt this prosperity?

3. **SPECULATING** Britain treated its sailors badly during the war with France. How might better treatment have prevented the practice of impressment?

My Notes

4 IDENTIFYING EFFECTS Congress passed the Embargo Act in 1807 to prevent trade with Britain. What unintended consequences did the Act have for the U.S. economy?

Cause	Effect
The United States embargos trade with Britain.	Effect
	Effect
	Effect
	Effect

5 IDENTIFYING PROBLEMS AND SOLUTIONS How did Tecumseh respond to the problem of white settlement in Native American lands?

ESSENTIAL QUESTION

Why does conflict develop?

A political cartoon illustrates the debate over entering war with Britain

DIRECTIONS: Look at the political cartoon and answer the accompanying questions.

INTRODUCTION: Congress was bitterly divided over how to respond to the British practice of impressment. Some members advocated war, while others opposed it. This cartoon illustrates the debate. In the cartoon, George Washington looks down from Heaven and reflects:

VOCABULARY

pillars: columns

casket: a box or container

desist: to stop

PRIMARY SOURCE: POLITICAL CARTOON

“I left you with a precious Casket of choicest Blessings Supported by three Pillars – Desist my sons from pulling at them. Should you remove one you destroy the whole.”

The casket Washington mentions is labeled “Liberty and Independence.” The pillars are labeled “Federalism,” “Republicanism,” and “Democracy.”

1 **ANALYZING VISUALS** Why does the cartoonist represent the casket containing liberty and independence as something supported by three pillars?

2 **IDENTIFYING POINTS OF VIEW** The figure on the left says, "This pillar Shall not stand. I am determined to support a just and necessary war." What political group does this figure most likely represent?

3 **INTERPRETING** Pulling at the pillar labeled "Democracy," the figure on the right says, "This pillar must come down. I am a friend of peace." How might the call for peace threaten democracy?

4 **PREDICTING** Based on this cartoon, what is likely to happen if the debate on war with Britain continues?

ESSENTIAL QUESTION

Why does conflict develop?

Primary Source: Speech by Tecumseh to a Council of the Choctaw and Chickasaw Nations

DIRECTIONS: Read this speech from Tecumseh to a council of Choctaw and Chickasaw nations. Then answer the accompanying questions.

INTRODUCTION: As settlement increased in the West, white settlers broke treaties with Native Americans and moved onto Native American lands. To prevent more lands from being taken, Shawnee chief Tecumseh decided to create a confederation of Native American nations.

1 **INFERRING** What can you infer about relations between the Choctaw, Chickasaw, and Shawnee nations based on Tecumseh's call for unity?

____

____

____

____

PRIMARY SOURCE: SPEECH

"The annihilation of our race is at hand unless we unite in one common cause against the common foe. Think not, brave Choctaws and Chickasaws, that you can remain passive and indifferent to the common danger, and thus escape the common fate. Your people, too, will soon be as falling leaves and scattering clouds before their blighting breath. You, too, will be driven away from your native land and ancient domains as leaves are driven before the wintry storms.

Sleep not longer, O Choctaws and Chickasaws, in false security and delusive hopes. Our broad domains are fast escaping from our grasp. Every year our white intruders become more greedy, exacting, oppressive and overbearing. Every year contentions spring up between them and our people and when blood is shed we have to make atonement whether right or wrong, at the cost of the lives of our greatest chiefs, and the yielding up of large tracts of our lands.

If there be one here tonight who believes that his rights will not sooner or later be taken from him by the avaricious American pale faces, his ignorance ought to excite pity, for he knows little of our common foe... Then listen to the voice of duty, of honor, of nature and of your

VOCABULARY

annihilation: complete destruction
atonement: making up for doing something wrong
foe: enemy
blighting: destroying
domains: lands
delusive: deceiving
intruders: invaders
exacting: demanding
avaricious: greedy

. . . *continued*

endangered country. Let us form one body, one heart, and defend to the last warrior our country, our homes, our liberty, and the graves of our fathers.”

Source “Sleep not longer, O Choctaws and Chickasaws,” Tecumseh, 1811

2 **ANALYZING** What metaphors does Tecumseh use in the first paragraph? Why does he use these images?

3 **INTERPRETING** What does Tecumseh mean when he says that year after year “we have to make atonement whether right or wrong?”

4 **DRAWING CONCLUSIONS** Based on the speech, how do you think Tecumseh would respond to the call for a new treaty with the settlers?

5 **CITING TEXT EVIDENCE** What words does Tecumseh use in the final sentence to convince his audience that they should unite?

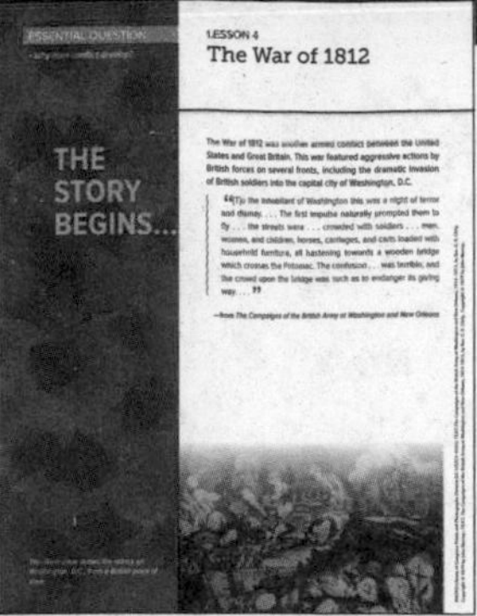

ESSENTIAL QUESTION

Why does conflict develop?

As you gather evidence to answer the Essential Question, think about

- how Americans were divided
- how conflict leads groups of people to form alliances with one another
- why people respond to conflict in different ways

My Notes

The War of 1812

DIRECTIONS: Search for evidence in Chapter 8, Lesson 4 to help you answer the following questions.

1A ANALYZING What were some strengths and weaknesses of the United States in the War of 1812? Complete the chart below.

War of 1812	
American Strengths	**American Weaknesses**

1B SUMMARIZING Use your responses in the chart to summarize the American position as war with Britain got underway.

2 **GEOGRAPHY** Why do you think that Lake Erie, Chesapeake Bay, and other waterways and coastal regions were so important to the War of 1812?

3 **IDENTIFYING EFFECTS** Why was the battle of Lake Champlain a crucial turning point in the war?

4 **SEQUENCING** Why did the British–Native American alliance come to an end? Complete the chart to show the sequence of events.

Event 1	Event 2	Event 3	Event 4	
				The British–Native American alliance ends

5 **IDENTIFYING CAUSE AND EFFECT** How did the American victory in the War of 1812 and a rising sense of patriotism affect the Federalists?

ESSENTIAL QUESTION

Why does conflict develop?

Dolley Madison Describes the British Attack on Washington, D.C.

DIRECTIONS: Read this excerpt from a letter written by Dolley Madison to her sister. Then answer the accompanying questions.

INTRODUCTION: Intent on destroying the American capital at Washington, D.C., British troops overpowered American resistance and entered the city. Dolley Madison bravely decided to remain in the White House until the last minute. She was determined to save documents that were important to the nation. In this letter, she also describes her determination to save a portrait of George Washington. The day after Dolley Madison wrote this letter, British forces set the capital city ablaze.

PRIMARY SOURCE: LETTER

“My husband left me yesterday morning to join General Winder. He inquired anxiously whether I had courage or firmness to remain in the President's house until his return on the morrow, or succeeding day, and on my assurance that I had no fear but for him, and the success of our army, he left, beseeching me to take care of myself, and of the Cabinet papers, public and private. I have since received two dispatches from him, written with a pencil. The last is alarming, because he desires I should be ready at a moment's warning to enter my carriage, and leave the city; that the enemy seemed stronger than had at first been reported, and it might happen that they would reach the city with the intention of destroying it. I am accordingly ready; I have pressed as many Cabinet papers into trunks as to fill one carriage; our private property must be sacrificed, as it is impossible to procure wagons for its transportation. I am determined not to go myself until I see Mr. Madison safe, so that he can accompany me, as I hear of much hostility towards him...

Wednesday Morning, twelve o'clock. -- Since sunrise I have been turning my spy-glass in every direction, and watching with unwearied anxiety, hoping to discover the approach of my dear husband and his friends; but, alas! I can descry only groups of military, wandering in all directions, as if there was a lack of arms, or of spirit to fight for their own fireside.

1 **INTERPRETING** How does Madison feel about her own safety? What does she worry most about?

____

____

____

____

2 **ANALYZING** Why do you think Madison saved the Cabinet papers but left her own property behind?

____

____

____

____

____

. . . continued

Three o'clock. -- Will you believe it, my sister? we have had a battle, or skirmish, near Bladensburg, and here I am still, within sound of the cannon! Mr. Madison comes not. May God protect us! Two messengers, covered with dust, come to bid me fly; but here I mean to wait for him... Our kind friend, Mr. Carroll, has come to hasten my departure, and in a very bad humor with me, because I insist on waiting until the large picture of General Washington is secured, and it requires to be unscrewed from the wall. This process was found too tedious for these perilous moments; I have ordered the frame to be broken, and the canvas taken out. It is done! and the precious portrait placed in the hands of two gentlemen of New York, for safe keeping. And now, dear sister, I must leave this house, or the retreating army will make me a prisoner in it by filling up the road I am directed to take. When I shall again write to you, or where I shall be tomorrow, I cannot tell!"

Source Letter from Dolley Madison, August 23, 1814

VOCABULARY

inquired: asked
morrow: tomorrow
succeeding: next
beseeching: pleading, asking urgently
dispatches: letters
procure: get
spy-glass: telescope
unwearied: tireless
descry: see
tedious: time-consuming
perilous: dangerous
skirmish: brief battle
bid me fly: flee; run away

3 **CITING TEXT EVIDENCE** In which sentence does Madison worry that American troops may have lost the will to fight?

4 **SPECULATING** Why do you think that Madison risked her own safety to save the painting of George Washington?

5 **EVALUATING** Do you think that Madison made the right decision in trying to save the painting? Why or why not?

ESSENTIAL QUESTION

Why does conflict develop?

Henry Clay Makes the Case for War

DIRECTIONS: Read the excerpt from a letter by Henry Clay. Then answer the accompanying questions.

INTRODUCTION: In 1812, Americans were bitterly divided about how to respond to British violations of American neutrality. Some members of Congress argued that the United States was unprepared for war. Others advocated war as the only way to protect American shipping interests. As Speaker of the House, Henry Clay played an important role in this debate. In this letter, he makes the case for an immediate declaration of war with Britain.

VOCABULARY

pusillanimous: cowardly
apprehend: perceive
idle: minor; insignificant
dominions: lands
gallant: noble
assail: attack
relinquish: give up
vigor; strength; energy
solemn: serious
infatuated: obsessed with

PRIMARY SOURCE: LETTER

"But it is said that we are not prepared for war, and ought therefore not to declare it. This is an idle objection, which can have weight with the timid and pusillanimous only. The fact is otherwise. Our preparations are adequate to every essential object. Do we apprehend danger to ourselves? From what quarter will it assail us? From England, and by invasion? The idea is too absurd to merit a moment's consideration. Where are her troops? But lately, she dreaded an invasion of her own dominions, from her powerful and menacing neighbor. That danger, it is true, has diminished, but it has not entirely, and forever, disappeared. A gallant effort, which called forth the whole energies of the nation, has put it at a distance, but still it is one of those sparks which peer above the horizon, & excite alarm even in those least liable to it. The war in the peninsula, which lingers, requires strong armies to support it. She maintains an army in Sicily; another in India; and a strong force in Ireland, and along her own coast and in the West Indies. Can anyone believe, that, under such circumstances, the British government could be so infatuated, or rather mad, as to send troops here for the purpose of invasion?

The great question on which the United States have to decide, is, whether they will relinquish the ground which they now hold, or maintain it with the firmness and vigor becoming freemen. That the sense of the nation favors the latter course, is proved by a series of important and solemn facts,

. . . continued

which speak a language not to be misunderstood. From the first attack by Great Britain on our neutral rights in 1805, to the present day, these facts have been multiplied, yearly, by the acts of Congress, by the proceedings of the state legislatures, and by the voice of the people. Let not the Representatives of the People, therefore, in either branch of the government, disappoint their reasonable wishes and just expectations. ”

Source *Letter in Support of the War of 1812,* Henry Clay, 1812

1 **INTERPRETING** How does Clay feel about members of Congress who oppose war with Britain?

2 **INFERRING** According to Clay, the argument that England will invade the United States is not worth considering. Why do you think he arrives at this conclusion?

3 **CITING TEXT EVIDENCE** In which sentence does Clay observe that England remains concerned about conflict with France?

4 **DRAWING CONCLUSIONS** Why does Clay point out that there are British troops in Sicily, Ireland, and the West Indies?

5 **SPECULATING** Clay insists that the United States is fully prepared for war. Do you think he still felt this way at the end of the war? Why, or why not?

ESSENTIAL QUESTION

Why does conflict develop?

1 Think About It

Review the supporting questions you developed at the beginning of the chapter, in the chapter opener. Review the evidence you gathered in Chapter 8. Were you able to answer each Supporting Question? If there was not enough evidence to answer your Supporting Questions, what additional evidence do you think you need to consider?

2 Organize Your Evidence

Fill in the chart below with the information you learned about the different conflicts that occurred in the years following American independence.

Conflict	Parties involved in the conflict	Reasons for the conflict	Effects of the conflict on the people
The Election of 1800			
War with Tripoli			
Violation of Neutral Rights			
The Embargo of 1807			
The Battle of Tippecanoe			
The War of 1812			
The Federalists' Grievances			

3 Talk About It

Work in small groups. Discuss the evidence you included in your organization chart in question 2. Did you include the same evidence, or were your classmates' responses different? Discuss any differences in your charts, then make notes below about anything you'd like to add to yours or change. Create a new chart that includes the responses of all your classmates.

4 Write About It

Write a summary for each conflict listed in the left column. Incorporate evidence from your chart. When possible, excerpt a line or phrase from a primary source that you think is significant in demonstrating the reasons for the conflict and the effects the conflict had on the people involved. Each summary should be about a paragraph long.

5 Connect to the Essential Question

Create a clear and interesting informational presentation. Imagine that you are introducing the conflicts that occurred in the years following American independence and that you will explain the reasons for the conflicts and the effect these conflicts had on those involved. Include a visual informational time line that includes when each conflict happened, who was involved, the reasons for the conflict, and ways in which the conflict was addressed. Be sure that you reference the primary sources discussed in the lessons of this chapter.

CITIZENSHIP

TAKING ACTION

The question of why conflict develops is just as important today as it was 200 years ago. In fact, many of the conflicts you have been reading about are somewhat similar to conflicts in today's world. For example, President Jefferson sent American warships abroad to deal with the Barbary pirates. These American sailors traveled far from home to defend American interests. The U.S. Navy—along with the Army, Air Force, Coast Guard, and Marines—travel all over the world to protect American interests today. Think what it must be like for American soldiers, sailors, and airmen stationed far away from the United States. They miss their country, their homes, and their families.

DIRECTIONS: With your teacher or other appropriate adult, use the Internet to identify one of the many websites that will guide you in writing a letter to a member of the U.S. military. Once you have chosen the organization, follow their guidelines on how to send your letter (or email).

Growth and Expansion

ESSENTIAL QUESTION

How does geography influence the way people live?

Think about how geography might affect the way people live as they move into new regions.

TALK ABOUT IT

Discuss with a partner what type of information you would need in order to understand American growth and expansion in the early 1800s. For example, you might wonder whether the American landscape helped or hurt people as they moved into new areas.

DIRECTIONS: Now write down three additional questions that will help you explain how American expansion in the early 1800s was affected by geography.

MY RESEARCH QUESTIONS

Supporting Question 1:

____

____

Supporting Question 2:

____

____

Supporting Question 3:

____

____

ESSENTIAL QUESTION

How does geography influence the way people live?

As you gather evidence to answer the Essential Question, think about

- how geography affected industrial growth.
- how geography affected agricultural growth.
- how cities developed.

My Notes

A Growing Economy

DIRECTIONS: Search for evidence in Chapter 9, Lesson 1 to help you answer the following questions.

1 IDENTIFYING CAUSES Complete the graphic organizer.

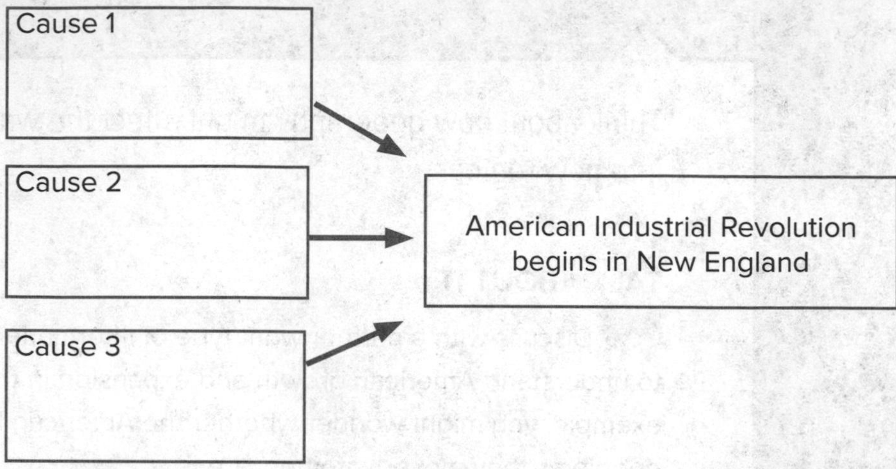

2 EXPLAINING What was the cotton gin? What effect did it have?

3 DESCRIBING Complete the table.

Person	Contributions to American Textile Manufacturing
Samuel Slater	
Francis Cabot Lowell	

4 EXPLAINING ISSUES Define the terms in the chart below.

Term	Definition
capitalism	
capital	
free enterprise	

5 CAUSE AND EFFECT Complete the chart below to explain how the invention of the cotton gin affected the economy.

Cause		Effect | Cause		Effect
invention of cotton gin	→	expanded cotton production	→	

ESSENTIAL QUESTION

How does geography influence the way people live?

Two Neighborhoods in New York City

DIRECTIONS: Read the following excerpt and answer the accompanying questions.

EXPLORE THE CONTEXT: The industrialization of New England led to the growth of cities in the early 1800s. Workers needed to be close to the new factories where they worked. Thus, industrialization led to urbanization, or the expansion of urban areas, or cities. Not everyone in the growing cities lived the same way, however. Consider this description of two neighborhoods in New York City.

PRIMARY SOURCE: JOURNAL

"The buildings were ruinous for the most part, as well as I could judge, & the streets & sidewalks muddy & ill lighted. Several of [the] houses had wooden shutters well closed & in almost [each] such case I found by stopping & listening, that there were many voices in the rooms & sometimes the sound of music & dancing. Grog shops, oyster cellars and close, obscure and suspicious looking places of every description abounded.

From these dark, filthy, violent & degraded regions, I passed into Broadway, where were lighted carriages with footmen, numerous well dressed passers by, cheerful light coming from behind curtained parlor windows, where were happy, affectionate & virtuous people connected by the ties of blood & friendship & enjoying the charities & honors of life. What mighty differences, what awful separations, wide as that of the great gulf & lasting for eternity, do what seem to be the merest chances place between human beings, of the same flesh & blood."

—Richard Henry Dana, Jr., 1844

VOCABULARY

ruinous: in ruins, dilapidated, old and broken
grog shops: places to buy and drink alcohol
oyster cellars: basement where oysters are served (located underground because ice kept longer there)
obscure: unknown
merest: smallest

1 DETERMINING CENTRAL IDEAS Why do you think the author wrote about what he saw in New York City?

2A ANALYZING POINT OF VIEW What attitude does the writer hold about the first neighborhood?

2B What attitude does the writer hold about the second neighborhood?

3 IDENTIFYING CAUSES According to the writer, what is the cause of the differences between the two neighborhoods?

4 GEOGRAPHY How does this excerpt reflect the idea that geography influences the way people live?

ESSENTIAL QUESTION

How does geography influence the way people live?

The Role of Cotton in the U. S. Economy

DIRECTIONS: Read the following excerpt and answer the accompanying questions.

EXPLORE THE CONTEXT: Eli Whitney invented the cotton gin in 1793. Soon, more and better textile mills were built, and the demand for cotton grew. These developments led to a sharp rise in cotton production. Just 30 years after the cotton gin was invented, the South was producing 100 times as much cotton than before. In this excerpt, the impact of this explosion of cotton production is assessed.

PRIMARY SOURCE: MAGAZINE ARTICLE

"The production of cotton in the southern and south-western States, may be fairly considered to have exercised a more important agency than any other single circumstance in retrieving the credit of the country both at home and abroad. By furnishing a staple commodity of general necessity to a great amount, this cultivation has enabled our citizens, in all sections of the United States, to follow their gainful commerce without being constantly exposed to the disturbing influence of the enormous sacrifices upon their remittance to foreign nations, to which they were before subjected. In connection with our tobacco, fish, lumber, rice, and bread-stuffs, cotton has mainly enabled us to pay for the articles of necessity as well as luxuries, which we have so largely imported from England, France, and other countries. It has accordingly become one of the principal sources of the wealth of our citizens, greatly advantageous even to the states which do not produce it. Our cotton crops have in fact placed Europe in a state of greater dependence upon us than we are upon Europe, inasmuch as this commodity is essential, not only to the prosperity, but to the very existence of a great portion of its manufacturing population. In this point of view the production of cotton in the United States may be regarded as the most important element of our actual commercial independence...."

—"Cotton and its Connection With the Currency Question," *The United States Magazine and Democratic Review,* March 1838

VOCABULARY

southern and south-western States: the southern states of today
agency: effect
retrieving: regaining; getting back
abroad: overseas; foreign countries
staple: main, basic
gainful: profitable
remittance: payment
inasmuch as: since
commodity: bulk agricultural product
bread-stuffs: grain or flour used to make bread

1 **SUMMARIZING** Write a one sentence summary that expresses the main idea of this excerpt.

2A **COMPARING** What other crops does the writer mention?

2B Are these other crops more important, less important, or equal in importance to cotton? How do you know?

3 **DETERMINING MEANING** What do you think the writer means by "commercial independence"?

4 GEOGRAPHY How does this source support the idea that geography influences the way people live?

ESSENTIAL QUESTION

How does geography influence the way people live?

As you gather evidence to answer the Essential Question, think about

- how roadways to the west developed
- how rivers and canals transported people and goods
- how people in new Western settlements lived

My Notes

Moving West

DIRECTIONS: Search for evidence in Chapter 9, Lesson 2 to help you answer the following questions.

1 DESCRIBING Complete the table below.

Road	Description
Wilderness Road	
turnpikes	
national road	

2 DESCRIBING Who was Robert Fulton? What was the Clermont?

3A DESCRIBING What is a canal?

3B What are locks on a canal?

3C Describe the location of the Erie Canal.

4 **IDENTIFYING EFFECTS** Identify three effects of canals.

canals → [ ] → [ ] → [ ]

5 **EXPLAINING** Why did pioneer families often settle in communities along rivers and canals?

ESSENTIAL QUESTION

How does geography influence the way people live?

Life in Frontier Wisconsin

DIRECTIONS: Read the following excerpt and answer the accompanying questions.

EXPLORE THE CONTEXT: Before telephones and the Internet, letters were the primary means of long-distance communication. Settlers often wrote long letters describing their new lives to family members back home. A great deal of what we know about frontier life comes from these sources. They provide fascinating glimpses of life in a time much different than our own. Yet, what they wrote about—where they live, what they do—reveals concerns not too different from our own.

VOCABULARY

beset: troubled

artisans: skilled workers who make things by hand

dispatched: dealt with; handled

1A ANALYZING TEXT PRESENTATION Does the writer generally view the settlements positively or negatively?

____

1B How can you tell?

____

____

____

PRIMARY SOURCE: LETTER

"Still the roads are good enough to make it possible to carry mail all over the country in stagecoaches drawn by four horses, except in the most recent settlements, where one cannot expect this. As to the houses, you have to build simply at first in the newest places to get a shelter while you grow something on the land and try to build a better house as soon as possible. In the areas where the land has been inhabited for some time, you will find houses as beautiful as those in Norway – and even more beautiful.

The oldest inhabitants of Wisconsin have only lived here ten or eleven years, and the majority not half that time, yet the land can already feed the population of the numerous bigger and smaller towns and the many thousands of people who arrive every year. And it is said that as early as 1842 forty thousand barrels of wheat and wheat flour were exported from Wisconsin. Since that time the land has been improved to more than the double of this capacity, because the difficulties which beset the first immigrants especially have gradually been almost completely overcome.

We have also many other advantages which one must value highly: all sorts of honest trades are open to everyone who has a liking and ability for them, and there are many opportunities for investment which pay off well if you go about them carefully and in the right

manner. As soon as a man has become known as honest and dependable, he is just as much respected here as anyone. Farmers and artisans are just as good as merchants and officials. They all have practically the same manners, and the appearance and dress of people are usually the same as they are in Norwegian towns, with the exception of the Norwegian mountain people, who stick to their old customs to some extent.

The English language is spoken everywhere, with the exception of a few smaller areas, settlements of colonies of Norwegians, Swedes, Germans, or French. In these settlements people usually speak their native language when they are among themselves, but this habit will generally die out with the second generation.

Though the degree of freedom is very great here and the nation is made up of people from almost all European countries, crimes are very rare. But if a crime has been committed it is punished according to the laws, which are very hard and explicit. The criminals do not have to wait long to be sentenced, and when sentence has been pronounced, it is carried out as soon as possible, for all business both public and private is dispatched quickly and is as little of burden to the public as possible. ”

—Letter from Nils Hansen Naerum at Muskego, Wisconsin to J.H. Naerum, Porsgrund, Norway. March 5, 1846

2 **INFERRING** The writer states that "you have to build simply at first in the newest places to get a shelter." Based on this excerpt and your knowledge of geography, what do you think settlers made their first shelters from?

3 ECONOMICS According to the letter, what are the different ways that people make their livings?

4 GEOGRAPHY How does this source support the idea that geography influences the way people live?

ESSENTIAL QUESTION

How does geography influence the way people live?

The Role of the Ohio River in Commerce

DIRECTIONS: Read the following excerpt and answer the accompanying questions.

EXPLORE THE CONTEXT: The Ohio River has long been a major transportation route By 1820, at least 60 steamboats plied its waters. Today, the Ohio remains an important waterway: only the Mississippi River carries more freight. In this excerpt, you get a glimpse of an Ohio River town in 1845. As you read, think about how the town is dependent on the river.

1 **DETERMINING CENTRAL IDEAS** What town is described in the excerpt?

______

2A **INFERRING** What do you think the difference is between an "upper" and a "lower" boatyard?

______

2B What can you infer about the boatyards being "busy the year round"?

______

PRIMARY SOURCE: BOOK

"It is necessary to tell you about Ripley in 1845. At that time it was as busy as beehive. There was no town along the Ohio River except Cincinnati that was in its class.

There were the upper and lower boatyards, busy the year round....One hundred flatboats were made here in one year for Vevay, Indiana, to float hay down the river. These boats were turned out in quantities and very rapidly all winter long. The mills would turn out the parts, so all that would have to be done in the spring and summer was to assemble the parts into flatboats.

The entire riverfront was filled with flatboats loading cargoes for New Orleans and all waypoints. Winter and summer there flowed down the river highways into the town a continuous stream of logs night and day. Only pork was packed, as the south did not feed beef to its slaves. The slaughterhouses were in full blast at all seasons. Flour mills, both water and steam, ground up the grain of the neighboring farms, which were very fertile. One mill located back from the river had an overhead gravity runway, sending the barrels from the mill across the creek down to the bank to the flatboats.

VOCABULARY

boatyard: a place where boats are built and repaired

flatboat: cargo boat with flat bottom

All winter long the farmer and his family were busily engaged making pork and flour barrels, and tobacco hogsheads. These were brought to town either on sleighs or by four-to-six-horse teams. At times the farmers killed and packed their own hogs. A woolen mill made most of the jeans for the town and flatboats. ”

—from *His Promised Land: The Autobiography of John P. Parker, Former Slave and Conductor on the Underground Railroad,* 1880s

VOCABULARY

overhead gravity runway: a raised wooden ramp down which barrels rolled

hogsheads: large barrels

3 ANALYZING POINT OF VIEW Does the author seem to have a positive view, a negative view, or a neutral view of Ripley?

4 CITING TEXT EVIDENCE List the businesses mentioned in the excerpt.

5 NARRATIVE WRITING Based on this excerpt, what are three adjectives that describe Ripley, Ohio in 1845?

6 ECONOMICS How does this source support the idea that geography influences the way people live?

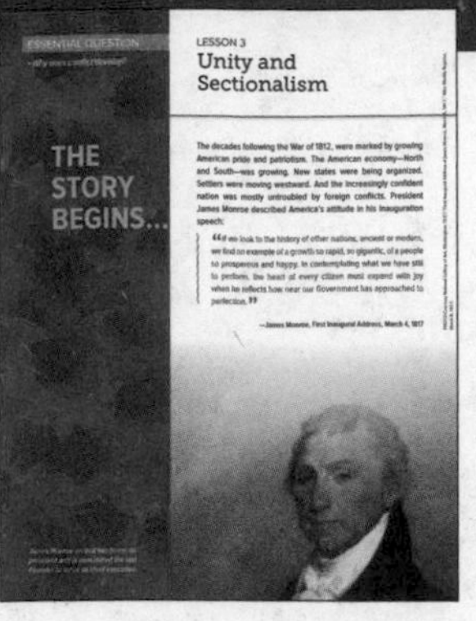

ESSENTIAL QUESTION

How does geography influence the way people live?

Unity and Sectionalism

DIRECTIONS: Search for evidence in Chapter 9, Lesson 3 to help you answer the following questions.

1 DESCRIBING Complete the table.

The American System	
Purpose	to help the nation grow
Main Parts	
1.	
2.	
3.	

2 IDENTIFYING CAUSES Complete the cause-effect diagram.

Cause

Effects

Tariff of 1816

Protective tariffs of 1818

Protective tariffs of 1824

3 DESCRIBING Complete the table.

Sectionalism in the Early 1800s		
Region (section)	Geographic Area	Leader in Congress
North		
South		
West		

My Notes

4 **ANALYZING** What did the Missouri Compromise aim to do?

____

____

____

____

____

5 **IDENTIFYING MAIN IDEAS** How did the Rush-Bagot Agreement of 1817 and the Convention of 1818 affect the geography of the United States?

____

____

____

6 The Convention of 1818 set the boundary of the Louisiana ________ between the ____________ and _______ at the 49th parallel.

____

____

7 **IDENTIFYING EFFECTS** What were the three major effects of the Adams-Onís Treaty?

1. ____

2. ____

3. ____

8 **INTERPRETING** What was purpose of the Monroe Doctrine? Do you think it was needed?

____

____

____

____

ESSENTIAL QUESTION

How does geography influence the way people live?

Citizens of Connecticut Lobby Congress Against Admission of Missouri as a Slave State

DIRECTIONS: Read the following excerpt and answer the accompanying questions.

EXPLORE THE CONTEXT By the early 1800s, three sections, or regions, had developed in the United States: the North, the South, and the West. In some ways, the West was a prize that the other two sections fought over. If the West developed into slave states, the South would gain power. If the West developed into free states, the North would gain power. The resolution excerpted here shows a state from the North trying to affect a new state in the West.

VOCABULARY

vicinity: local area
pursuant: according to
hereafter: from now on
lamented: grieved over
repugnant: disgusting
peculiar phraseology: unique wording
prescribe: determine
prostrate: defeat

1A DETERMINING MAIN IDEAS There are six paragraphs that begin "RESOLVED." If they were numbered from one to six in order, which paragraph states the purpose of the entire document?

____

1B What is the purpose of the other paragraphs?

____

____

PRIMARY SOURCE: PUBLIC DOCUMENT

"At a meeting of the citizens of Hartford and its vicinity, held at the State-house, on Friday, the 3rd day of December, 1819, pursuant to public notice, for the purpose of taking into consideration the subject of permitting slavery in such states as may hereafter be admitted into the Union...

The following resolutions were adopted:

RESOLVED, That the existence of slavery in this republic is an evil deeply to be lamented, and utterly repugnant to the principles of a republican government.

RESOLVED, That, in the opinion of this meeting, the peculiar phraseology of the preamble to the declaration of independence, declaring that "all men are created equal,' et cetera, shows conclusively that the illustrious authors of that document never contemplated the further extension of slavery in these United States.

RESOLVED, That, in the opinion of this meeting, Congress possesses the clear and indisputable right to prescribe the terms upon which any Territory may be admitted into the Union as an independent State; and that a contrary doctrine would not only tend to destroy that order and harmony so indispensable to the happiness and union of these states, but would prostrate the powers confided to the General Government by the constitution.

RESOLVED, That it is a duty the American people owe to their republican character, and the honor and glory of their country, to endeavor, by all honorable and lawful means, to prevent the further extension of slavery, which we consider to be contrary to the spirit of our free and excellent constitution, and injurious to the highest interests of the nation.

RESOLVED, That, while we lament the efforts which the Representatives in the last Congress from the slaveholding states made to extend an evil which all unite in deploring, the thanks of this meeting are eminently due to those members who so ably and zealously opposed the admission of slavery into the proposed State of Missouri.

RESOLVED, that the Senators and Representatives in Congress from this state be requested to use every honorable and constitutional exertion to prevent the admission of slavery into any new state which may be formed.”

—Prohibition of Slavery in Missouri, Communicated to the Senate, January 18, 1820

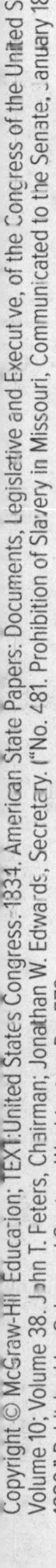

2 **ANALYZING ISSUES** Was it proper for American citizens in one state to try to influence life in another state? Explain both answers (yes and no) to this question.

3 GEOGRAPHY How does this source support the idea that geography influences the way people live?

ESSENTIAL QUESTION

How does geography influence the way people live?

President Monroe's Statement to Congress: the Monroe Doctrine

DIRECTIONS: Read the following excerpt and answer the accompanying questions.

EXPLORE THE CONTEXT A *doctrine* is a stated principle of government policy. One of the most important doctrines in American history is the Monroe Doctrine. What makes it so important? When you read this excerpt from it, you will understand. To help you, remember that the United States was only 50 years old when the doctrine was issued.

VOCABULARY

comport: agree
candor: openness; honesty
amicable: friendly
interposition: interference
indispensable: essential
de facto: in effect

1 IDENTIFYING CENTRAL IDEAS What are the two main points President Monroe makes?

PRIMARY SOURCE: PRESIDENTIAL STATEMENT

"The occasion has been judged proper for asserting, as a principle in which the rights and interests of the United States are involved, that the American continents, by the free and independent condition which they have assumed and maintain, are henceforth not to be considered as subjects for future colonization by any European powers....

The citizens of the United States cherish sentiments the most friendly in favor of the liberty and happiness of their fellow-men on that side [the European side] of the Atlantic. In the wars of the European powers in matters relating to themselves we have never taken any part, nor does it comport with our policy so to do. It is only when our rights are invaded or seriously menaced that we resent injuries or make preparation for our defense. With the movements in this hemisphere we are of necessity more immediately connected, and by causes which must be obvious to all enlightened and impartial observers. The political system of the allied powers is essentially different in this respect from that of America.... We owe it, therefore, to candor and to the amicable relations existing between the United States and those powers to declare that we should consider any attempt on their part to extend their system to any portion of this hemisphere as dangerous to our peace and safety. With the existing colonies or dependencies of any European power we have not interfered and shall

not interfere. But with the Governments who have declared their independence and maintained it, and whose independence we have, on great consideration and on just principles, acknowledged, we could not view any interposition for the purpose of oppressing them, or controlling in any other manner their destiny, by any European power in any other light than as the [appearance] of an unfriendly disposition toward the United States. In the war declared between those new Governments and Spain we declared our neutrality at the time of their recognition, and to this we have adhered, and shall continue to adhere, provided no change shall occur which, in the judgment of the competent authorities of this Government, shall make a corresponding change on the part of the United States indispensable to their security....

Our policy in regard to Europe, which we adopted at an early stage of the wars which have so long agitated that quarter of the globe, nevertheless remains the same, which is not to interfere in the internal concerns of any of its powers; to consider the government de facto as the legitimate government for us; to cultivate friendly relations with it, and to preserve those relations by a frank, firm, and manly policy, meeting in all instances the just claims of every power, submitting to injuries from none. ”

—Seventh Annual Message (Monroe Doctrine), December 2, 1823

2 **CITING TEXT EVIDENCE** Which sentence do you think is the key passage in this document?

3 **PREDICTING** What effect do you think the Monroe Doctrine had on European countries?

4 GEOGRAPHY How does this source support the idea that geography influences the way people live?

ESSENTIAL QUESTION

How does geography influence the way people live?

1 Think About It

Review the supporting questions that you developed at the beginning of the chapter. Review the evidence that you gathered in Chapter 9. Were you able to answer each Supporting Question?

If there was not enough evidence to answer your Supporting Questions, what additional evidence do you think you need to consider? Write them below.

____

____

____

____

____

2 Organize Your Evidence

Use a chart like the one below to organize the evidence you will use to support your Position Statement.

Source of information	Specific evidence from the source to cite	How evidence helps support my Position Statement

3 Write About It

A position statement related to the Essential Question should reflect your conclusion about the evidence. Write a Position Statement for the ESSENTIAL QUESTION: ***How does geography influence the way people live?***

4 Talk About It

Work in a small group to present your position statement and evidence. Gather feedback from your classmates before you write your final conclusion. You may choose to refine your position statement after you have discussed it with your classmates. Group members should listen to one another's arguments, ask questions, and offer constructive advice about the statement.

5 Connect to the Essential Question

On a separate piece of paper, develop an argumentative essay to answer the ESSENTIAL QUESTION: ***How does geography influence the way people live?***

CITIZENSHIP

TAKING ACTION

MAKE CONNECTIONS California has some of the most beautiful geographic features in the world. The Golden Gate, Yosemite, the Cascade Mountains, beautiful rivers, amazing forests...the list is endless. However, air pollution can make it difficult to actually see these features.

People have been concerned about air pollution in California for decades. However, many individuals still do not realize how important an issue this is. Air pollution not only spoils the view of California's geographic wonders, but it also threatens the health of people and creatures living in the state and beyond.

Fortunately, you can help raise awareness!

Have you ever heard of the Air Quality Index (AQI)? You might have heard it mentioned by a weather reporter on television. According to the United States Environmental Protection Agency, "The AQI is an index for reporting daily air quality. It tells you how clean or polluted your air is, and what associated health effects might be a concern for you."

DIRECTIONS: Working with a teacher or other trusted adult, use social media to raise awareness about air pollution and the AQI. Develop a blog, Facebook page, or Twitter feed that explains the AQI and shares the air quality index daily. Also research and post easy things that everyone can do to help lower air pollution.

The Jackson Era

ESSENTIAL QUESTION

What are the consequences when cultures interact?

Think about how this question might relate to the Jackson Era.

TALK ABOUT IT

Discuss with a partner what information you would need to know to answer this question. For example, one question might be: Who is harmed when cultures interact?

DIRECTIONS: Now write down three additional questions that you need to answer to be able to explain what happened when cultures interacted during the presidency of Andrew Jackson.

MY RESEARCH QUESTIONS

Supporting Question 1:

Supporting Question 2:

Supporting Question 3:

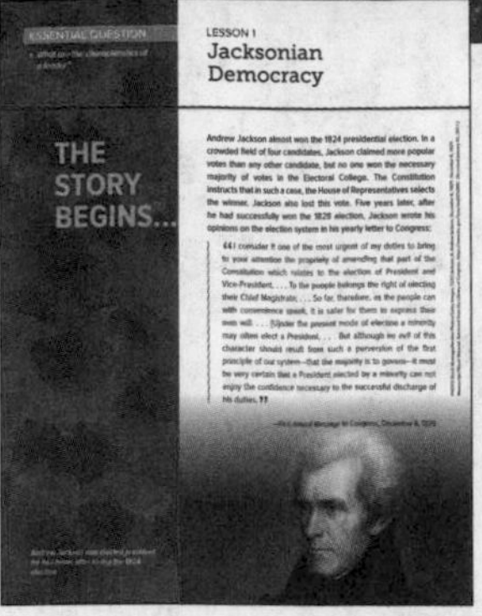

Jacksonian Democracy

DIRECTIONS: Search for evidence in Chapter 10, Lesson 1 to help you answer the following questions.

1 CIVICS In what two ways were candidates chosen in 1816?

2 **INFERRING** How might having more than one way to choose candidates have complicated the election process?

3 **COMPARING** Use the chart below to analyze the 1824 election results by filling in the percentages each candidate earned.

	Popular Vote	Electoral Vote	House of Representatives Vote
John Q. Adams			
Andrew Jackson			
Henry Clay			
William H. Crawford			

ESSENTIAL QUESTION

What are the consequences when cultures interact?

As you gather evidence to answer the Essential Question, think about:

- how voting rights began to expand in the early 1800s.
- which groups of people had a voice in the elections of this time.
- why voting matters to members of a society.
- how everyday citizens might have felt about the election of 1824.

My Notes

4 **INTERPRETING** What did Andrew Jackson mean when he said Adams and Clay had made a "corrupt bargain"?

5 HISTORY In what ways might Adams's means of winning the election have negatively impacted his presidency?

ESSENTIAL QUESTION

What are the consequences when cultures interact?

The Address to Richmond against Andrew Jackson

DIRECTIONS: Read the following statement by the Republican party, then answer the accompanying questions.

INTRODUCTION: The election of 1824 divided the Democratic Republican Party between supporters of Andrew Jackson and those who opposed him, led by Henry Clay and John Quincy Adams. In 1828 opponents of Jackson held a convention to oppose the election of Andrew Jackson.

PRIMARY SOURCE: POLITICAL ADDRESS

"We are left to the alternative of choosing between Jackson and Adams; and however; we may differ in opinion as to the merits of the latter, we heartily concur in giving him a decided preference over his competitor...

...Reflect on the character of the office you are about to fill,—inquire what feeling, what temper, what talent, what accomplishments, what habits, are best suited to the discharge of its high duties;—and then carefully compare John Quincy Adams with Andrew Jackson, in reference to the great questions,—which of these is best qualified for the first office in the nation,—which most likely to preserve to us, the distinguished blessings we enjoy,— from which is most danger to be apprehended, to our peace and happiness, of lives and liberties?

...For civil government,—and in no station more emphatically than in that of President of the United States,—a well governed temper is of admitted importance; Gen. Jackson's friends lament the impetuosity of his, and all the world has evidence of its fiery misrule."

—Proceedings of the Anti-Jackson Convention held at the capitol in the city of Richmond, with their address to the people of Virginia

VOCABULARY

concur: agree
decided: clear
character: personality/temperament
office: job (in this case, the presidency)
discharge: performance
preserve: protect
apprehended: feared
emphatically: strongly stated
impetuosity: recklessness
fiery: angry

1 **IDENTIFYING PERSPECTIVES** What does the first paragraph imply about how the Republicans feel about John Quincy Adams? What language tells you this?

2 **SUMMARIZING** In the first half of the second paragraph, what two things does the speaker ask listeners to do?

3 **INFERRING** In the second half of the second paragraph, what might the speaker mean by "the distinguished blessings we enjoy"?

4 In the second half of the second paragraph, the speaker implies that Andrew Jackson is a dangerous candidate for president. Where does the speaker offer reasoning to support this concern? What aspect of Jackson's personality does the speaker warn against?

ESSENTIAL QUESTION

What are the consequences when cultures interact?

A Vindication of the Character and Public Services of Andrew Jackson

INTRODUCTION: Henry Lee IV, the son of Major Henry Lee, was a speechwriter for Andrew Jackson during his candidacy for president who also wrote Jackson's inaugural address. This source is one of many pamphlets written to refute Adams's attacks on Jackson's character and directly responds to the Richmond Address.

DIRECTIONS: Read the following pamphlet excerpt, then answer the accompanying questions.

PRIMARY SOURCE: PAMPHLET

"While General Jackson was braving the ambushed shaft of the Indian, and foiling the discipline shock of British columns; was performing toilsome marches; was enduring thirst and hunger, relieved only by the fruit of the oak and the wave of the torrent; was periling his life and pledging his fortune, to save the lives and fortunes of his countrymen, these diplomatic gentlemen [Adams and Clay] "were brewing mysteries of ruin" against each other, in sumptuous chambers at Ghent—were preparing that hostile rivalship, which, in due dramatic succession, rose into the production of separate interests, and sunk into the soft catastrophe of the coalition. Mr. Adams carefully duplicating his charges against our "weak and penurious government," and Mr. Clay gratifying his love of pleasure by excursions to Paris! ...Absurdity and injustice like this, gentlemen, can never find favour in the renowned commonwealth..."

—Henry Lee, *A Vindication of the Character and Public Services of Andrew Jackson; in Reply to the Richmond Address.*

VOCABULARY

vindication: freeing from blame
ambushed: attacked by surprise
shaft: arrow
foiling: stopping
columns: marching troops
toilsome: exhausting
torrent: rushing river
sumptuous: luxurious
Ghent: city currently in Belgium, then in France
catastrophe: disaster
coalition: alliance
penurious: poor or stingy
excursions: trips

1 **DETERMINING PURPOSE** How does Lee indicate the intended purpose of his pamphlet in the title?

2A **ANALYZING POINTS OF VIEW:** What seem to be Lee's feelings about Jackson? What leads you to this conclusion?

2B How does Lee feel about Adams and Clay? What leads you to this conclusion?

3 **INFERRING** How might the clash between Jackson and Adams be considered a cultural clash?

ESSENTIAL QUESTION

What are the consequences when cultures interact?

As you gather evidence to answer the Essential Question, think about:

- how the Indian Removal Act impacted the lives of people known as the Five Civilized Tribes.
- the choice the Native Americans were given.

My Notes

Conflicts Over Land

DIRECTIONS: Search for evidence in Chapter 10, Lesson 2 to help you answer the following questions.

1 In the chart below, compare the ways in which Chief John Ross and George Hawkins spoke out against the forced removal of their peoples westward, their decision to stay or leave, and their reasons for their decisions.

Leader	Nation	Arguments Made to US Government	Decision	Reason for Decision
John Ross				
George Hawkins				

1A **DETERMINING MEANING** Hawkins says the Choctaw have decided not to "live under the degrading influence of laws, which our voice could not be heard in their formation." Why might the Choctaw people have found it degrading not to have had a voice in the laws governing their own state?

1B What language does Ross use that is similar to Hawkins's reference to degrading treatment?

2A **RESEARCHING** Using the Internet, find out the approximate distance between Georgia and Oklahoma. About how far were the Cherokee people forced to march?

2B **HISTORY** What was the Cherokee name for this march? How has that name been more commonly translated?

2C **INFERRING** What are the reasons for this name?

3 What was the outcome of the Seminole resistance?

Indian Removal Act

ESSENTIAL QUESTION

What are the consequences when cultures interact?

DIRECTIONS: Read the following excerpt from the Indian Removal Act, then answer the accompanying questions.

INTRODUCTION: The Indian Removal Act passed in 1830. Pushed by President Jackson, it allowed the federal government to force Native Americans to move west.

PRIMARY SOURCE: CONGRESSIONAL ACT

"CHAP CXLVIII.—An Act to provide for an exchange of lands with the Indians residing in any of the states or territories, and for their removal west of the river of Mississippi.

Be it enacted by the Senate and House of Representatives of the United States of America, in Congress assembled, That it shall and may be lawful for the President of the United States to cause so much of any territory belonging to the United States, west of the river Mississippi, not included in any state or organized territory, and to which the Indian title has been extinguished, as he may judge necessary, to be divided into... districts, for the reception of such tribes or nations of Indians as may choose to exchange the lands where they now reside...

And be it further enacted...it shall and may be lawful for the President solemnly to assure the tribe or nation with which the exchange is made, that the United States will forever secure and guaranty to them, and their heirs or successors, the country so exchanged with them...Provided always, That such lands shall revert to the United States, if the Indians become extinct, or abandon the same.

And be it further enacted, That if, upon any of the lands now occupied by the Indians, and to be exchanged for, there should be such improvements as add value to the land claimed by any individual or individuals of such tribes or nations, it shall and may be lawful for...ascertained value to be paid to the person or persons rightfully claiming such improvements. And upon the payment of such valuation, the improvements so valued and paid for, shall pass to the United States...

VOCABULARY

title: real estate ownership
reception: accommodation
improvements: buildings (houses)
ascertained: determined
valuation: determined value
furnished: supplied
subsistence: survival
superintendence: oversight

And be it further enacted, That upon the making of any such exchange as is contemplated by this act, it shall and may be lawful for the President to cause such aid and assistance to be furnished to the emigrants as may be necessary and proper to enable them to remove to, and settle in, the country for which they may have exchanged; and also, to give them such aid and assistance as may be necessary for their support and subsistence for the first year after their removal.

And be it further enacted, That it shall and may be lawful for the President to cause such tribe or nation to be protected, at their new residence, against all interruption or disturbance from any other tribe or nation of Indians, or from any other person or persons whatever.

And be it further enacted, That it shall and may be lawful for the President to have the same superintendence and care over any tribe or nation in the country to which they may remove...”

1 **INFERRING** Why might the word “choose” be misleading in the phrase “to be divided into...districts, for the reception of such tribes or nations of Indians as may choose to exchange the lands where they now reside”?

2 **DETERMINING MEANING** What do you think the word “extinguished” refers to in the phrase, “and to which the Indian title has been extinguished”? How would the title to their lands have been extinguished? What lands are the Native Americans being removed to?

ESSENTIAL QUESTION

What are the consequences when cultures interact?

Birthday Story of Private John G. Burnett

DIRECTIONS: Read the following excerpt. Then answer the accompanying questions.

INTRODUCTION: In 1890, on his 80th birthday, Private John G. Burnett wrote a letter to his children describing his experiences after he had been ordered to accompany the Cherokee in their removal westward. Burnett's moving account was recorded many years later by famous country musician Johnny Cash. Cash supported Native American causes, and his spoken-word recording honored the memory of the native peoples involved in the removal.

VOCABULARY

exiles: outcasts
martyr: someone who dies to help others or a cause
alleviate: lessen
detailed: given a job to do
unconfined: without a coffin
cavalcade: procession

1 HISTORY Why was John Burnett sent to accompany the Cherokee on the Trail of Tears?

____

____

____

____

PRIMARY SOURCE: LETTER

"...On these long hunting trips I met and became acquainted with many of the Cherokee Indians, hunting with them by day and sleeping around their camp fires by night. I learned to speak their language, and they taught me the arts of trailing and building traps and snares... By this time I had become an expert rifleman and fairly good archer and a good trapper and spent most of my time in the forest in quest of game.

The removal of Cherokee Indians from their life long homes in the year of 1838 found me a young man in the prime of life and a Private soldier in the American Army. Being acquainted with many of the Indians and able to fluently speak their language, I was sent as interpreter into the Smoky Mountain Country in May, 1838, and witnessed the execution of the most brutal order in the History of American Warfare. I saw the helpless Cherokees arrested and dragged from their homes, and driven at the bayonet point into the stockades. And in the chill of a drizzling rain on an October morning I saw them loaded like cattle or sheep into six hundred and forty-five wagons and started toward the west.

...I made the long journey to the west with the Cherokees and did all that a Private soldier could do to alleviate their sufferings. When on guard duty at night I have many times walked my beat in my blouse in order that some sick child might have the warmth of my overcoat. I was on guard duty the night Mrs. Ross died. When relieved at midnight I did not retire, but remained around the wagon out of sympathy for Chief Ross, and at daylight was detailed by Captain McClellan to assist in the burial like the other unfortunates who died on the way. Her unconfined body was buried in a shallow grave by the roadside far from her native home, and the sorrowing Cavalcade moved on....

At this time, 1890, we are too near the removal of the Cherokees for our young people to fully understand the enormity of the crime that was committed against a helpless race. Truth is, the facts are being concealed from the young people of today. School children of today do not know that we are living on lands that were taken from a helpless race at the bayonet point to satisfy the white man's greed....

Let the historian of a future day tell the sad story with its sighs, its tears and dying groans. Let the great Judge of all the earth weigh our actions and reward us according to our work.

Children–Thus ends my promised birthday story. This December the 11th 1890. ”

—Private John G. Burnett

2 INFERRING How do you think John Burnett felt about accompanying the Cherokee on the Trail of Tears? Cite an excerpt from Burnett's account that supports your inference.

3 ANALYZING SOURCES Why does Burnett feel the story of the Trail of Tears isn't known by younger people of his time?

4 ASSESSING CREDIBILITY Do you think Burnett is a credible source about the Trail of Tears? Why or why not?

ESSENTIAL QUESTION

What are the consequences when cultures interact?

As you gather evidence to answer the Essential Question, think about:

- strategies political parties use to try to win elections.
- how strategies can backfire.
- why people choose to follow certain politicians.

My Notes

Jackson and the Bank

DIRECTIONS: Search for evidence in Chapter 10, Lesson 3 to help you answer the following questions.

1 HISTORY Why did Andrew Jackson oppose the federal bank? How was his opposition to the bank consistent with his upbringing and background?

2 How did Harrison use the Democrats' tactics to his advantage?

3 Why did Harrison choose John Tyler as a running mate?

4A After the Panic of 1837, what did President Van Buren do to help prevent further bank crises?

4B Was this a popular decision among Democrats (Van Buren's own party)?

5 Use the graphic organizer below to analyze how political scheming backfired against the schemers.

Schemers	Plan	Goal	Actual Result
Henry Clay and Daniel Webster			
Democratic Party			
Whig Party/Harrison Campaign			

ESSENTIAL QUESTION

What are the consequences when cultures interact?

Tippecanoe and Tyler Too

DIRECTIONS: Analyze the political illustration below and carefully read the caption before answering the questions that follow.

INTRODUCTION: Martin Van Buren was known by members of his party as "Old Kinderhook" because he came from the town of Kinderhook, NY. His predecessor, Andrew Jackson, was nicknamed "Old Hickory." A Democratic newspaper tried to discredit Van Buren's Whig opponent, William Henry Harrison, as too old to be president. They described him as someone who sits in his log cabin drinking hard cider and collecting his retirement pension. The illustration shown here is from the sheet music for a pro-Harrison song.

PRIMARY SOURCE: POLITICAL ILLUSTRATION

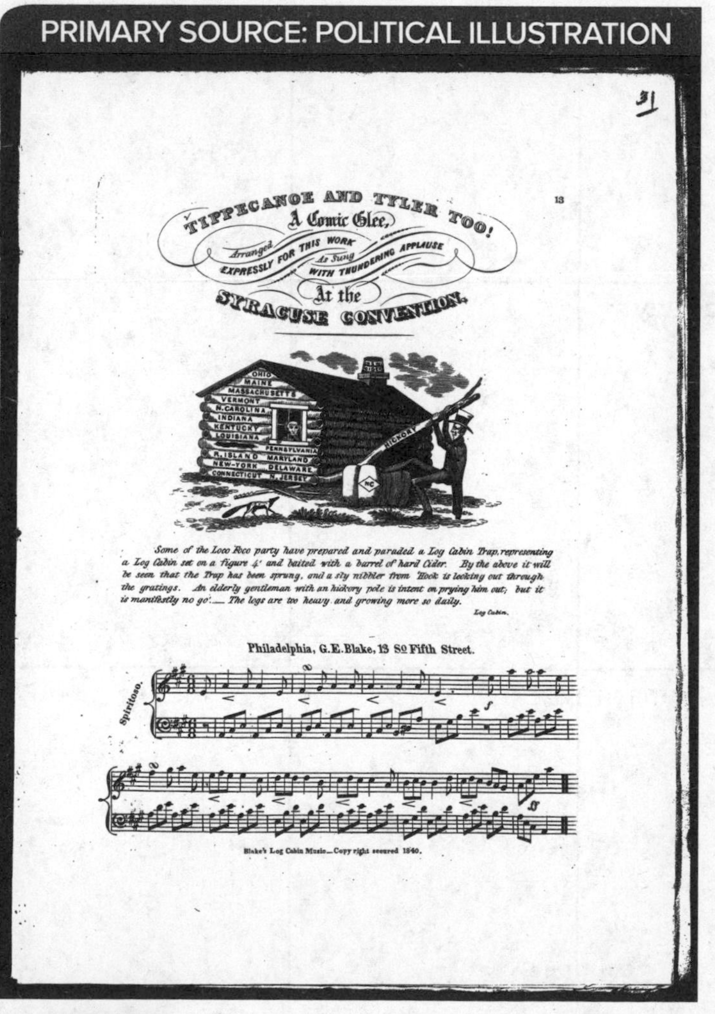

VOCABULARY

Loco Foco: nickname for the Democrats
manifestly: evidently
sly: sneaky

1 HISTORY According to the illustration's caption, who set the log cabin "trap"?

____

____

____

2 INFERRING Who is caught inside the trap? What details in the caption tell you who the man inside looking out the window is?

3 MAKING CONNECTIONS Poltiical illustrations often rely on symbolism—an image standing for a group or idea—to convey meaning. If the old man with the hickory stick is a symbol, whom does he represent? What details help you to know who he is?

4A INTEGRATING VISUAL INFORMATION If the log cabin is a symbol, what idea did the Democrats intend for it to represent when they "set the trap"?

4B IDENTIFYING Why are the logs too heavy for the man to be pried out of the cabin? What visual clues tell you what the log cabin has come to represent, from the perspective of the Whig party?

5 DETERMINING CENTRAL IDEAS What is the tone of this illustration and its caption? Back up your answer with details from the primary source.

ESSENTIAL QUESTION
What are the consequences when cultures interact?

"Tippecanoe and Tyler Too!" by Alexander Coffman Ross

INTRODUCTION: "Tippecanoe and Tyler Too" was written by Alexander Coffman Ross, a jeweler from Ohio, who wrote it to support the Whig candidate, William Henry Harrison. After performing it at a Whig gathering in his Ohio hometown of Zanesville, he shared it again at a Whig political meeting in Syracuse, New York, where the song caught on and became popular across the nation. The full song has twelve stanzas. Here is an excerpt from the song.

VOCABULARY

commotion: excitement
Loco: Democrat
standard: flag
tottering: falling over
spoilsmen, leg-treasurers: government thieves

1 ANALYZING STRUCTURE Notice the structure of the song. The chorus is the part that is repeated, and the verse is the part that changes. On the lines below, write the lines that make up the chorus.

____

____

____

____

____

____

____

PRIMARY SOURCE: SONG

"Tippecanoe and Tyler Too

What's the cause of this commotion, motion, motion, 1
Our country through?
It is the ball a-rolling on
For Tippecanoe and Tyler too.
For Tippecanoe and Tyler too.
And with them we'll beat little Van, Van, Van,
Van is a used up man.
And with them we'll beat little Van.

...

Have you heard from old Vermount, mount, mount, 4
All honest and true?
The Green Mountain Boys are rolling the ball
For Tippecanoe and Tyler too.
For Tippecanoe and Tyler too.
And with them we'll beat little Van, Van, Van,
Van is a used up man.
And with them we'll beat little Van...

Let them talk about hard cider, cider, cider, 5
And Log Cabins too,
It will only help to speed the ball
For Tippecanoe and Tyler too.
For Tippecanoe and Tyler too.
And with them we'll beat little Van, Van, Van,

Van is a used up man.
And with them we'll beat little Van...
He always had his tables set, set, set, 6
For all honest and true,
To ask you in to take a bite
With Tippecanoe and Tyler too.
For Tippecanoe and Tyler too.
And with them we'll beat little Van, Van, Van,
Van is a used up man.
And with them we'll beat little Van.

...

Little Matty's days are numbered, numbered,
numbered, 8
Out he must go!
And in his place we'll put the good
Old Tippecanoe and Tyler too.
For Tippecanoe and Tyler too.
And with them we'll beat little Van, Van, Van,
Van is a used up man.
And with them we'll beat little Van. ”

2 **INFERRING** What is the tone of the song? How do you know?

3 **EVALUATING MEDIA** What do you think is the purpose of a political song? How are political songs useful and different from other means of political advertising?

4 Can you detect any of the songwriter's feelings toward President Van Buren in the song? Support your opinion with reasoning based on details.

ESSENTIAL QUESTION

What are the consequences when cultures interact?

1 Think About It

Review the questions in the chapter opener along with the evidence that you gathered in Chapter 10. Were you able to answer each question? If there was not enough evidence to answer the questions, what additional evidence do you think you need to consider?

2 Organize Your Evidence & Draw Conclusions

Create a graphic organizer like the one below to examine the interactions between specific cultures detailed in Chapter 10. Create one for each pair of cultures you found in the chapter.

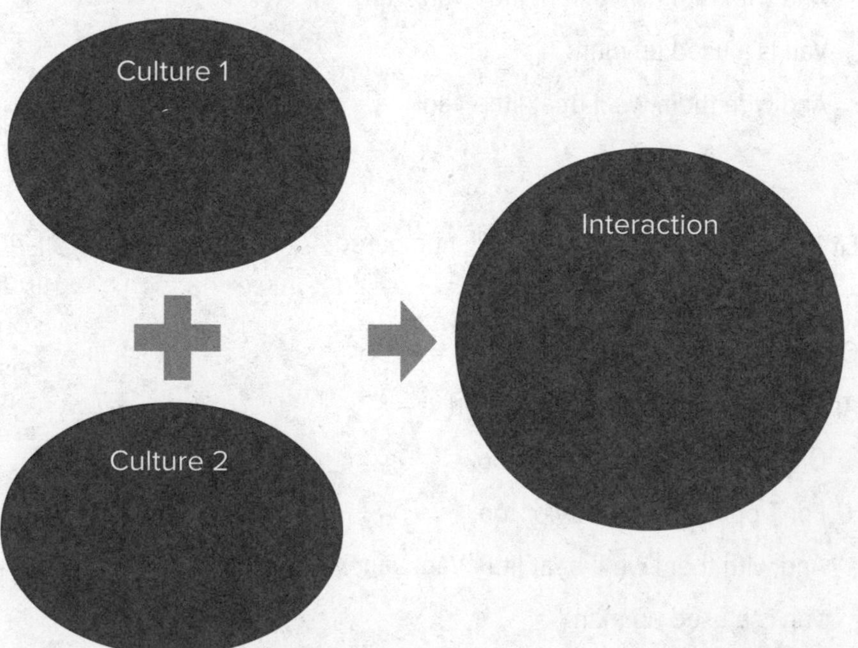

3 Talk About It

Get together with a friend and discuss your findings. Were you both able to answer the questions in the chapter opener? Did either of you think of things the other missed?

4 Write About It

In your "My Notes" box on the opening page, take a moment now to fill in any information you neglected to include.

5 Connect to the Essential Question

Using your notes and information gleaned from this chapter, write the lyrics to a song about what happens when cultures interact. Here are some ideas:

- A political song advertising for one of the candidates in the chapter other than Harrison and Tyler.
- A protest song about a policy you read about in the chapter that adversely affected a particular group.
- A song of hope for bringing cultures together.

Most songs use a "verse/chorus" structure where the chorus is repeated after every one or two verses and the verses change throughout the song. Observe the structure of "Tippecanoe and Tyler Too." Most songs today have fewer verses than this song. Aim to make your song include three to four verses and a repeated chorus. Set your lyrics to the tune of a popular song of today or make up your own music.

Present your song in one of the following ways:

- Submit it to your teacher in writing with a recording of the song whose tune you are using.
- Sing your song to your teacher privately.
- Perform your song for your class.
- Ask a friend to perform your song for your class.
- Have someone film you performing your song and submit it to your teacher or play it for your class.

Be creative and have fun; don't worry about whether or not you have musical ability. If you don't feel comfortable performing your song, then submit it in the first way or have a friend sing it for you.

CITIZENSHIP

TAKING ACTION

The United States has long attracted people of different cultural backgrounds. The Statue of Liberty, in New York Harbor, bears a poem by Emma Lazarus on its base, a welcome to people from all over the world. Some people have called the United States a "melting pot" where cultures all become part of one big American stew. Others consider it something more like a tossed salad, where cultures are tossed together, but each retains its distinct flavor and adds something special to the whole.

Immigration has long been a part of the American conversation. Immigrants contribute to our culture and have helped to build this country. However, the government must make decisions about how many immigrants it welcomes at any one time.

DIRECTIONS: Write down your favorite things about your own culture or cultures. These might include your favorite foods, holidays, music, clothing, or traditions. Then create a classroom calendar on posterboard. For each month, each student in the class will contribute a cultural holiday, food, or practice to add to the calendar. If you wish, decorate your calendar with drawings, stickers, or photos.

Manifest Destiny

ESSENTIAL QUESTION

How does geography influence the way people live?

Think about how this question might relate to the settlers of the American West in the first half of the 1800s.

TALK ABOUT IT

Discuss with a partner what information you would need to know to answer the Essential Question. What questions would you ask to get this information? For example, you might ask, "Did the landscape make it easier or harder for settlers to reach western lands?"

DIRECTIONS: Now, write down three additional questions that you need to answer to help you understand how geography influences the way people live.

MY RESEARCH QUESTIONS

Supporting Question 1:

____

____

Supporting Question 2:

____

____

Supporting Question 3:

____

____

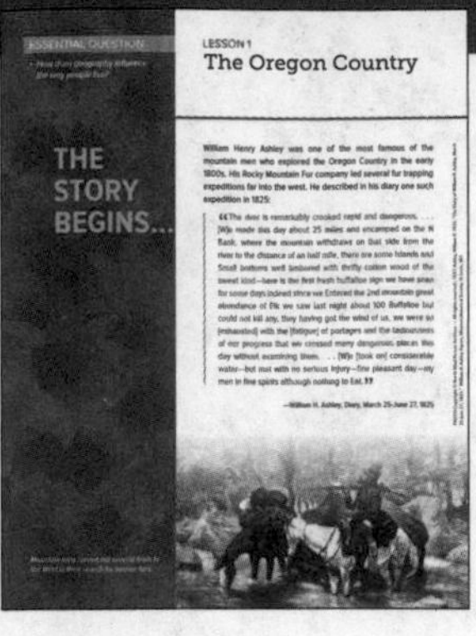

The Oregon Country

DIRECTIONS: Search for evidence in Chapter 11, Lesson 1 to help you answer the following questions.

ESSENTIAL QUESTION

How does geography influence the way people live?

As you gather evidence to answer the Essential Question, think about:

- why people were attracted to the Oregon country.
- what the trip to Oregon was like for settlers.
- what life in Oregon was like for them.

My Notes

1 **DESCRIBING** Where was the Oregon Country?

2 **IDENTIFYING CAUSES** Why did Americans want to control the Oregon Country?

3 **IDENTIFYING** What three countries did the United States compete with for control of the Oregon territory? Complete the table with your answers.

Rivals for the Oregon Country

4A IDENTIFYING Who were the first Americans to move to the Oregon Country?

4B What drew them there?

4C What were wilderness trappers called?

5 IDENTIFYING CAUSES Complete the graphic organizer.

Why Americans Headed to the Oregon Country	
Problems in the East	
Promise in the West	

6 EXPLAINING Why were Marcus and Narcissa Whitman and others killed by the Cayuse?

7A DESCRIBING About how long was the Oregon Trail?

7B What were prairie schooners?

8 EXPLAINING Explain the idea of Manifest Destiny.

ESSENTIAL QUESTION

How does geography influence the way people live?

An image of a Prairie Schooner

DIRECTIONS: Use the image to answer the questions.

INTRODUCTION: Between about 1840 and 1860, close to 50,000 people traveled the Oregon Trail. Each person experienced an epic journey. The trail was long—2,000 miles. Today, traveling in a car at highway speed, it would take more than 30 hours driving nonstop to cover that distance. For emigrants on the trail, walking or riding in prairie schooners, the trip took about five months. As you study the image, imagine what traveling so long riding in or walking by a prairie schooner must have been like.

SECONDARY SOURCE: IMAGE

1 **INFERRING** What part of the covered wagon earned it the nickname "prairie schooner"?

2A ANALYZING SOURCES What is the purpose of the cover?

2B Do you think it fulfilled its purpose well? Why or why not?

3 INFERRING What provided the power to move the prairie schooner?

4A HUMAN-ENVIRONMENT INTERACTION What were the tires made of?

4B What do you think better describes the ride of the wagon for its passengers: smooth or rough? Why?

ESSENTIAL QUESTION

How does geography influence the way people live?

"Experience that Can Never Be Forgotten"

DIRECTIONS: Read the excerpt. Then answer the questions.

INTRODUCTION: Travel on the Oregon Trail was rough. Why? The trail was long—about 2,000 miles. It crossed plains, and mountains, and deserts. It also crossed rivers. But one geographic threat was not from the ground below, but from the skies above. Let J. Henry Brown, who traveled the Oregon Trail in 1847, tell you about it.

PRIMARY SOURCE: AUTOBIOGRAPHY

"In a few days we reached the Platte [River], and entered the edge of the buffalo country. The first night we camped upon this stream, we were visited by one of those thunder storms for which that part of the country is famous. The day had been very warm, and in the evening about sundown, Mr. Bradshaw discovered a small black cloud in the west, and immediately ordered 20 men to saddle horses and remain on them while the rest were securely tied to the wagons, tents extra pinned, the cattle herded closely by horse and footmen. The storm could now plainly be seen coming by the flashes of lightening and the rapidly increasing roar of the thunder. It was well that these precautions had been taken, although not wholly successful. When the storm struck us, it was quite dark, which of course added to the confusion. It seemed as if the very elements were at war with each other. The blinding brightness of lightning as it apparently covered acres, followed instantaneously by the deafening crash that seemed to shake the earth, accompanied by large hailstones and a terrific wind, when all combined was well calculated to throw everything into confusion. Tents were prostrated, thus increasing the fright of the occupants; cattle bellowing as they rushed by with the storm; horses struggling franticly to break their fastenings to the wagons, mingled with the shouting of men, made an hours experience that can never be forgotten when once endured.

But the storm went by as rapidly as it came, leaving a heavy coating of hail in its track, with all the cattle gone and the horsemen in

VOCABULARY

tents extra pinned: extra stakes were added to the tents to keep them from blowing away in a strong wind

precautions: safeguards taken beforehand to prevent damage

prostrated: knocked flat

endured: suffered through

. . . continued

pursuit. As the clouds cleared away and the moon and stars came out, they were enabled to follow and gradually herd them together, and by 10 o'clock next morning we were again on the move.”

—*The Autobiography of J. Henry Brown*, 1938

1A IDENTIFYING CENTRAL IDEAS What geographic event is Brown describing?

1B EXPLAINING Why are the emigrants frightened?

1C ANALYZING What protection do the travelers have?

2 INFERRING Why do you think Mr. Bradshaw ordered 20 men to get and stay on horses?

3 HUMAN-ENVIRONMENT INTERACTION How does this passage show how geography influences the way people live?

ESSENTIAL QUESTION

How does geography influence the way people live?

As you gather evidence to answer the Essential Question, think about:

- how geography affected Florida's path to statehood.
- how geography affected Texas's path to statehood.

My Notes

Statehood for Florida and Texas

DIRECTIONS: Search for evidence in Chapter 11, Lesson 2 to help you answer the following questions.

1 DESCRIBING Complete the table.

Settler Population of Florida	
1824	**1837**
< 8,000	

2 HUMAN-ENVIRONMENT INTERACTION How did early American settlers in Florida use the land? Complete the table.

Land Use of Early Florida Settlers	
Region	**Land Use**
Northern Florida and the Panhandle	
Central Florida	

3 INFERRING Florida became a territory in 1821. Yet it was not until more than 15 years later that the settlers in Florida voted to form a state. What geographical reason related to human movement caused this delay?

4 IDENTIFYING CAUSES How was the admission of Florida as a state affected by the state of Iowa?

5A **IDENTIFYING CAUSES** Why did so many Americans move to Mexican Texas?

5B What caused tensions between the American settlers in Texas and the Mexican government?

5C Why did Santa Anna attack and massacre the defenders of the Alamo?

6A **IDENTIFYING CAUSES** What battle led to the Texas victory in the war for independence?

6B Who were the leaders on the battlefield?

ESSENTIAL QUESTION

How does geography influence the way people live?

Florida Land Claim, 1827

DIRECTIONS: Study the image. Then answer the accompanying questions.

INTRODUCTION: Spain encouraged settlement in Florida by granting, or giving away, land. After Florida became a possession of the United States, landowners there had to confirm their land claims. The map shown here was part of a land claim filed on behalf of Geronimo Alvarez.

PRIMARY SOURCE: GOVERNMENT DOCUMENT

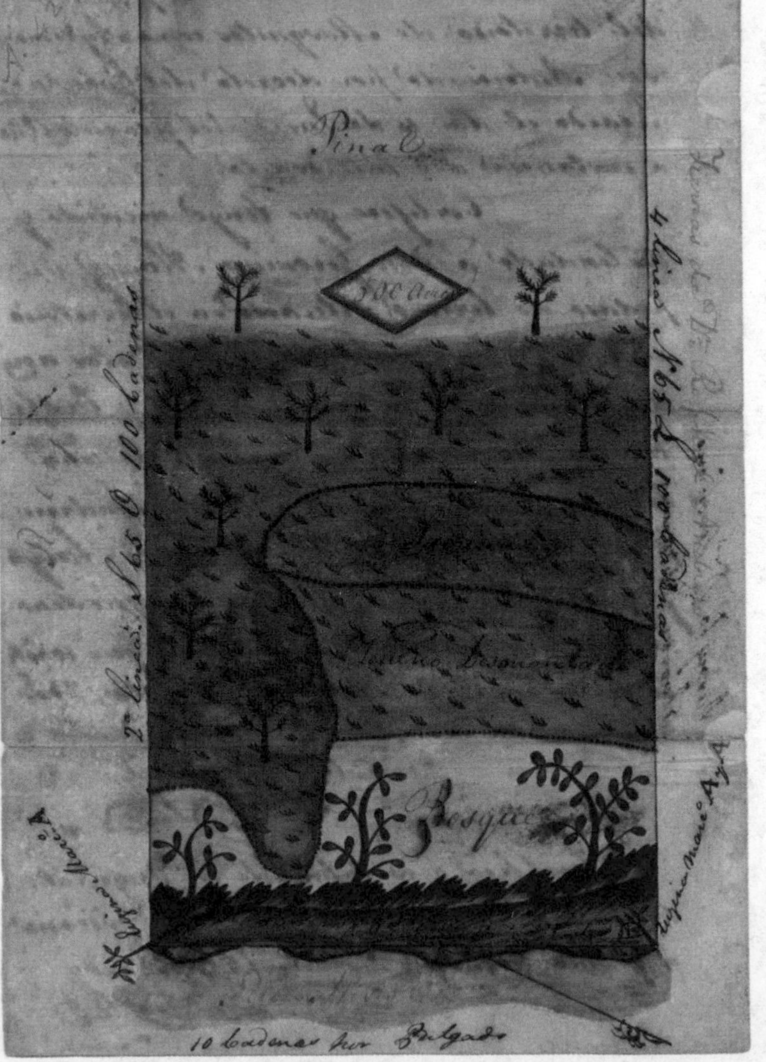

VOCABULARY

land claim: official document showing transfer of ownership

1 **INFERRING** This map from a land claim being presented to the U.S. government has notations written in Spanish. What might you infer from this?

2 **DETERMINING PURPOSE** Consider the image. What does it show?

3 **DESCRIBING** What natural or geographical resources are depicted in the image?

4 Use your answer to 3 and your knowledge of social studies to complete the table.

Land Uses Shown on Florida Claim	
Natural Resource	**How Used**

ESSENTIAL QUESTION

How does geography influence the way people live?

Letter from William Barret Travis

DIRECTIONS: Read the letter. Then answer the accompanying questions.

INTRODUCTION: The Alamo is world famous. Almost two million people from all over the globe come to San Antonio, Texas, each year to visit it. Why? The story of the Alamo is the story of bravery in the face of certain death. The bravery is best expressed by a commander of the forces there, William Barret Travis. Surrounded and hugely outnumbered by Mexican forces under General Santa Anna, Travis sent a messenger with a letter asking for help. It is one of the most moving documents in American history.

PRIMARY SOURCE: LETTER

"Fellow citizens & compatriots—

I am besieged, by a thousand or more of the Mexicans under Santa Anna I have sustained a continual Bombardment & cannonade for 24 hours & have not lost a man The enemy has demanded a surrender at discretion, otherwise, the garrison are to be put to the sword, if the fort is taken I have answered the demand with a cannon shot, & our flag still waves proudly from the walls I shall never surrender or retreat. Then, I call on you in the name of Liberty, of patriotism & everything dear to the American character, to come to our aid, with all dispatch The enemy is receiving reinforcements daily & will no doubt increase to three or four thousand in four or five days. If this call is neglected, I am determined to sustain myself as long as possible & die like a soldier who never forgets what is due to his own honor & that of his country VICTORY OR DEATH."

—William Barret Travis, Lt. Col. comdt.
February 24, 1836

VOCABULARY

compatriots: fellow citizens or sympathizers
besieged: surrounded
surrender at discretion: unconditional surrender; no promises made to the people who surrender
garrison: fort
dispatch: speeding to a purpose
beeves: heads of beef cattle

. . . *continued*

P.S. The Lord is on our side. When the enemy appeared in sight we had not three bushels of corn. We have since found in deserted houses 80 or 90 bushels and got into the walls 20 or 30 head of Beeves. Travis ❞

1 GEOGRAPHY In geography, there are five themes, or major ideas. Think about each theme as it relates to the letter. Complete the table.

Geography and the Alamo		
Theme	**Meaning**	**Evidence in Letter**
Location	where something is	
Place	physical and human features	
Interaction	people and environment affecting each other	
Movement	travel and exchange of goods and ideas	
Region	areas united by physical or cultural traits	

2A **IDENTIFYING CENTRAL IDEAS** What geographic thing are the Mexicans and the Texans fighting over?

2B People have fought over land for thousands of years. Why?

War With Mexico

DIRECTIONS: Search for evidence in Chapter 11, Lesson 3 to help you answer the following questions.

1 **DESCRIBE** Describe the location of New Mexico in the early 1800s.

2 What was the most important early Spanish settlement in New Mexico?

3 **IDENTIFYING CAUSES** How did geography affect the route of the Santa Fe trail that William Becknell laid out?

4 **IDENTIFYING CAUSES** Why did Americans in the 1840s want to add California to the country?

ESSENTIAL QUESTION

How does geography influence the way people live?

My Notes

5A **EXPLAINING** What roles did rivers play in the start of the Mexican War?

5B What were the three parts of America's plan to defeat Mexico?

6 **IDENTIFYING** What were the results of the Treaty of Guadalupe Hidalgo on the geography of the United States and Mexico?

ESSENTIAL QUESTION

How does geography influence the way people live?

The Battle of Cerro Gordo

DIRECTIONS: Read the excerpt from the letter. Then answer the accompanying questions.

INTRODUCTION: March 9, 1847. The United States is at war with Mexico. General Winfield Scott lands near Veracruz with a fighting force of 10,000 men. His ultimate goal: the capture of Mexico City. He will have to fight his way to the inland Mexican capital. On April 17 and 18, Scott storms the mountain pass at Cerro Gordo ("Big Hill"). Below is part of Scott's letter to William L. Marcy, Secretary of War, about the Battle of Cerro Gordo.

PRIMARY SOURCE: LETTER

"Headquarters of the Army,
Plan del Rio, 50 miles from Vera Cruz
April 19, 1847

Sir –

The brigade ascended the long and difficult slope of Cerro Gordo, without shelter, and under the tremendous fire of artillery and musketry with the utmost steadiness, reached the breastworks, drove the enemy from them, planted the colors of the 1st artillery, 3d and 7th infantry — the enemy's flag still flying — and, after some minutes' sharp firing, finished the conquest with the bayonet....

Worth's division of regulars coming up at this time, he detached Brevet Lieutenant-colonel C. F. Smith, with his light battalion, to support the assault, but not in time. The general, reaching the tower a few minutes before me, and observing a white flag displayed from the nearest portion of the enemy towards the batteries below, sent out Colonels Harney and Childs to hold a parley. The surrender followed in an hour or two.

Major-general Patterson left a sick-bed to share in the dangers and fatigues of the day; and after the surrender went forward to command the advanced forces towards Xalapa ....

VOCABULARY

brigade: small part of an army; typically foot soldiers
ascended: climbed up
musketry: from muskets, long arms similar to rifles
breastworks: temporary barrier or wall built as a defensive measure
bayonet: blade attached to the end of a rifle for use in hand-to-hand fighting
parley: negotiation for peace

. . . continued

President Santa Anna, with Generals Canalizo and Almonte, and some six or eight thousand men, escaped towards Xalapa just before Cerro Gordo was carried, and before Twiggs' division reached the National road above....

Being much occupied with ... prisoners, and all the details of a forward movement, besides looking to the supplies which are to follow from Vera Cruz, I have time to add no more — intending to be at Xalapa early to-morrow. We shall not, probably, again meet with serious opposition this side of Perote — certainly not, unless delayed by the want of the means of transportation.

I have the honor to remain, sir, with high respect, your most obedient servant,

WINFIELD SCOTT. ”

1 **INFERRING** Why do you think Scott attacked the Mexicans head-on instead of going around them?

2 **EXPLAINING** What does "finished the conquest with the bayonet" mean?

3 GEOGRAPHY Does this document support the idea that geography influences the way people live, or not? Explain.

ESSENTIAL QUESTION

How does geography influence the way people live?

The Treaty of Guadalupe Hidalgo

DIRECTIONS: Read the excerpt from the treaty. Then answer the accompanying questions.

INTRODUCTION: The Treaty of Guadalupe Hidalgo ended America's war with Mexico. It also transferred an enormous amount of land from Mexico to the United States. Mexico gave the United States more than 500,000 square miles of land—what is now the states of California, Nevada, and Utah, as well as most of Arizona and New Mexico and parts of Colorado and Wyoming.

PRIMARY SOURCE: TREATY

"ARTICLE V

The boundary line between the two Republics [the United States and Mexico] shall commence in the Gulf of Mexico, three leagues from land, opposite the mouth of the Rio Grande, otherwise called Rio Bravo del Norte, or Opposite the mouth of its deepest branch, if it should have more than one branch emptying directly into the sea; from thence up the middle of that river, following the deepest channel, where it has more than one, to the point where it strikes the southern boundary of New Mexico; thence, westwardly, along the whole southern boundary of New Mexico (which runs north of the town called Paso) to its western termination; thence, northward, along the western line of New Mexico, until it intersects the first branch of the river Gila; (or if it should not intersect any branch of that river, then to the point on the said line nearest to such branch, and thence in a direct line to the same); thence down the middle of the said branch and of the said river, until it empties into the Rio Colorado; thence across the Rio Colorado, following the division line between Upper and Lower California, to the Pacific Ocean."

—The Treaty of Guadalupe Hidalgo

VOCABULARY

league: a measure of distance of about three miles

from thence: from the place just mentioned

termination: end

1A **ANALYZING SOURCES** What is the purpose of Article V of the Treaty of Guadalupe Hidalgo?

____

____

1B What rivers are used to mark a boundary?

____

1C What large bodies of water are used to mark a boundary?

____

____

2 **INFERRING** Why are geographic features used to make borders?

____

____

3 **INFERRING** How might setting the border as a river impact life along the Rio Grande?

____

____

____

California and Utah

DIRECTIONS: Search for evidence in Chapter 11, Lesson 4 to help you answer the following questions.

1A IDENTIFY CAUSE AND EFFECTS What was discovered at Sutter's Mill in California in 1848?

1B What historic event did it lead to?

2 MOVEMENT Complete the table.

The Forty-niners: Where They Came From and How They Got There	
Origins of Miners	Routes to California

ESSENTIAL QUESTION

How does geography influence the way people live?

My Notes

3 EXPLAINING Complete the table

Gold Rush Terms	
forty-niner	
boomtown	
panning	
Levi's	
vigilantes	

4 EXPLAINING What role did geography play in the settlement of California?

5 DESCRIBING Complete the table.

The Mormon Migration	
Name of Route	
Starting Point	
Ending point	
Number of Travelers	

6 EXPLAINING What role did geography play in the Mormon settlement of Utah?

ESSENTIAL QUESTION

How does geography influence the way people live?

Routes to California

DIRECTIONS: Read the account below. Then answer the accompanying questions.

INTRODUCTION: Jedediah Strong Smith (1799-1831) was a legendary mountain man. His descriptions of the west provided Americans with vital information about the vast lands located there. Here, he tells of a terrifying encounter with some native people of California along what is today known as the Stanislaus River.

VOCABULARY

procure: obtain
futurity: future time
sandbar: narrow stretch of sand along or reaching into the water
breastwork: temporary barrier or wall built as a defensive measure
lance: spear

PRIMARY SOURCE: JOURNAL

"After weighing all the circumstances of my situation as calmly as possible, I concluded to again try the hospitality of the Californians. I had left with my party on the Appelamminy [River] a quantity of Beaver furs, and if the Governor would permit me to trade, and I could find any person acquainted with the value of furs, I might procure such supplies as would enable me to continue my journey to the North.

But to return from this anticipation, I was yet on the sand bar in sight of My dead companions and not far off were some hundreds of indians who might in all probability close in upon us and with an Arrow or Club terminate all my measures for futurity. Such articles as would sink I threw in to the river and spread the rest out on the sand bar. I told the men what kind of Country we had to pass through and gave them permission to take such things as they chose from the bar.

After making their selection, the rest was scattered over the ground, knowing that whilst the indians were quarreling about the division of the spoils we would be gaining time for our escape. We then moved on in the almost hopeless endeavor to travel over the desert Plain, where there was not the least probability of finding game for our subsistence. Our provision was all lost in the affray, with the exception of about 15 lbs of dried Meat.

We had not gone more than 1/2 Mile before the indians closed around us, apparently watching the proper moment to fall on us. I thought it most

. . . continued

prudent to go in to the bank of the river while we had it in our power, and if the indians allowed us time, select the spot on which we might sell our lives at the dearest rate. We were not molested and on arriving on the bank of the river we took our position in a cluster of small Cotton Wood trees, which were generally 2 or 3 inches in diameter and standing verry close.

With our knives we lopped down the small trees in such a manner as to clear a place in which to stand, while the fallen poles formed a slight breast work. We then fastened our Butcher knives with cords to the end of light poles so as to form a tolerable lance, and thus poorly prepared we waited the approach of our unmerciful enemies.

On one side the river prevented them from approaching us, but in every other direction the indians were closing in upon us, and the time seemed fast approaching in which we were to come to that contest which must, in spite of courage, conduct and all that man could do, terminate in our destruction.

It was a fearful time. Eighth men with but 5 guns were awaiting behind a defence made of brush the charge of four or five hundred indians whose hands were yet stained with the blood of their companions.

Some of the men asked me If I thought we would be able to defend ourselves. I told them I thought we would. But that was not my opinion. I directed that not more than three guns should be fired at a time and those only when the Shot would be certain of killing. Gradually the enemy was drawing near, but kept themselves covered from our fire.

Seeing a few indians who ventured out from their covering within long shot I directed two good marksmen to fire they did so and two indians fell and another was wounded. Uppon this the indians ran off like frightened sheep and we were released from the apprehension of immediate death.”

—Jedediah Smith's journal, Second Expedition to California

ESSENTIAL QUESTION

How does geography influence the way people live?

1A HUMAN-ENVIRONMENT INTERACTION Name two ways Smith uses the river to help his party survive.

1B Name two ways Smith uses the trees to help his party survive.

2 ANALYZING SOURCES What emotion or emotions do you think Smith felt during this encounter?

3 **CITING TEXT EVIDENCE** What happened to make the Native Americans run off "like frightened sheep"?

4 **MAKING CONNECTIONS** Do you think this type of encounter was common as Americans opened the West? Explain your answer.

ESSENTIAL QUESTION

How does geography influence the way people live?

All Was Not Gold That Glittered

DIRECTIONS: Read the excerpt from the report. Then answer the questions that follow.

INTRODUCTION: San Francisco during the 1849 gold rush was a boomtown. It grew from a tiny village of about 800 people to a city of about 25,000 people in just a year. One witness recalled that the number of people grew so fast that the government could not keep up.

VOCABULARY

vulgar parlance: straight talk
quarters: where someone lives
speculating in real estate: buying land hoping the value will go up and so could be sold at a profit
wharf: platform for loading and unloading ships
municipal: related to a city government

PRIMARY SOURCE: DIARY

"A short experience of the mines had satisfied most of the citizens of San Francisco that, in vulgar parlance, all was not gold that glittered, and that hard work was not easy, — sorry truisms for weak or lazy men. They returned very soon to their old quarters, and found that much greater profits, with for less labor, were to be found in supplying the necessities of the miners, and speculating in real estate.

For a time everybody made money, in spite of himself. The continued advance in the price of goods, and especially in the value of real estate, gave riches at once to the fortunate owner of a stock [goods] or of a single advantageously situated lot of the latter. ... Coin was scarce, but bags of gold dust furnished a circulating medium, which answered all purposes. ...

There were few regular houses erected, for neither building materials nor sufficient labor were to be had ; but canvas tents, or houses of frame, served the immediate needs of the place. Great quantities of goods continued to pour in from the nearer ports, till there were no longer stores to receive and cover them. ...

Seamen deserted their vessels soon as they dropped anchor in the bay, and hastened to the mines. Society, not merely there, but in San

... continued

Francisco, was in a state of utter disorganization, which became worse and more terrible as the autumn and winter months brought new thousands of immigrants upon the place.

We have seen that there [were] no ... municipal authorities, who could have protected the citizens, and established order, and made provision for the systematic extension of the town and reception of the coming crowds. ... Thefts, robberies, murders, and other outrages of the most desperate and criminal nature were taking place, and there was no proper officials to take [notice] of them and bring the offenders to justice. Every man was intent on merely making money [and] was content to shut his eyes... ”

SOURCE: The Annals of San Francisco. 1855. by Soulé, Frank; Nisbet, Jim, joint author.

1 **IDENTIFYING CAUSES** What turned San Francisco into a boomtown in 1849?

2 **ANALYZING TEXT** What is the meaning of the first paragraph? Use your own words.

3 CIVICS How does this document demonstrate the need for government?

4 GEOGRAPHY Does this document show how geography can affect the way people live? Explain.

ESSENTIAL QUESTION

How does geography influence the way people live?

1 Think About It

Review the supporting questions that you developed at the beginning of the chapter. Review the evidence that you gathered in Chapter 11. Were you able to answer each supporting question? If there was not enough evidence to answer your supporting questions, what additional evidence do you think you need to include?

____

____

____

____

2 Organize Your Evidence

Use the graphic organizer below to list what you have learned about how geography influences the way people live.

Part of Geography (land, water, trees, etc.)	How It Influences the Way People Live
1.	
2.	
3.	
4.	
5.	
6.	
7.	
8.	
9.	
10.	

Review your list. Is there any way to organize your items into categories? Your categories might be based on time, or place, or type of geography.

3 Talk About It

Talk with a partner about how geography influences your own lives, every day. Does it have as strong an influence as it did on the Americans of the 19th century? Discuss this and similar questions. Use the space below to organize your thoughts.

4 Connect to the Essential Question

Using your work from step 2 above, plan a visual essay that answers the Essential Question: How does geography influence the way people live? Your essay can be based on individual items, or categories, or both. Your visual essay should be in the form of a poster that has the Essential Question as its title and illustrations (that you draw or print or cut out) that provide an answers or multiple answers to the Essential Question. You may caption the images as you wish. Create your visual display for classroom presentation to your own class or the class of students one year younger.

CITIZENSHIP

TAKING ACTION

It can be helpful when studying history to think of geography as the "stage" on which the "actors" of history perform. For example, the peninsula where San Francisco became a boomtown would be a stage. The actors were the Forty-niners and other settlers.

Unlike a theater stage, however, the "stage" of the landscape directly affects the "actors," or actual people. For example, people headed to California because of something in the landscape: gold. They docked ships there because of the bay. These are just two examples of the countless ways geography influences how people live every day.

This sense of geography being central to our lives is deep in the human spirit. That is one reason why we preserve nature—think about Yosemite National Park in California. We also preserve areas of historical importance—think about the Oregon Trail wagon wheel ruts in Wyoming.

Unfortunately many of these places face serious trouble. Years of neglect, loss of funding, overuse, and other problems can threaten them.

DIRECTIONS: Using the Internet, conduct research to learn more about a geographic location of your choice. Find out if this location is facing any particular difficulties (neglect, lack of funding, etc.). Find out too if they have any ways you can help, perhaps through volunteering. If not, find another location. Jot down what you learn below. Then perform a task to help preserve your local geography. Volunteer, write a letter to the editor, start a petition for preservation, or take some other concrete action. Report what you do to your teacher in an explanatory essay.

North and South

ESSENTIAL QUESTION

How does technology change the way people live?

Think about the innovations in transportation, production, and agriculture of the early to mid-1800s.

TALK ABOUT IT

Discuss with a partner what type of information you would need in order to understand how technology changes the way people live. What questions would you need to answer in order to explore this topic? For instance, one question might be, "What new technological advances came into existence during the early to mid-1800s?"

DIRECTIONS: Now write down three additional questions that will help you explain how technology changed the way people lived during the period 1820 to 1860.

MY RESEARCH QUESTIONS

Supporting Question 1:

Supporting Question 2:

Supporting Question 3:

The Industrial North

DIRECTIONS: Search for evidence in Chapter 12, Lesson 1 to help you answer the following questions.

1 ANALYZING Use the graphic organizer below to analyze the innovations in technology during the early 1800s. The first two have been done for you.

Impact of Major Technological Innovations of the Early 1800s		
INVENTOR	INNOVATION	IMPACT ON LIFE
Engineers	Canals	Improved shipping
Robert Fulton	Steamboat	Improved river shipping and expanded leisure travel

ESSENTIAL QUESTION

How does technology change the way people live?

As you gather evidence to answer the Essential Question, think about

- improvements in factory production.
- agricultural improvements.
- new modes of transportation.
- evolving modes of communication.

My Notes

2 DRAWING CONCLUSIONS How did technological innovations lead to economic growth in the United States?

3 GEOGRAPHY How did technology lead to geographic expansion and growth of cities in the Midwest?

4 INFERRING Why did technological innovations in farming and factory production lead to the creation of more jobs?

ESSENTIAL QUESTION

How does technology change the way people live?

Notice from the Michigan Central Railroad, c. late 1880s

DIRECTIONS: Look closely at the image below. Then respond to the questions that follow.

EXPLORE THE CONTEXT: This advertisement, or "notice," for the Michigan Central Railroad promotes "The Niagara Falls Route," a major attraction of the time. Notices such as these were often displayed in public places.

PRIMARY SOURCE: ADVERTISEMENT

1. **INTEGRATING VISUAL INFORMATION** Why do you think the railway advertised itself as "The Niagara Falls Route" and also used an illustration of the falls?

2A **GEOGRAPHY** According to the ad, what other geographic feature would passengers see on this route if they continued to Bar Harbor?

2B How would a person have traveled from Chicago to Bar Harbor, Maine, before the advent of the railroad? How long do you think it might have taken?

3 **RESEARCHING** Using the Internet, find out how long it takes today to travel the 281 miles from Chicago to Detroit—the halfway point in the trip to Niagara Falls. Track the time over four different modern modes of transportation, such as train, car, plane, and bus. Record your findings in the table below. (Round times to the nearest quarter hour.)

Average Time to Travel from Chicago to Detroit in Different Eras						
Time period	BEFORE 1857	1857	TODAY	TODAY	TODAY	TODAY
Mode of Transport		Train				
Journey Time						

4 **COMPARING AND CONTRASTING** How might a person riding a train for the first time in 1857 have felt about the time it took to travel this distance? How might someone from today feel about traveling for that same amount of time?

5 **ANALYZING SOURCES** Why do you think the ad uses words such as “A Modern Pilgrimage” and “Through Sleeping Cars, without change”?

ESSENTIAL QUESTION

How does technology change the way people live?

Clipper Ships at Anchor

DIRECTIONS: Read this article dated May 26, 1851, from a San Francisco newspaper. Then answer the questions that follow.

EXPLORE THE CONTEXT: The advent of clipper ships excited observers, who were amazed to note the size and stability in their design. One such observer was a reporter from a San Francisco newspaper, *The Daily Alta California,* who observed clipper ships anchored in San Francisco Bay.

PRIMARY SOURCE: NEWSPAPER ARTICLE

"In the tremendous wind of yesterday, which made the whole bay white with foam, and caused sizeable brigs and schooners to pitch and roll, as they lay at anchor, like chips pawing over rapids, it was a study to mark the difference between the sharp clippers and the old fashioned, tub-prowed ships, as they lay at anchor, facing the tide and wind. One of the large, sharp ocean giants lay directly in the full range of the gale as it swept up from the Golden Gate, yet there was not a ripple at her bows. A number of the full built ships lay near her, and at their bows it was all "feather white," like the waves as they dash down over a cataract. She had not even a "white bone in her mouth," while the rest of the fleet had whole skeletons.

She lay at her anchor as quietly as if on a summer lake, and did not seem to give anchor or chain any trouble. There were ships of five hundred tons which gave their ground tackle more strain than did that immense ship of three or four times the tonnage. This shows how much more safe such ships would be on a lee shore, or in a gale of wind anywhere at anchor, than those of the former usual construction. Their length also, as well as their sharp model, giving them less motion, renders the chances of dragging anchors and parting chains much less. The clippers will prove one of the greatest improvements of the age."

—from The *Daily Alta California,* San Francisco newspaper, May 26, 1851

VOCABULARY

brig: a two-masted sailing ship

schooner: a sailing ship with two or more masts

prow: protruding tip of a ship

gale: strong wind

bows: front section of a ship

cataract: waterfall

ground tackle: anchor and chain

lee: protected from wind

1 **DETERMINING MEANING** What do you suppose the writer means by "tub-prowed"?

2 **DETERMINING MEANING** What do you suppose the writer means by "She had not even a 'white bone in her mouth,' while the rest of the fleet had whole skeletons"?

3 **INFERRING** Why does the writer feel clipper ships must be safer than standard ships?

4 **ANALYZING POINT OF VIEW** How does the writer show that the clipper ships are a new technology that will change the way people live?

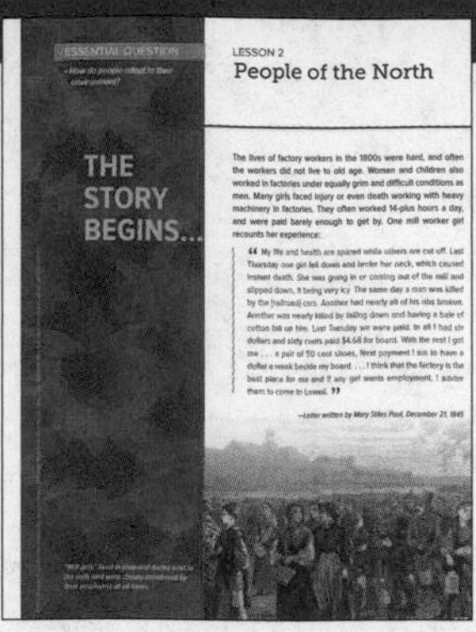

ESSENTIAL QUESTION

How does technology change the way people live?

As you gather evidence to answer the Essential Question, think about

- the long hours and dangerous conditions faced by factory workers.
- children operating machines for 12 hours a day, 6 days a week.
- factors that led to increased immigration.
- how African Americans living in the free North were treated.

My Notes

People of the North

DIRECTIONS: Search for evidence in Chapter 12, Lesson 2 to help you answer the following questions.

1 Why was life hard and unfair for African Americans living in the North?

2 **INFERRING** What circumstances led to increased immigration during the mid-1800s?

3A **IDENTIFYING PERSPECTIVES** What were the complaints of nativists about immigrants?

3B Was Orestes Brownson accurate about the future of immigrants in America? What evidence would support his view?

4 **DRAWING CONCLUSIONS** How did the rise of trade unions begin to change the way people worked?

5 **EXPLAINING CAUSE AND EFFECT** Use the chart below to list some problems with working conditions in factories in the 1800s. Also record laws that labor unions worked to have passed that eventually changed those conditions. Extend your observations into the present day.

Changes in Factory Conditions Over Time	
CONDITIONS IN THE 1800S	CONDITIONS TODAY
12-hour days	
wages that barely allowed subsistence	minimum wage, higher wages for skilled professions

ESSENTIAL QUESTION

How does technology change the way people live?

Speech to the African Lodge

DIRECTIONS: Read the following report from a Masonic lodge president to his members. Then respond to the questions that follow.

EXPLORE THE CONTEXT: Prince Hall (1735—1807) was an African American Revolutionary War veteran and abolitionist. In 1787, he obtained a charter from England to establish in Boston the first African American Masonic lodge. This is an excerpt from Hall's report to the members of his lodge in 1797. It brings to light the challenges facing African Americans living in a Northern city.

VOCABULARY

stedfast: lasting

tabernacle: church

letter learning: formal education

indispensible: essential

1 **ANALYZING** What does Hall mean by his opening sentence?

____

____

____

____

____

____

2 What is Hall's recommendation to his fellow African American masons in dealing with daily discrimination and harassment?

____

PRIMARY SOURCE: REPORT

"Now my brethren, as we see and experience, that all things hear [sic] are frail and changeable and nothing here to be depended upon: Let us seek those things which are above, which are sure and stedfast... and unchangeable, and at the same time let us pray to Almighty God, while we remain in the tabernacle, that he would give us the grace of patience and strength to bear up under all our troubles, which at this day God knows we have our share. Patience I say, for were we not possess'd of a great measure of it you could not bear up under the daily insults you meet with in the streets of Boston; much more on public days of recreation; how are you shamefully abus'd, and that at such a degree, that you may truly be said to carry your lives in your hands . . .

Although you are deprived of the means of education; yet you are not deprived of the means of meditation; by which I mean thinking, hearing and weighing matter, men and things in your own mind, and making that judgment of them as you think reasonable to satisfy your minds and give an answer to those who may ask you a question. This nature hath furnished you with, without letter learning; and some have made great progress therein, some of those I have heard repeat psalms and

hymns, and a great part of a sermon, only by hearing it read or preached and why not in other things in nature: how many of this class of our brethren that follow the seas, can foretell a storm some days before it comes; whether it will be a heavy or light, a long or short one; foretell a hurricane whether it will be destructive or moderate; without any other means than observation and consideration. . . .

Live and act as Masons, that you may die as Mason; let those despisers see, altho' many of us cannot read, yet by our searches and researches into men and things, we have supplied that defect, and if they will let us we shall call ourselves a charter'd lodge, of just and lawful Masons; be always ready to give an answer to those that ask you a question; give the right hand of affection and fellowship to whom it justly belongs let their colour and complexion be what it will; let their nation be what it may, for they are your brethren, and it is your indispensible duty so to do . . . ”

—Prince Hall, from his report to the African (Masonic) Lodge, June 24, 1797

3. **DETERMINING CENTRAL IDEAS** Hall says that even though the men present might not have access to education, they have something else they can use as a strength to better themselves. What do they have that they can use, and how can they use it?

4. In the last paragraph, what does Hall indicate is the purpose of the organization?

5. **INFERRING** What might have motivated Hall to try to obtain a charter from England for an African American Masonic lodge?

ESSENTIAL QUESTION

How does technology change the way people live?

"Factory Girls"

DIRECTIONS: Read the excerpt below from a magazine article. Then respond to the questions that follow.

EXPLORE THE CONTEXT: The following excerpt is from an article about the experiences of young women working in the factories. It was published in December 1840, in the *Lowell Offering,* a literary magazine by and for the "mill girls." Attributed to "A factory girl," it was very likely written by Harriet Jane Farley, who later became the *Lowell Offering*'s editor.

PRIMARY SOURCE: ARTICLE

"It has been asserted that to put ourselves under the influence and restraints of corporate bodies, is contrary to the spirit of our institutions, and to that love of independence which we ought to cherish. . . . We are under restraints, but they are voluntarily assumed; and we are at liberty to withdraw from them, whenever they become galling or irksome. Neither have I ever discovered that any restraints were imposed upon us but those which were necessary for the peace and comfort of the whole, and for the promotion of the design for which we are collected, namely, to get money, as much of it and as fast as we can; and it is because our toil is so unremitting, that the wages of factory girls are higher than those of females engaged in most other occupations. It is these wages which, in spite of toil, restraint, discomfort, and prejudice, have drawn so many worthy, virtuous, intelligent, and well-educated girls to Lowell, and other factories; and it is the wages which are in great degree to decide the characters of the factory girls as a class."

—from an article "Factory Girls" in the *Lowell Offering*, December 1840

VOCABULARY

asserted: claimed
galling: aggravating
irksome: annoying
toil: work
unremitting: without end or relief
imposed: placed
worthy: deserving
virtuous: wholesome; of good moral character

1 **DETERMINING PURPOSE** Why does it seem this article was written? To what assertions is this article responding?

2 **DETERMINING MEANING** In this context, what might the author mean by "restraints"?

3 **ANALYZING** Why does the writer feel that others don't need to complain about the "restraints" placed on women factory workers?

4 **IDENTIFYING PERSPECTIVES** What does she say are the downsides of factory work?

5 **ANALYZING** What aspect of the job attracts her and so many other women factory workers?

6 **DETERMINING CENTRAL IDEAS** What type of women does the writer say is attracted to this work?

ESSENTIAL QUESTION

How does technology change the way people live?

As you gather evidence to answer the Essential Question, think about

- how technology helped cotton become "king."
- why industry developed slowly in the South.
- the extent of the South's transportation networks.

My Notes

Southern Cotton Kingdom

DIRECTIONS: Search for evidence in Chapter 12, Lesson 3 to help you answer the following questions.

1 **CONTRASTING** Complete the table.

The Changing Agriculture of the South	
Chief Crop(s) During Colonial Times	Chief Crop(s) in 1850

2 **IDENTIFYING CAUSES AND EFFECTS** Complete the cause-effect flowchart.

A New Technology Changes Life in the South

separating cotton _____ from cotton _____ is difficult

Eli Whitney invents _________

this new technology enables workers to process cotton ___ times faster

______ production spreads

demand for _______ increases

institution of _______ spreads

________ slave trade expands

3A INFERRING Why does your textbook refer to cotton as "king"?

3B EXPLAINING Industry grew slowly in the South. Why? Complete the table.

The Slow Development of Southern Industry
1
2

4 DESCRIBING Was there no, little, or extensive industry in the South?

5 EXPLAINING What did Southern cities rely on to transport their goods. Why?

ESSENTIAL QUESTION

How does technology change the way people live?

Letter from Thomas Jefferson to Eli Whitney, November 16, 1793

DIRECTIONS: Read the letter. below. Then respond to the questions that follow.

EXPLORE THE CONTEXT: The cotton gin proved to be a technology that changed the way people lived. It was the cotton gin that expanded cotton production across the South. This led to an ever-growing demand for enslaved labor. The debate over slavery would soon lead to war. Thus, this seemingly simple device changed the way millions of people lived.

In 1793, Eli Whitney wrote a letter to the government about his cotton gin. He described it and also drew a picture of it. He was asking for a patent on his machine. A patent is a government document guaranteeing ownership of an invention. Whitney wanted this because other inventors were also trying to make good cotton gins.

Thomas Jefferson was Secretary of State at the time. In those early days of American government, responding to patent applications was part of the Secretary of State's job. This letter is Jefferson's reply to Eli Whitney's application for a patent.

VOCABULARY

favor: something very welcomed
inclosing: including
inst.: of this month
requisite: requirement
uncomplied: not done
patent: government document guaranteeing ownership of an invention
embarrassments: problems
induce: make
obedt. servt: obedient servant; a friendly way to end a letter during this time
ginning: separating the cotton fiber from the seeds

PRIMARY SOURCE: LETTER

"Germantown, Nov. 16. 1793

Sir, —Your favor of Oct. 15. inclosing a drawing of your cotton gin, was received on the 6th inst. The only requisite of the law now uncomplied with is the forwarding a model, which being received your patent may be made out & delivered to your order immediately.

As the state of Virginia, of which I am, carries on household manufactures of cotton to a great extent, as I also do myself, and one of our great embarrassments is the clearing the cotton of the seed, I feel a considerable interest in the success of your invention, for family use. Permit me therefore to ask information from you on these

. . . continued

points. Has the machine been thoroughly tried in the ginning of cotton, or is it as yet but a machine of theory? What quantity of cotton has it cleaned on an average of several days, & worked by hand, & by how many hands? What will be the cost of one of them made to be worked by hand? Favorable answers to these questions would induce me to engage one of them to be forwarded to Richmond for me. I am Sir Your most obedt. servt

Thomas Jefferson

P.S. Is this the machine advertised the last year by Pearce at the Patterson manufactory?”

—Thomas Jefferson, letter to Eli Whitney, November 16, 1793

1. **DETERMINING CENTRAL IDEAS** A What is the main idea of the letter?

2. **INFERRING** In the postscript (P.S.), Jefferson asks about the gin advertised by Pearce. What can you infer from this?

3. **DETERMINING POINT OF VIEW** Does Jefferson think Whitney's cotton gin is a useful new invention? How can you tell?

ESSENTIAL QUESTION

How does technology change the way people live?

Eli Whitney's Cotton Gin

DIRECTIONS: Read the passage below. Then respond to the questions that follow.

EXPLORE THE CONTEXT: Eli Whitney invented the cotton gin in 1793. It was the first mechanical cotton gin. Before this, enslaved workers would process cotton by hand in the United States. This invention changed the cotton industry. It brought more money into the United States and stimulated the economy. However, it also increased the demand for enslaved people and expanded the market for enslaved people.

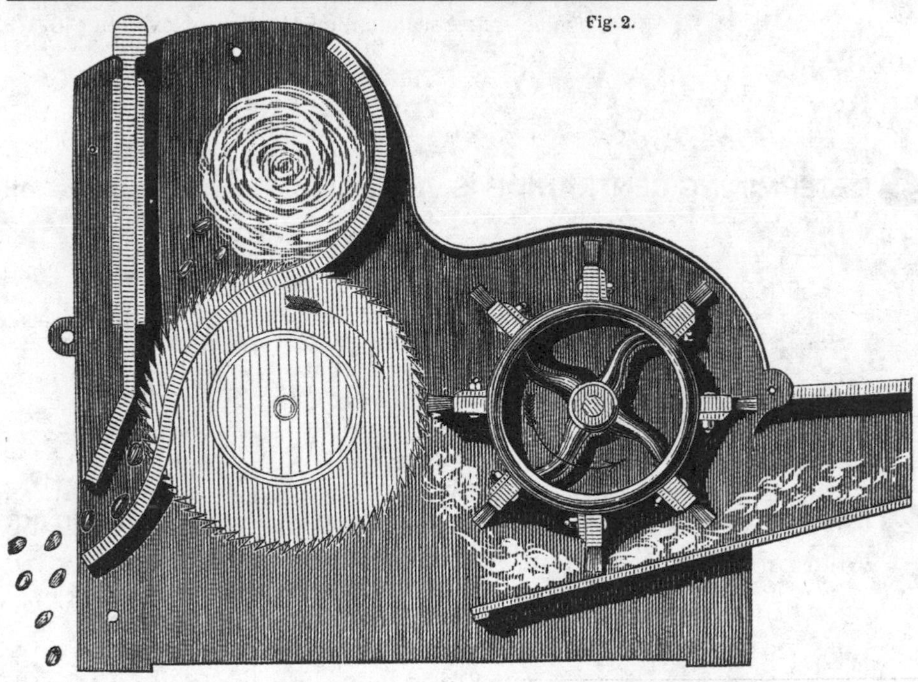

Cross-section of Eli Whitney's cotton gin, 1795

1 ECONOMICS **EXPLAINING** What impact did the cotton gin have on the nation's economy?

2 **IDENTIFYING CAUSE AND EFFECT** What circumstances allowed the cotton gin to have such a huge impact?

3 **INFERRING** How did the cotton gin specifically change the way people lived?

4 **DRAWING CONCLUSIONS** What other technological inventions have significantly impacted the economy?

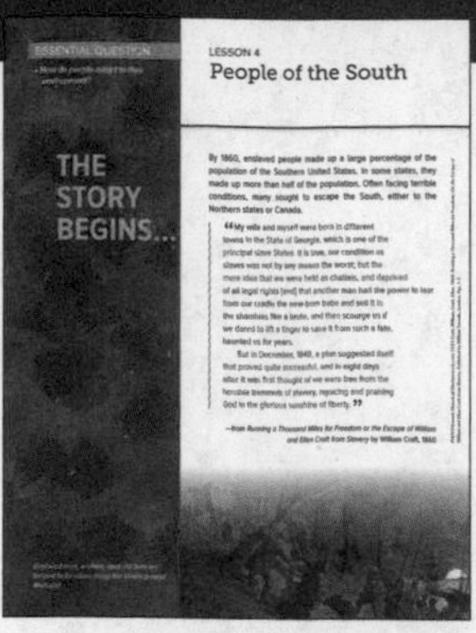

People of the South

DIRECTIONS: Search for evidence in Chapter 12, Lesson 4 to help you answer the following questions.

ESSENTIAL QUESTION

How does technology change the way people live?

As you gather evidence to answer the Essential Question, think about

- how white society in the South was organized.
- what the lives of enslaved people were like.
- how much urbanization affected the South.

My Notes

1 DESCRIBING Complete the table.

White Society in the South	
Group	**Description**
yeomen	
tenant farmers	
rural poor	
plantation owners	

2 INFERRING Did the majority or the minority of white people in the South hold enslaved people?

3 IDENTIFYING CAUSES Why did large, close-knit extended families become an important part of African American culture?

4 **IDENTIFYING CAUSES** What were the purposes of the black codes?

5 **IDENTIFYING EFFECTS** What were the effects of Nat Turner's rebellion?

6 What was the "Underground Railroad"?

7 **DESCRIBING** By the mid-1800s, was the South mostly agricultural or mostly industrial?

8 GEOGRAPHY The ten largest cities in the South were either seaports or river ports. Why do you think this was the case?

ESSENTIAL QUESTION

How does technology change the way people live?

Milling by Hand

DIRECTIONS: Read the passage below. Then respond to the questions that follow.

EXPLORE THE CONTEXT: This excerpt is taken from a collection of narratives that were compiled from formerly enslaved people about their everyday lives. In this excerpt, Gus Smith recalls how his grandfather decided to develop the means to grind his own grain.

PRIMARY SOURCE: NARRATIVE

“My granddad, Godfry, owned a place called [the] old Potter's place, near Vichey Springs, Vichey, Missouri, not far from where we lived. He bought it from a man who used to make pottery. Grandfather made his own mill to grind grain for bread. In those days there was no steam operated mill and few water mills. Sometimes we had to go as much as twenty miles to grind corn. So grandfather made his own burr to grind corn and wheat. It was as big as any burr in [the] large mills, but it was turned by hand power. It was made of limestone rock, a great big stone about two and a half foot across. [The] top burr would probably weigh about three or four hundred pounds. [The] bottom case would weigh a thousand pounds or more. There was a hole in the top stone, where [the] grain flowed freely to [the] bottom and ground out on the big thick stone below.”

—from the narrative of Gus Smith, an enslaved person, recalling his grandfather's life

VOCABULARY

mill: a workshop where grain is ground into flour

grind: to reduce something to small pieces

burr: a type of stone used for milling

limestone: kind of rock used in buildings and cement

1 **EXPLAINING** What does Godfry do at his mill?

___

___

___

2 **IDENTIFYING POINT OF VIEW** Who is the narrator of this passage?

3 **INFERRING** What technology would have saved Godfry some time and energy?

4 **DRAWING CONCLUSIONS** Why doesn't Godfry have technology that would make his job easier?

5 ECONOMICS **DRAWING CONCLUSIONS** How would new technology help Godfry's finances?

ESSENTIAL QUESTION

How does technology change the way people live?

A Year of Cotton Picking

DIRECTIONS: Read the passage below. Then respond to the questions that follow.

INTRODUCTION: When cotton was king in the Southern states, it ruled the economy and the lives of landowners and enslaved people. This excerpt is from an archaeological investigation of Cannon's Point, a cotton plantation that was located on an island off the coast of Georgia.

PRIMARY SOURCE: BOOK

"Cotton dominated the slaves' lives on a year-round basis. Cotton season actually began in late winter when the slaves listed, manured and bedded the cotton fields. (*Listing* was hoeing down the old cotton beds or ridges.) A full hand listed ½ acre per day. Then using plows and hoes, the slaves created new beds set 5 feet apart. This was easier work than listing, so a full hand bedded ¾ of an acre. Cotton planting began in March: Two hands walked down a bed, hoeing open holes 18 inches apart; another slave followed dropping about 50 seeds into each hole....Then in late August or early September, when the cotton began to open in "good blow," the slaves began the long process of picking. A typical hand picked about 100 pounds a day, although women usually picked more than men. After ginning, groups of slaves—usually women and invalid men—sorted the cotton lint according to quality..."

—from *Cannon's Point Plantation, 1794–1860: Living Conditions and Status Patterns in the Old South.* by John Solomon Otto

VOCABULARY

hand: farm worker

list: to hoe down the cotton ridges

bed: a patch of ground where plants are grown

invalid: sick, unwell

1 EXPLAINING: What was picking cotton like for enslaved workers?

2 DETERMINING MEANING Recalling Lesson 3, "Cotton is King" in your textbook, how would you define "ginning"?

3 INFERRING Why would women be able to pick more pounds of cotton than men?

4A CITING TEXT EVIDENCE Was cotton an easy or a difficult crop to grow and harvest?

4B How did the cotton gin affect slaves' lives?

ESSENTIAL QUESTION

How does technology change the way people live?

1 Think About It

Review the supporting questions you developed at the beginning of the chapter. Review the evidence you gathered in Chapter 12. Were you able to answer each Supporting Question? If there was not enough evidence to answer your Supporting Questions, what additional evidence do you think you need to consider?

2 Organize Your Evidence

Complete the chart below with information you learned about new technologies of the early to mid-1800s and how they changed the way people of that time lived.

How Technology Changed Lives in the Early to Mid-1800s

NEW TECHNOLOGY	POSITIVE CHANGES	NEGATIVE CHANGES

3 Talk About It

Work in small groups. Talk with your group about the evidence you included in your chart. Did you include the same evidence, or were your classmates' responses different from your responses? Overall, which technologies did your group feel had the best overall effect on people's lives?

4 Write About It

Of all of the new technologies of the early to mid-1800s, which two do you feel had the most positive effect on people's lives? Which two were more negative than positive? Describe these technologies and explain your reasons for classifying each as either positive or negative.

5 Connect to the Essential Question

Choose one of the two technologies you wrote about in question 4. Pretend you are an advertising person who has been hired to make an impressive ad campaign for that technology. Create one of each of the following:

- a print ad on poster board
- a flyer, handmade or laid out on the computer
- a commercial, either in video or performed live for the class

Do your best to "sell" the technology. Imagine that your job depends on convincing people that your technology will change their lives dramatically for the better.

CITIZENSHIP

TAKING ACTION

The Internet is considered by many to be the most life-changing technology of our time. It has become the place where people communicate with one another, read the news of the day, research topics, enjoy media, and find instant answers to questions.

As a student raised in the world of the Internet, you have never known anything different, but many people who experienced the Internet for the first time as adults may have viewed it with surprise or apprehension, not unlike people in the mid-1800s viewing a railroad journey for the first time. Write a list of questions you would like to ask an older person about how the Internet changed life for his or her generation. Assume the role of a journalist and write questions that start with one of the "Five W's and an H": Who? What? When? Where? Why? How?

Interview an older adult about life before the Internet. Take notes or, with their permission, record them speaking about their experience. Find out what it was like for them using the Internet for the first time, but most of all, find out how it changed life for them and others they know, for the better or the worse.

Using your notes, your audio recording, and your memory, write a paragraph or two about what you learned about how the Internet changed people's lives. Next, think about a topic important to you and write a paragraph about how the Internet might help you to make a difference in people's lives. Some suggestions might include animal welfare, the environment, or helping people your age in other cities or parts of the world

____

____

____

____

Use the Internet to research the topic you chose. Take note of the resources you use. How might you use the Internet to change lives for the better? For example, you could raise awareness about an organization that rescues animals or create a fundraiser to help people in need.

The Spirit of Reform

ESSENTIAL QUESTION

How do new ideas change the way people live?

Think about how this question might relate to the social reform movements of the early to mid-1800s.

TALK ABOUT IT

Discuss with a partner what information you would need to know to answer this question. For example, one question might be, "What were the social reform movements of the early to mid-1800s?"

DIRECTIONS: Now, write down three additional questions that you need to answer to be able to explain how new ideas change the way people live.

MY RESEARCH QUESTIONS

Supporting Question 1:

____

____

Supporting Question 2:

____

____

Supporting Question 3:

____

____

ESSENTIAL QUESTION

How do new ideas change the way people live?

As you gather evidence to answer the Essential Question, think about

- how the Second Great Awakening moved people to reform society.
- the temperance movement.
- how public education was a new idea.
- how people with disabilities were treated.
- how prisoners were treated.

My Notes

Social Reform

DIRECTIONS: Search for evidence in Chapter 13, Lesson 1 to help you answer the following questions.

1 **EXPLAINING** Why were revival meetings so popular on the frontier?

2 **INFERRING** Why might some people have opposed the idea of compulsory education for both boys and girls? For African Americans? For the poor?

3 **DRAWING CONCLUSIONS** How might colleges and universities opening their doors to women and African Americans offer the potential for major changes in society?

____

____

____

____

____

____

____

4 **DETERMINING CONTEXT** Using your textbook, fill in the graphic organizer below and examine the connections between social reform movements and Transcendentalism in the arts by filling in a word or phrase describing each individual's contribution to the area described in the column header. Some will have entries in more than one column. The first one has been provided as an example.

Connections Between Transcendentalism in Art and the Social Reform Movement				
REFORMER OR THINKER	SELF-AWARENESS/ IMPROVEMENT	CIVIL DISOBEDIENCE	CARING ABOUT/ HELPING OTHERS	CONNECTION TO NATURE
Mann			School reform	
Gallaudet				
Howe				
Dix				
Fuller				
Emerson				
Thoreau				
Whitman				
Longfellow				
Dickinson				
Hudson River School				

ESSENTIAL QUESTION

How do new ideas change the way people live?

Seventh Annual Report of the Secretary of the Massachusetts Board of Education and a Response

DIRECTIONS: Read the following excerpts from a report by education reformer Horace Mann and a response by schoolmaster Joseph Hale. Then answer the accompanying questions.

EXPLORE THE CONTEXT: Horace Mann was an education reformer who worked to further public education for all. He served as the secretary of the Massachusetts Board of Education from the time of its founding, as a Massachusetts state legislator, and later, as a member of the U.S. House of Representatives. In his 1844 annual report for the Massachusetts Board of Education, he made arguments for the abolition of corporal (physical) punishment in schools. The Association of Masters of the Boston Public Schools responded to points Mann made in the report, and a heated written exchange ensued. Below is an excerpt from Mann's annual report that sparked a formal response by the Boston Masters. On the next page, there is a response from Joseph Hale, a schoolmaster in Boston, Massachusetts, who was one of the Boston Masters.

VOCABULARY

authority: control
doctrine: policy
prevails: succeeds
nay: no
sentiment: warm feeling
estimation: respect
eminence: high rank
refining: purifying

PRIMARY SOURCE: ANNUAL REPORT

"... These are the motives, by which the children of Boston,--and if this doctrine prevails, the children of the State also,--are to be trained.... Throughout this whole section, conscience is no where referred to, as one of the motive-powers in the conduct of children. The idea seems not to have entered into the mind of the writer, that nay such agency could be employed in establishing the earliest, as well as the latest relations, between teacher and pupil. That powerful class of motives which consists of affection for parents, love for brothers and sisters, whether older or younger than themselves, justice and the social sentiment toward schoolmates, respect for elders, the pleasures of acquiring knowledge, the duty of doing as we would be done by, the connection between present conduct, and success, estimation, eminence, in future life, the presence of an unseen eye,--not a syllable of all these is set forth with any earnestness, or insisted upon, as the true source and spring of human actions....

. . . continued

"Authority, Force, Fear, Pain! These are the four cornerstones of 'School Discipline.' Not Duty, Affection, Love of Knowledge, and Love of Truth; but Power, Violence, Terror, Suffering!

"Was it not, and is it not, one of the grand objects in the institution and support of Common Schools, to bring those children who are cursed by a vicious parentage, who were not only "conceived and brought forth," but have been nurtured in "sin"; who have never known the voice of love and kindness; who have daily fallen beneath the iron blows of those parental hands that should have been outstretched for their protection;--was it not, and is it not, I say, one of the grand objects of our schools to bring this class of children under humanizing and refining influences; to show them that there is something besides wrath ... and suffering in God's world?"

--Horace Mann, from *Seventh Annual Report of the Secretary of the Massachusetts Board of Education,* 1844

1 DETERMINING MEANING What does Mann mean by "the unseen eye"?

2 ANALYZING POINTS OF VIEW In his first paragraph, Mann lists nine true motivations for good behavior instead of "Authority, Force, Fear, Pain." What are these?

ESSENTIAL QUESTION

How do new ideas change the way people live?

PRIMARY SOURCE: PUBLISHED RESPONSE TO A REPORT

“"...Let me avow...that physical coercion is, in certain cases, necessary, natural, and proper;...and to...[discredit] the sickly and ridiculous notion, that all use of pain and compulsion is disgraceful and degrading.... Children should not hear the authority of their parents and teachers called in question. They should not be allowed to speak disrespectfully of their own or of each other's parents and teachers, and he who through the press, or in any other way, encourages this, whatever he may intend, is a disorganizer; is weakening and dissolving the primal bond of civil society, and sapping the foundations of social order.”

—Joseph Hale, Boston schoolteacher and member of the Boston Masters

3 **DETERMINING CONTEXT** What is Mann's argument about the role of schools in the last paragraph of the excerpt?

4 **INFERRING** Hale states that children should not be allowed to disagree with or speak disrespectfully of their parents and teachers. What does he mean when he says, "...he who through the press, or in any other way, encourages this, whatever he may intend, is a disorganizer; is weakening and dissolving the primal bond of civil society, and sapping the foundations of social order."

5 **DRAWING CONCLUSIONS** Which man—Mann or Hale—has the more well-reasoned argument, in your opinion? Be sure to address the logic of the points made by each man.

ESSENTIAL QUESTION

How do new ideas change the way people live?

A Contrast of Two Trees: Intemperance and Temperance

DIRECTIONS: Examine the lithographs of the "Intemperance Tree" and "Temperance Tree" and answer the questions that follow.

EXPLORE THE CONTEXT: The two lithographs below were created in 1849 by Nathaniel Currier of the famous printmaking firm Currier and Ives. They were part of a larger campaign to discourage drinking alcohol. With these two lithographs, Currier uses juxtaposition—the placing of opposites next to each other—to powerful effect.

One tree is titled "The Tree of Temperance." Temperance means not drinking alcohol. The other tree is titled "The Tree of Intemperance." Intemperance means drinking alcohol, especially too much.

1A **COMPARING AND CONTRASTING** With just a quick glance, you can tell which is the healthy tree and which is the sickly tree. What visual clues help you?

1B What is happening in the scene surrounding the Temperance Tree?

PRIMARY SOURCE: TWO LITHOGRAPHS

VOCABULARY

lithograph: type of print popular in the mid- to late 1800s

temperance: not drinking alcohol

intemperance: drinking alcohol, especially too much

1C What is happening in the scene surrounding the Intemperance Tree?

2 **SUMMARIZING** What is the artist's message?

3 **ANALYZING TEXT PRESENTATION** Is Currier's message clear and persuasive? Why or why not?

4 **ANALYZING ISSUES** How do these two images help you answer the Essential Question: How do new ideas change the way people live?

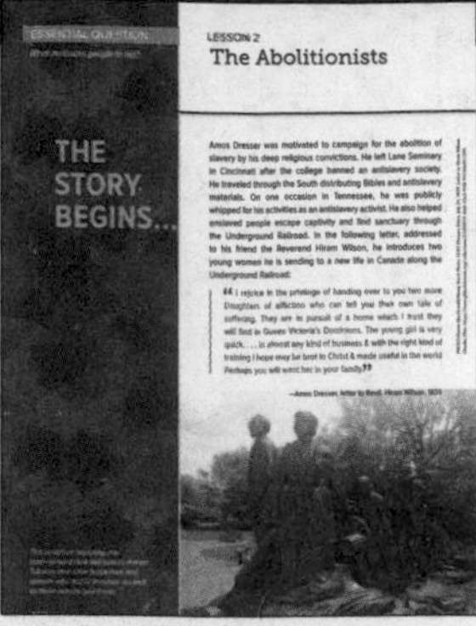

ESSENTIAL QUESTION

How do new ideas change the way people live?

As you gather evidence to answer the Essential Question, think about

- the courage abolitionists showed in speaking out against slavery.
- how abolishing slavery gradually became a goal for many Americans.
- how people thought of different ways to end slavery.
- why some people continued to resist ending slavery.
- the courage formerly enslaved people demonstrated in escaping from slavery and making a new life.

My Notes

The Abolitionists

DIRECTIONS: Search for evidence in Chapter 13, Lesson 2 to help you answer the following questions.

1 **EXPLAINING** What was gradualism?

2 **INFERRING** What were some problems with gradualism? Why do you think it did not end slavery?

3A **GEOGRAPHY** What was colonization and why did some abolitionists favor it as a solution?

3B What were some problems with the colonization plan?

4 **ANALYZING POINTS OF VIEW** What were the problems with the Southern plantation owners' claims that enslaved African Americans had a better life than African Americans working in the North?

5 **GATHERING EVIDENCE** In the graphic organizer below, fill in at least one important detail about each of the abolitionists listed.

Abolitionists and Their Accomplishments	
NAME OF ABOLITIONIST	IMPORTANT DETAIL(S)
Benjamin Lundy	
William Lloyd Garrison	
Sarah and Angelina Grimké	
Harriet Beecher Stowe	
Samuel Cornish & John Russwurm	
David Walker	
Frederick Douglass	
Sojourner Truth	
Elijah Lovejoy	

ESSENTIAL QUESTION

How do new ideas change the way people live?

A Methodist Minister's Observations of Slavery in Georgia and South Carolina

DIRECTIONS: Read the following excerpt and answer the questions that follow.

EXPLORE THE CONTEXT: Horace Moulton was a Methodist minister from Massachusetts who spent five years—between 1817 and 1824—working in the brickmaking industry in Savannah, Georgia, during which time he closely observed the daily routines of enslaved laborers on plantations. The following is an excerpt from one of his letters.

VOCABULARY

barbarous: brutal inhuman
viper: poisonous snake
infested: filled
moulders: those who shape

1 HISTORY How long does Moulton state the enslaved laborers were required to work each day?

____

____

____

____

2 DESCRIBING What did they eat, and how often did they eat?

____

____

____

____

PRIMARY SOURCE: LETTER

“The rule was to work them from sun to sun. But when I was burning brick they were obliged to take turns, and *sit up all night* about every other night, and work all day... On one plantation, where I spent a few weeks, the slaves were called up to work long before daylight, when business pressed, and worked until late at night; and sometimes some of them *all night*. . .

“Women are seen bringing their infants into the field to their work, and leading others who are not old enough to stay at the cabins with safety. When they get there, they must set them down in the dirt, and go to work. Sometimes they are left to cry until they fall asleep.

“Others are left at home, shut up in their huts. Now, is it not barbarous, that the mother, with her child or children around her, half starved, must be whipped at night if she does not perform her task? But so it is. Some who have very young ones, fix a little sack, and place the infants on their backs, and work. One reason, I presume is, that they will not cry so much when they can hear their mother's voice. Another is, the mothers fear that the poisonous vipers and snakes will bite them. Truly, I never knew any place where the land is so infested with all kinds of the most venomous snakes, as in the low lands round about Savannah...The females, in order to secure their infants from these poisonous snakes, do, as I have said, often work with their infants on their backs. Females are sometimes called to take the hardest part of

the work. On some brick yards where I have been, the women have been selected as the moulders of brick, instead of the men...

"The custom was to blow the horn early in the morning, as a signal for the hands to rise and go to work, when commenced; they continued work until about eleven o'clock, A.M., when, at the signal, all hands left off, and went into their huts, made their fires, made their corn-meal into homony or cake, ate it, and went to work again at the signal of the horn, and worked until night, or until their tasks were done. Some cooked their breakfast in the field while at work. Each slave must grind his own corn in a hand-mill after he has done his work at night. There is generally one hand-mill on every plantation for the use of slaves...

"As soon as it was thought they had had sufficient time to swallow their food they were called to their work again. *This was the only meal they ate through the day. . .*"

—Horace Moulton, a Methodist minister, from a letter dated February 18, 1839

3 DETERMINING CONTEXT Why did the mothers take their infants and small children to the fields with them?

4 DETERMINING POINT OF VIEW What do you think is Moulton's attitude about what he observed on the plantations? What clues are offered in the excerpt?

ESSENTIAL QUESTION

How do new ideas change the way people live?

Narrative of the Life of Frederick Douglass, an American Slave, Written by Himself

DIRECTIONS: Read the following excerpt from Frederick Douglass's first autobiography and answer the questions that follow.

EXPLORE THE CONTEXT: After escaping from slavery, Frederick Douglass became a powerful voice for the abolition of slavery and equality for African Americans. His writings and speeches are quoted widely today and valued for Douglass's eloquence in delivering his message. In this excerpt from his 1845 autobiography, Douglass describes being deeply moved by the songs sung by his fellow enslaved African Americans as they walked to the main house on the plantation where they worked, to receive their monthly allowance.

VOCABULARY

reverberate: echo
rapturous: delighted
rude: rough
without: outside of
feeble: weak
comprehension: understanding
anguish: suffering
deliverance: freedom
ineffable: indescribable
obdurate: stubborn
contentment: peaceful happiness

PRIMARY SOURCE: AUTOBIOGRAPHY

"The slaves selected to go to the Great House Farm, for the monthly allowance for themselves and their fellow-slaves, were peculiarly enthusiastic. While on their way, they would make the dense old woods, for miles around, reverberate with their wild songs, revealing at once the highest joy and the deepest sadness. They would compose and sing as they went along, consulting neither time nor tune. The thought that came up, came out—if not in the word, in the sound;—and as frequently in the one as in the other. They would sometimes sing the most pathetic sentiment in the most rapturous tone, and the most rapturous sentiment in the most pathetic tone. Into all of their songs they would manage to weave something of the Great House Farm. Especially would they do this, when leaving home. They would then sing most exultingly the following words:—

"*I am going away to the Great House Farm! O, yea! O, yea! O!*"

This they would sing, as a chorus, to words which to many would seem unmeaning jargon, but which, nevertheless, were full of meaning to themselves. I have sometimes thought that the mere hearing of those songs would do more to impress some minds with the horrible character of slavery, than the reading of whole volumes of philosophy on the subject could do.

I did not, when a slave, understand the deep meaning of those rude and apparently incoherent songs. I was myself within the circle; so that I neither saw nor heard as those without might see and hear. They told a tale of woe which was then altogether beyond my feeble comprehension; they were tones loud, long, and deep; they breathed the prayer and complaint of souls boiling over with the bitterest anguish. Every tone was a testimony against slavery, and a prayer to God for deliverance from chains. The hearing of those wild notes always depressed my spirit, and filled me with ineffable sadness. I have frequently found myself in tears while hearing them. The mere recurrence to those songs, even now, afflicts me; and while I am writing these lines, an expression of feeling has already found its way down my cheek. To those songs I trace my first glimmering conception of the dehumanizing character of slavery. I can never get rid of that conception. Those songs still follow me, to deepen my hatred of slavery, and quicken my sympathies for my brethren in bonds. If any one wishes to be impressed with the soul-killing effects of slavery, let him go to Colonel Lloyd's plantation, and, on allowance-day, place himself in the deep pine woods, and there let him, in silence, analyze the sounds that shall pass through the chambers of his soul,—and if he is not thus impressed, it will only be because "there is no flesh in his obdurate heart.

. . . continued

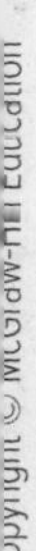

1 **SUMMARIZING** In your own words, explain what Douglass means by this passage: "They would compose and sing as they went along, consulting neither time nor tune. The thought that came up, came out—if not in the word, in the sound;—and as frequently in the one as in the other. They would sometimes sing the most pathetic sentiment in the most rapturous tone, and the most rapturous sentiment in the most pathetic tone."

2 **ANALYZING POINT OF VIEW** What does Douglass mean when he says, "I have sometimes thought that the mere hearing of those songs would do more to impress some minds with the horrible character of slavery, than the reading of whole volumes of philosophy on the subject could do."

ESSENTIAL QUESTION

How do new ideas change the way people live?

PRIMARY SOURCE: (CONTINUED)

I have often been utterly astonished, since I came to the north, to find persons who could speak of the singing, among slaves, as evidence of their contentment and happiness. It is impossible to conceive of a greater mistake. Slaves sing most when they are most unhappy. The songs of the slave represent the sorrows of his heart; and he is relieved by them, only as an aching heart is relieved by its tears. At least, such is my experience. I have often sung to drown my sorrow, but seldom to express my happiness. Crying for joy, and singing for joy, were alike uncommon to me while in the jaws of slavery. The singing of a man cast away upon a desolate island might be as appropriately considered as evidence of contentment and happiness, as the singing of a slave; the songs of the one and of the other are prompted by the same emotion.”

—Frederick Douglass, from *Narrative of the Life of Frederick Douglass, an American Slave, Written by Himself*, 1845

3 **INFERRING** Why do you think Douglass was unable to understand the songs when he heard them from “within the circle” of slavery?

4 **ANALYZING SOURCES** What aspect of the songs was he able to understand that continued to affect him even after attaining his freedom?

5 **IDENTIFYING MAIN IDEAS** What does Douglass say was the purpose of the songs? How do outsiders greatly misinterpret the songs to mean the opposite of what they really indicate?

The Women's Movement

DIRECTIONS: Search for evidence in Chapter 13, Lesson 3 to help you answer the following questions.

1. **HISTORY** How many people attended the Seneca Falls Convention? How many of that number were women?

2. **CIVICS** What rights did the Declaration of Sentiments and Resolutions call for?

3. **DETERMINING CONTEXT** Who stood by Elizabeth Cady Stanton in her efforts to include women's suffrage in the Declaration?

ESSENTIAL QUESTION

How do new ideas change the way people live?

As you gather evidence to answer the Essential Question, think about

- how abolitionism influenced women to focus on their own unequal standing in society.
- the rights that women demanded at the Seneca Falls Convention.
- how men responded to their demands.
- why some people respond to change with fear.

My Notes

4 What rights were women demanding? Complete the table.

Women's Rights	Did women have by the late 1800s?	Do women have today?
RIGHT		
Suffrage		
Divorce and guardianship		

ESSENTIAL QUESTION

How do new ideas change the way people live?

Editorial in Opposition to the Seneca Falls Convention

DIRECTIONS: Read the following editorial opposing the Seneca Falls Convention and answer the questions that follow.

EXPLORE THE CONTEXT: The *Oneida Whig,* an upstate New York newspaper, published an editorial that opposed the Seneca Falls Convention that was held July 19–20, 1848. The excerpt below states some of the arguments that were used to support its opposition.

VOCABULARY

usurpations: takeovers
evinces: reveals
invariably: always
despotism: tyranny
candid: critical
inalienable: natural
elective franchise: right to vote
illustrious: esteemed
willful: stubborn
predestined: unavoidable

PRIMARY SOURCE: NEWSPAPER EDITORIAL

"A Woman's Rights Convention was held at Seneca Falls on the 19th and 20th inst., at which the opposers of female slavery adopted a declaration of sentiments, declaring that these truths are self-evident–that all men and women are created equal, &c., &c. and that when a long train of abuses and usurpations, pursuing invariably the same object, evinces a design to reduce then under absolute despotism, it is their right, it is their duty, to throw off such government . . . but the Woman's Rights Convention glory in the publicity of such an exchange. They have let the facts be submitted to a candid world: "He has never permitted to exercise her [in]alienable right to the elective franchise. He has compelled her to submit to laws in the formation of which she has had no voice." Was there ever such a dreadful revolt?–They set aside the statute, "wives submit yourselves unto your husbands." . . . This bolt is the most shocking and unnatural incident ever recorded in the history of womanity. If our ladies will insist on voting and legislating, where, gentlemen, will be our dinners and our elbows? where our domestic firesides and the holes in our stockings? Here is another shot: "Having deprived her of this first right of a citizen, the elective franchise, thereby leaving her without representation in the halls of legislation, he has oppressed her on all sides. "He has made her, if married, in the eye of the law, civilly dead. "He has taken from her all right in property, even to the

1 DETERMINING MEANING Why do you think is the author uses the term to "female slavery" in the first sentence of his editorial?

______

______

______

______

2 INFERRING What does the author mean when he says the women at the convention "glory in the publicity of such an exchange"?

______

______

______

______

. . . continued

wages she earns." ... the bolters are too wise, too witty and too wilful to endure such a state of bondage, and the lords of creation will hardly escape the "predestined scratched face."”

—from an editorial in the *Oneida Whig*, August 1, 1848

3 **DETERMINING CONTEXT** What is the reference for the following argument: "They set aside the statute, 'wives submit yourselves unto your husbands'"?

4 **ANALYZING POINT OF VIEW** What opinion does the author express in the following quote? "This bolt is the most shocking and unnatural incident ever recorded in the history of womanity. If our ladies will insist on voting and legislating, where, gentlemen, will be our dinners and our elbows? where our domestic firesides and the holes in our stockings?"

5 **IDENTIFYING PERSPECTIVES** Who do you suppose the "lords of creation" are, and what is significant about his reference to their inability to escape a "scratched face"?

6 **ASSESSING CREDIBILITY** Do you feel this author is a credible source? Why or why not?

ESSENTIAL QUESTION

How do new ideas change the way people live?

Frederick Douglass's Support of the Seneca Falls Convention

DIRECTIONS: Read the following editorial about the Seneca Falls Convention and answer the questions that follow.

EXPLORE THE CONTEXT: Abolitionist Frederick Douglass published a newspaper called *The North Star* in Rochester, New York. On July 28, 1848, Douglass published this editorial in support of the Seneca Falls Convention.

VOCABULARY

conducted: run
novel: unusual
disposed: inclined
dispositions: attitudes
deliberative: discussing topics for and against
animated: lively
decorum: politeness, courtesy
deterred: turned away
approbation: approval
elective franchise: right to vote for elected officials

PRIMARY SOURCE: NEWSPAPER EDITORIAL

"One of the most interesting events of the past week, was the holding of what is technically styled a Women's Rights Convention, at Seneca Falls. The speaking, addresses, and resolutions of this extraordinary meeting were almost wholly conducted by women ; and although they evidently felt themselves in a novel position, it is but simple justice to say, that their whole proceedings were characterized by marked ability and dignity. No one present, we think, however much he might be disposed to differ from the view advanced by the leading speakers on that occasion, will fail to give them credit for brilliant talents and excellent dispositions. In this meeting, as in other deliberative assemblies, there were frequently differences of opinion and animated discussion ; but in no case was there the slightest absence of good feeling and decorum. Several interesting documents, setting forth the rights as well as the grievances of women were read. Among these was a declaration of sentiments, to be regarded as the basis of a grand movement for attaining all the civil, social, political, and religious rights of woman. . . .

. . . Standing as we do upon the watchtower of human freedom, we cannot be deterred from an expression of our approbation of any movement, however humble, to improve and elevate the character and condition of any members of the human family. While it is impossible for us to go into this subject at length, and dispose of the various

1 CITING TEXT EVIDENCE
Comparing this editorial with the previous editorial, how is Douglass's language in describing the women different from the language used by the writer of the editorial in the *Oneida Whig?*

. . . continued

objections which are often urged against such a doctrine as that of female equality, we are free to say, that in respect to political rights, we hold woman to be justly entitled to all we hold for man. . . . All that distinguishes man as an intelligent and accountable being is equally true of woman; and if that government is only just which governs by the free consent of the governed, there can be no reason in the world for denying to women the exercise of the elective franchise, or a hand in making and administering the laws of the land. Our doctrine is, that "Right is of no sex." We therefore bid the women engaged in this movement our humble God-speed. ”

—Frederick Douglass, from his editorial in *The North Star,* July 28, 1848

2 DETERMINING POINT OF VIEW What is Douglass's tone towards the women and their movement? How can you tell?

3 **DRAWING CONCLUSIONS** What does Douglass mean by, "Standing as we do upon the watchtower of human freedom, we cannot be deterred from an expression of our approbation of any movement, however humble, to improve and elevate the character and condition of any members of the human family"?

4 **ANALYZING ISSUES** How is this source related to the Essential Question: How do new ideas change the way people live?

ESSENTIAL QUESTION

How do new ideas change the way people live?

1 Think About It

Review the supporting questions you developed at the beginning of the chapter. Review the evidence you gathered in Chapter 13. Were you able to answer each Supporting Question? If there was not enough evidence to answer your Supporting Questions, what additional evidence do you think you need to consider?

2 Organize Your Evidence

Complete the chart below to organize what you feel is the most significant information you learned about the social reform movements in Chapter 13.

Spirit of Reform			
MOVEMENT	IDEAS INFLUENCED BY	ACTIVISTS & INFLUENCERS	GOALS

❸ Talk About It

Talk with a classmate about what you thought were the most important aspects of social reform to come out of this period of history. Do you have differences of opinion? Can you support your own opinions with evidence from the chapter?

❹ Write About It

Write a paragraph about the importance of social reform movements in American history.

____

____

____

____

____

____

❺ Connect to the Essential Question

Create a "Before and After" poster board that connects to the Essential Question by showing how people lived before social reforms and how things changed after. Here are some suggested ways to create your board:

- draw pictures
- paint
- use stenciled or printed and cut-out words from the computer to create a "text collage"
- use photos printed out from the Internet (be sure to use only appropriate photos; see your teacher with any questions before you glue questionable images down)
- your own idea

For the "after" section, you may use images or words describing how people live today.

CITIZENSHIP

TAKING ACTION

One of America's basic beliefs is that of popular sovereignty: the idea that the power of government comes from the people. If citizens are unhappy with the country, they have the freedom to try to make a change. That is why the Bill of Rights protects the freedom of speech, the freedom of the press, the freedom of assembly, and the freedom to ask the government to change.

How might social movements today be similar to the abolition movement or the women's rights movement of the 1800s? How might they be different?

Get together in a small group and share ideas for ways new ideas could change our society today for the better. How might you and your classmates solve a problem in the world today, such as poverty, war, or climate change? Why might some people oppose your idea? Think back to those who opposed the abolition of slavery or women's rights. Considering your potential opposition can help you to better frame your idea.

Choose an idea from your group brainstorming session and write a pitch, selling your idea to potential supporters. It's okay for multiple people in the group to choose to pitch the same topic, but your way of writing your pitch must be your own. What help might you need to implement your idea and change society? Whom can you ask to support you? Some ideas of people to pitch your idea to:

- your parents
- your school principal
- your city or town mayor
- your state governor
- your state senator or representative
- your federal congressperson or senator
- the president of the United States

Do your best to make your pitch clearly written and free of mistakes, then send it to someone whose support you would like. Good luck!

Toward Civil War

ESSENTIAL QUESTION

Why does conflict develop?

Think about how this question might relate to the national discussion of slavery and the movement toward the Civil War.

TALK ABOUT IT

Discuss with a partner what information you would need to know to answer this question. For example, one question might be, "What were some steps taken by congressional leaders that moved the country toward war?"

DIRECTIONS: Now, write down three additional questions that you need to answer to be able to describe the characteristics of a leader.

MY RESEARCH QUESTIONS

Supporting Question 1:

____

____

Supporting Question 2:

____

____

Supporting Question 3:

____

____

ESSENTIAL QUESTION

Why does conflict develop?

As you gather evidence to answer the Essential Question, think about

- how pro- and anti-slavery politicians tried to find ways to compromise.
- how compromises inflamed tempers rather than calming them.
- how the nation became increasingly divided.

My Notes

The Search for Compromise

DIRECTIONS: Search for evidence in Chapter 14, Lesson 1 to help you answer the following questions.

1 **ANALYZING SOURCES** What is strange about the drawing captioned *Peace Convention*? What do you think is the artist's point of view portrayed in this drawing?

2 **ANALYZING POINTS OF VIEW** What was the motto of the Free-Soil Party? Why do you suppose they chose this name?

3 **IDENTIFYING PERSPECTIVES** What were Henry David Thoreau's words regarding the justness of civil disobedience?

4 **EXPLAINING** What was meant by the expression "Bleeding Kansas"?

5 UNDERSTANDING CHRONOLOGY In the table below, list the acts, events, and proposals that contributed to the growing divide between North and South. The years have been completed for you.

Acts, Events & Proposals Leading to the Civil War		
Year	**Act, Event, or Proposal**	**Description**
1820		
1845		
1845		
1845		
1848		
1850		
1854		

ESSENTIAL QUESTION

Why does conflict develop?

VOCABULARY

contempt: disgust
execration: loathing
esteem: judgment
effectual: effective
peril: endanger, risk
exaction: cost
effected: brought about
St. Domingo Emancipation: the slave revolt in Haiti that ended in independence

1 **SUMMARIZING** How do the authors feel about people who cooperate in upholding the act?

2 **ANALYZING** What is meant by, "Resolved, that it is our duty to peril life, liberty, and property, in behalf of the fugitive slave, to as great an extent as we would peril them in behalf of ourselves"?

Opposition to Fugitive Slave Act

DIRECTIONS: Read the following Resolution and Address and then answer the accompanying questions.

EXPLORE THE CONTEXT: On January 9, 1851, the Anti–Fugitive Slave Law meeting was held in Syracuse, New York, drawing abolitionists from throughout the state and region. At the meeting, Frederick Douglass delivered an address in which he laid out resolutions for opposing the Fugitive Slave Act. This list of resolutions—adopted unanimously at the meeting— was co-written by Gerrit Smith, a philanthropist, abolitionist, supporter of women's rights, and congressman from New York. Smith also delivered the same address at the state convention that same week. The speech has been excerpted below (some resolutions are not included).

PRIMARY SOURCE: RESOLUTION AND ADDRESS

"1st. Resolved, that we pour out upon the Fugitive Slave Law the fullest measure of our contempt and hate and execration; and pledge ourselves to resist it actively, as well as passively, and by all such means, as shall, in our esteem, promise the most effectual resistance.

2d. Resolved, that they who consent to be the agents of Southern oppressors for executing this law, whether as Commissioners or Marshals, or in any other capacity, are to be regarded as kidnappers and land-pirates.

3d. Resolved, that it is our duty to peril life, liberty, and property, in behalf of the fugitive slave, to as great an extent as we would peril them in behalf of ourselves.

4th. Resolved, that obviously and grossly Unconstitutional as is this Law, nevertheless this is not the chief reason why we condemn and defy it:--for equally, whether they are Constitutional or Unconstitutional, we do condemn and defy all laws, which insult Him, who is above all Constitutions, and which, aiming not to protect, but to destroy, rights, are, therefore to be regarded as no laws.

. . . continued

5th. Resolved, that horrible as is this law, we must bear in mind, that it is but a perfectly natural and not at all to be wondered at exaction of slavery; and that, hence our first and great work is to get rid, not of the law, but of slavery--as it would be our first and great work to pursue and kill the mad-dog, instead of pausing, until we had effected the cure of one of his bites.

...

8th. Resolved, that when the immortal writer of the Declaration of Independence said: "If we do not liberate the enslaved by that generous energy of our own minds, they must, they will, be liberated by the awful process" of St. Domingo Emancipation, he uttered words, which there is but too much reason to believe are rapidly approaching their fulfillment. ”

Frederick Douglass and Gerrit Smith, from "Anti-Fugitive Slave Law Meeting," Syracuse, New York, January 9, 1851

3 **DETERMINING POINT OF VIEW** In the "4th" section, the authors say the act is unconstitutional, but they condemn it for other reasons. What are those reasons?

4 **INFERRING** What is meant by the comparison to a mad dog in the section numbered "5th"?

5 **EXPLAINING ISSUES** What do you think is the "fulfillment" the writers hint at in the final paragraph?

ESSENTIAL QUESTION

Why does conflict develop?

Charles Sumner, "The Crime Against Kansas," May 19, 1856

DIRECTIONS: Read the excerpt below from a congressional speech and answer the questions that follow.

EXPLORE THE CONTEXT: After the passage of the Kansas-Nebraska Act, Charles Sumner, an anti-slavery congressman from Massachusetts, delivered a fiery speech during a congressional debate. This excerpt is a passage from his speech, "The Crime Against Kansas."

1 ANALYZING What does Sumner mean when he says, "It was a swindle of the North by the South. On the part of those who had already completely enjoyed their share of the Missouri Compromise, it was a swindle of those whose share was yet absolutely untouched"?

PRIMARY SOURCE: SPEECH

"Sir, the Nebraska Bill was in every respect a swindle. It was a swindle of the North by the South. On the part of those who had already completely enjoyed their share of the Missouri Compromise, it was a swindle of those whose share was yet absolutely untouched; and the plea of unconstitutionality set up—like the plea of usury after the borrowed money has been enjoyed—did not make it less a swindle. Urged as a bill of peace, it was a swindle of the whole country. Urged as opening the doors to slave-masters with their slaves, it was a swindle of Popular Sovereignty in its asserted doctrine. Urged as sanctioning Popular Sovereignty, it was a swindle of slave-masters in their asserted rights. It was a swindle of a broad territory, thus cheated of protection against slavery. It was a swindle of a great cause, early espoused by Washington, Franklin, and Jefferson, surrounded by the best fathers of the Republic. Sir, it was a swindle of God-given, inalienable rights. Turn it over, look at it on all sides, and it is everywhere a swindle. ... No other word will adequately express the mingled meanness and wickedness of the cheat. Its character is still further apparent in the general structure of the bill. Amidst overflowing professions of regard for the sovereignty of the people in the Territory, they are despoiled of every essential privilege of sovereignty. They are not allowed to choose governor, secretary, chief justice, associate justices, attorney, or marshal,—all of whom are sent

. . . *continued*

from Washington; nor are they allowed to regulate the salaries of any of these functionaries, or the daily allowance of the legislative body, or even the pay of the clerks and door-keepers; but they are left free to adopt slavery. And this is nicknamed Popular Sovereignty!

Suffice it to say that slavery is in itself an arrogant denial of human rights, and by no human reason can the power to establish such a wrong be placed among the attributes of any just sovereignty. ”

—Charles Sumner, from his speech to Congress, "The Crime Against Kansas," May 19, 1856

VOCABULARY

swindle: scam, deception
usury: lending money at a high interest rate
sanctioning: approving
espoused: embraced
professions: claims, statements
despoiled: deprived
functionaries: representatives
arrogant: self-important
attributes: positive aspects

2 **DETERMINING CONTEXT** What is meant by, "It was a swindle of a great cause, early espoused by Washington, Franklin, and Jefferson, surrounded by the best fathers of the Republic. Sir, it was a swindle of God-given, inalienable rights"?

3 CIVICS According to Sumner, in what way does the law deliberately mislead in claiming to champion popular sovereignty for residents of the Nebraska Territory?

4 **DETERMINING CENTRAL IDEAS** What does Sumner find contradictory between the notion of popular sovereignty and slavery?

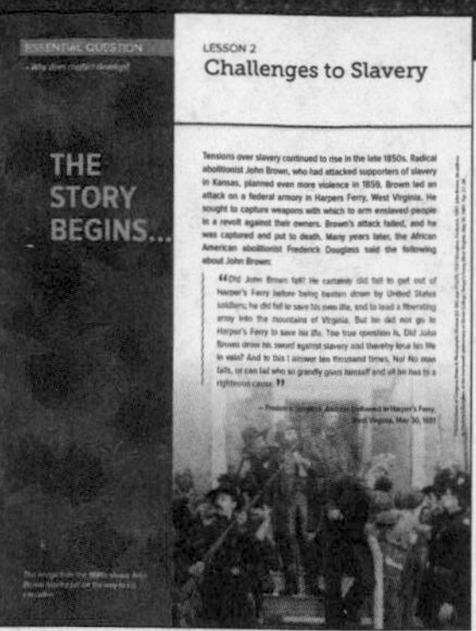

Challenges to Slavery

DIRECTIONS: Search for evidence in Chapter 14, Lesson 2 to help you answer the following questions.

1 CIVICS In the 1854 election, why did Democrats lose almost three-fourths of their elections in free states?

2 **SUMMARIZING** Which party was too badly damaged by the slavery issue to offer a candidate in the presidential election of 1856? Explain.

3 **ANALYZING** What is popular sovereignty and why did the Democratic Party support it?

ESSENTIAL QUESTION

Why does conflict develop?

As you gather evidence to answer the Essential Question, think about

- why political parties shifted during the elections of the 1850s.
- the issue at the center of the Dred Scott decision and the responses of citizens on both sides.
- how the Lincoln–Douglas debates affected the national discussion about slavery.
- the increasingly bitter division between North and South.

My Notes

4 HISTORY What was the basis of the U.S. Supreme Court decision in the Dred Scott case that protected slavery as an institution and made it unconstitutional to outlaw slavery?

5 How were the 1858 Lincoln–Douglas debates helpful to Abraham Lincoln?

ESSENTIAL QUESTION

Why does conflict develop?

"Northern Outrage over *Scott v. Sandford*," March 7, 1857

DIRECTIONS: Read the following excerpt from "Northern Outrage over *Scott v. Sandford*," an editorial published in the New York *Tribune*, March 7, 1857, and answer the questions that follow.

EXPLORE THE CONTEXT: After the Supreme Court ruled that Dred Scott had no ability to sue for his freedom since he was the property of his master and, further, that all laws banning slavery were unconstitutional, the North registered its outrage. A New York *Tribune* editorial cut to the heart of the matter. An excerpt appears below.

VOCABULARY

trumpeted: discussed
flagrantly: blatantly
cardinal: central
redress: remedy
thence: afterward
abominable: hated
dissents in toto: disagrees entirely
eminence: prestige
preponderance: greater in number
dictum: idea, philosophy
annihilates: destroys, nullifies
ascendancy: rise
henceforth: from now on

PRIMARY SOURCE: NEWSPAPER EDITORIAL

"The long trumpeted decision of the Supreme Court in the Dred Scott case was pronounced by Judge Taney yesterday, having been held over from last year in order not too flagrantly to alarm and exasperate the Free States on the eve of an important Presidential election. Its cardinal points are reported as follows:

1. A negro, because of his color, is denied the rights of a citizen of the United States--even the right to sue in our Courts for the redress of the most flagrant wrongs.

2. A slave being taken by his master into a Free State and thence returning under his master's sway, is not therefore entitled to his freedom.

3. *Congress has no rightful power to prohibit Slavery in the Territories:* hence the Missouri Restriction was unconstitutional.

Justice Nelson, we are happy to say, does not fully concur in this abominable judgment. Justice McLean of course dissents in toto; so, we presume, does Justice Curtis in the main, despite his eminence in Union saving. Justice Grier, we presume, went all lengths, with the five slaveholders who compose a majority of the Court, leaving but four-ninths to the immense preponderance of population in the Free States.

1 IDENTIFYING POINT OF VIEW How does the writer of the editorial feel about the Supreme Court's decision in the Dred Scott case? How do you know?

____

____

____

____

____

____

. . . *continued*

This decision, we need hardly say, is entitled to just so much moral weight as would be the judgment of a majority of those congregated in any Washington bar-room. It is a dictum prescribed by the stump to the bench—the Bowie knife sticking in the stump ready for instant use if needed

This judgment annihilates all Compromises and brings us face to face with the great issue in the right shape. Slavery implies slave laws—that is, laws sustaining and enforcing the claim of one man to own and sell another. In the absence of such laws, Slavery cannot exist; and a Republican ascendancy in the nation, insuring Republican rule over the Territories, will prove a shield against the enactment of any such laws. Under any other role, all our Territories are henceforth Slave Territories, on the way to be ripened into Slave States.... ”

—from an editorial in the New York *Tribune*, March 7, 1857

2 **ANALYZING** What meaning is implied by "the five slaveholders who compose a majority of the Court, leaving but four-ninths to the immense preponderance of population in the Free States"?

3 **IDENTIFYING POINT OF VIEW** How does the writer demonstrate contempt for the judgment in the paragraph that begins, "This decision..."?

4 **DETERMINING MEANING** When the writer describes territories on the way to being "ripened" into slave states, what is he comparing them to? What could stop this?

ESSENTIAL QUESTION

Why does conflict develop?

1 ANALYZING POINT OF VIEW What does the writer think will be the outcome of this ruling? What language in this article tells you this?

____

____

____

____

____

____

____

____

____

____

____

____

____

VOCABULARY

ardent: strong
soberness: seriousness
diffusing: spreading
venerable: respected
jurists: judges
deviation: movement away
agitators: troublemakers
sectional: devotion to one region
itinerant: traveling
harangue: rant
deprecated: criticized
adjudication: judgment
alienation: hostile withdrawal
unbridled: reckless
license: freedom to act
intemperate: extreme
advocated: supported

"The Dred Scott Case," March 12, 1857

DIRECTIONS: Read the following excerpt from an editorial, "The Dred Scott Case," in the Washington, D.C. *Union* reflecting the South's opinion on the Dred Scott decision. Then answer the questions that follow.

EXPLORE THE CONTEXT: Five days after the editorial "Northern Outrage over *Scott* v. *Sandford,*" was published in the New York *Tribune*, the following editorial appeared in the Washington, D.C. *Union.* Note the parallels in the way the writers address areas of controversy.

PRIMARY SOURCE: NEWSPAPER EDITORIAL

"...We cherish a most ardent and confident expectation that this decision will meet a proper reception from ... our intelligent countrymen; that it will be regarded with soberness and not with passion; and that it will thereby exert a mighty influence in diffusing sound opinions and restoring harmony...

The court ... is entirely independent of the legislative branch of the government. It is elevated above the schemes of party politics, and shielded alike from the effects of sudden passion and of popular prejudice. Little motive, therefore, can the venerable jurists ... have for a deviation from the true principles of law...

But we expect this decision will for a while be questioned, and even ridiculed by the anti-slavery press.... "We have a race of agitators all over the country," said Daniel Webster; "their livelihood consists in agitating...." To this class...this decision will be a fresh topic of sectional agitation.

In 1842 the Supreme Court decided...that Congress had the constitutional power to legislate for the return of fugitive slaves. The opinion of the court was...delivered by...one of the ablest jurists of the country...Nevertheless...that decision has been attacked by the press and by itinerant lecturers as if it was nothing more than the harangue of a stump orator...

We know that in the non-slaveholding States there are many who sincerely deprecated the repeal of the Missouri Compromise...They,

. . . continued

perhaps, have not examined both sides of the question.... We would appeal to such men in a spirit of candor and patriotism; and...only invite them to review their opinions, and to conform their action to the adjudication of the highest judicial tribunal in the land.

Never perhaps, in the history of the country, has there existed so much bitterness between the North, and the South.... But the chief cause of alienation was the unbridled license of a portion of the press and the intemperate language employed by many of our public speakers... No State or community is perfect. The North and the South have different institutions. ...[I]t is morally and constitutionally wrong for the people of one State to assail the institutions of another State. Nor is it at all remarkable to expect that people who have been differently advocated by social habits, by tradition... will think entirely alike. There must be toleration... It is gratifying to see that a better feeling is beginning to exist between both sections of the country.... ”

Source: *Washington Union*, March 12, 1857

2 INFERRING What purpose would the author have to quote Daniel Webster about anti-slavery "agitators"?

3 CONTRASTING What does the writer say about the relationship between the judges and the legislative branch? How does his perspective differ from that of the writer of the New York *Tribune* editorial?

4 INFERRING How does the writer take a moral stance at the end of the excerpt?

ESSENTIAL QUESTION

Why does conflict develop?

As you gather evidence to answer the Essential Question, think about:

- how parties continued to shift during the election of 1860.
- the justification for secession.
- the final events leading up to the Civil War.

My Notes

Secession and War

DIRECTIONS: Search for evidence in Chapter 14, Lesson 3 to help you answer the following questions.

1A CIVICS How did Abraham Lincoln win a majority of electoral votes in the 1860 election, despite not being on the ballot in most Southern states?

1B Which parties and party factions supported which candidates and policies?

2 HISTORY How did the Southern states justify secession?

3 **EXPLAINING** How did Senator John Crittenden of Kentucky attempt a compromise to avert secession and war? How was it received?

4 **DRAWING CONCLUSIONS** In the years leading up to the Civil War, attempts at compromise either failed outright or served to further inflame tensions. Why do you suppose the compromises of this era failed?

____

____

____

____

5 **ORGANIZE YOUR EVIDENCE** Complete this graphic organizer by listing in chronological order the compromises you learned about in this chapter with a summary of each.

COMPROMISES MADE PRIOR TO THE CIVIL WAR	

ESSENTIAL QUESTION

Why does conflict develop?

VOCABULARY

enthroned: empowered
pretext: reason
prosperity: well-being
unprecedented: unique
conferred: granted
audacity: nerve
infringed: violated
monopolize: control
unremitting: constant
despotism: tyranny, cruel rule

1 **ANALYZING POINT OF VIEW** What is the writer's perspective on the secession of the South? How does he feel about their actions?

Harrisburg *Telegraph* Editorial on Secession, February 23, 1861

DIRECTIONS: Read the following editorial from the Harrisburg, Pennsylvania *Telegraph* and answer the questions that follow.

EXPLORE THE CONTEXT: When several Southern states seceded from the Union in February 1861 and set up a new nation with Jefferson Davis as its president, Northerners were quick to respond publicly. The editorial "The Southern Confederacy—What Secession Means" expresses the anger felt by Northerners at these actions.

PRIMARY SOURCE: NEWSPAPER EDITORIAL

"Secession is at last enthroned in the Cotton States says the Springfield Journal. Jefferson Davis has been inaugurated as the first President of the Southern Confederacy.... But what is it that they want, and what is the pretext for this attempt at overthrowing the government under which they have lived for the greater part of a century in a peace and prosperity rarely paralleled in the history of mankind? Well may [Davis] call this 'a revolution unprecedented in the history of nations,' for never before did this number of sane people thus undertake to destroy a government, the power of which they had felt only in the blessings which it had conferred upon them. Mr. Davis has the audacity to declare that the Union has failed to secure the great objects for which it was professedly established, that is 'to establish justice, insure domestic tranquility, and secure the blessings of liberty to ourselves and our posterity.' Yet all the world knows that if the Union has failed in any of these objects, it was because those who are now making this charge would have it so. They can not point to a single instance in which the government of the Union has denied them justice, interfered with their domestic tranquility, or infringed upon their liberties. If any of these things have been done it has been by themselves, and their great complaint at this time is, that they are not permitted to make slaves of the white freemen of the North, as well as the black natives of Africa, and their...posterity.

. . . *continued*

[A]mbitious Southern leaders find that they can no longer be at the head of our National affairs and monopolize the power, honors and offices of this Government, as they have done for the greater part of national existence.... Thomas Jefferson...in his 'Notes on the State of Virginia,' chapter 18, ... pointed out the disturbing influence and danger of slavery in a Republican Government. He there says: 'There must, doubtless, be an unhappy influence on the manners of our people, produced by the existence of slavery among us. The whole commerce between master and slave is a perpetual exercise of...the most unremitting despotism on the one part, and degrading submission on the other....'

The immortal author of the Declaration of Independence was... convinced that slavery was...incompatible with the spirit and existence of a Republican Government... Hence, we have...States... throwing aside their allegiance to a government which they had so often and so solemnly sworn to support, and the great mass of their population excited to madness against their Northern brethren.... ”

—from an editorial in the Harrisburg, Pennsylvania Telegraph, February 23, 1861

2 **DETERMINING CENTRAL IDEAS** What does the writer say about the South's charge that the Union has failed its promises 'to establish justice, insure domestic tranquility, and secure the blessings of liberty to ourselves and our posterity'?

3 **INFERRING** What is the writer's point in the sentence "[A]mbitious Southern leaders find..."?

4 **INTERPRETING** Why does the writer quote Jefferson on the issue of slavery?

ESSENTIAL QUESTION

Why does conflict develop?

VOCABULARY

conviction: strong belief
adduce: show
sentiment: belief
restrained: held back

1 DETERMINING PURPOSE What is the purpose of Benning's address?

______

______

______

______

______

2. DETERMINING CENTRAL POINTS What does Benning say is the main reason for Georgia's decision to secede?

______

______

______

Henry L. Benning of Georgia Urges Virginia to Secede from the Union, February 1861

DIRECTIONS: Read the following address to the Virginia State Convention and answer the questions that follow.

EXPLORE THE CONTEXT: Henry L. Benning, the Commissioner of Georgia, delivered this speech to the state of Virginia's convention, urging them to join Georgia in seceding from the Union.

PRIMARY SOURCE: CONVENTION ADDRESS

"Mr. President and Gentlemen of the Convention,

I have been appointed by the Convention of the State of Georgia, to present to you the ordinance of secession of Georgia, and further, to invite Virginia, through you, to join Georgia and the other seceded States in the formation of a Southern Confederacy...

What was the reason that induced Georgia to take the step of secession?... It was ... a deep conviction... that a separation from the North was the only thing that could prevent the abolition of her slavery.... The effect of this conviction was strengthened by a further conviction that such a separation would be the best remedy for the fugitive slave evil, and also the best, if not the only remedy, for the territorial evil. But, doubtless, if it had not been for the first conviction the step would not have been taken....

In the first place, I say that the North hates slavery...Hate is the feeling, and it is the whole North that bears it...The first proof that I shall adduce consists in two or three sentences from a speech of Mr. Lincoln's, made in October, 1858...: "I have always hated slavery as much as any abolitionist... and if I were in Congress and a vote should come up on the question, whether slavery should be excluded from the territory, in spite of the Dred Scott decision, I would vote that it should."

. . . continued

... [These sentences] contain both a sentiment and a principle of political conduct. The former is that his hatred of slavery equals that of an abolitionist, and, therefore, that it equals that of Sumner or John Brown. The latter is that his action against slavery is not to be restrained by the Constitution of the United States...He is a representative man; his sentiments are the sentiments of his party; his principles of political action are the principles of political action of his party. ...

My next proposition is, that the Republican party is the North. That party is in a permanent majority there.... The minority is powerless if the majority is permanent...That party is so deeply seated at the North that you cannot overthrow it.... ”

–Henry L. Benning, address to the Virginia State Convention, February 1861

3 IDENTIFYING PERSPECTIVES What does Benning mean by the word “evil” when he says, “the fugitive slave evil, and ... the territorial evil”? In his eyes, what are these evils? What does his use of this word indicate about his view of slavery overall?

4 ANALYZING What are Benning’s objections to Lincoln and his position on slavery?

ESSENTIAL QUESTION

Why does conflict develop?

1 Think About It

Review the supporting questions you developed at the beginning of the chapter. Review the evidence you gathered in Chapter 14. Were you able to answer each Supporting Question? If there was not enough evidence to answer your Supporting Questions, what additional evidence do you think you need to consider?

____

____

____

____

2 Organize Your Evidence

What is the most significant information you learned in Chapter 14? Complete the chart below to organize this information into Northern and Southern actions and viewpoints leading up to the Civil War.

Actions & Viewpoints that Led to the Civil War	
North	South

3 Talk About It

Talk with a classmate about what you thought were the significant differences and issues that led the nation to the brink of Civil War. Was there any way war could or should have been avoided? Listen to any feedback your classmate provides and incorporate it into your conclusion.

4 Write About It

Write a paragraph about the conflict between the North and the South and whether you think war could or should have been avoided. Did the complexities of the situation make it impossible for the two sides to agree and avert war? Be sure to use evidence from the text to support your position.

5 Connect to the Essential Question

What happens when compromise doesn't seem possible because both sides in a conflict feel strongly that they are right? Is there a way to avoid violence? Imagine you are living in the 1850s. Write a letter to one of the politicians discussed in the chapter who had the power to influence others and tell him how you feel he could use his influence to encourage others to change course to avoid a civil war.

CITIZENSHIP

TAKING ACTION

MAKE CONNECTIONS The civil war in Syria is a major world crisis. Millions of civilians—ordinary people who are not soldiers—have been forced to flee their homes as refugees, often with nothing more than the clothing on their backs. Other countries have opened their doors to accommodate the flood of refugees.

Get together in small groups and use the Internet to research the Syrian refugee crisis. Have Syrian refugees been resettled in your community or nearby? If so, are there refugees with immediate needs such as clothing, school supplies, household items, or toys? Be sure to research what type of help the refugees or organizations working to help them have requested.

How can you reach out to refugees from Syria and other countries that have resettled in your community? Is there a way your school might extend friendship and help to welcome refugee families in your community?

Take action to help refugees in your town, city, or state. Organize a group to help fulfill the needs of refugees from Syria or other areas of the world. Ask your classmates if they would be willing donate any of the needed items. Or brainstorm ways to raise money to buy the needed supplies, such as a bake sale or charity sports event.

The Civil War

ESSENTIAL QUESTION

Why does conflict develop?

Think about how this question relates to the American Civil War.

TALK ABOUT IT

Discuss with a partner what type of information you would need to know to answer this question. For example, one question might be: Did the North and the South go to war for the same reasons?

DIRECTIONS: Now write down three additional questions that you need to answer to be able to explain why conflict develops.

MY RESEARCH QUESTIONS

Supporting Question 1:

____

____

Supporting Question 2:

____

____

Supporting Question 3:

____

____

The Two Sides

DIRECTIONS: Search for evidence in Chapter 15, Lesson 1 to help you answer the following questions.

1 SUMMARIZING Complete the table.

The Border States

2 COMPARING AND CONTRASTING Complete the graphic organizer.

The Stage Is Set for Civil War: North versus South		
	The North	The South
Strengths		
Goals		
Strategies		

ESSENTIAL QUESTION

Why does conflict develop?

As you gather evidence to answer the Essential Question, think about

- the differences between the North and South.
- the importance of the border states.
- what life was like for the soldiers of the Civil War.

My Notes

3 **INFERRING** "To get into the army, many teenagers ran away from home or lied about their ages." What do you think motivated these teenagers?

4 **DESCRIBING** How many soldiers were in each army by the end of the war? Complete the table.

Americans Against Americans	
Union Army Strength	
Confederate Army Strength	

5A **EXPLAINING** What fraction of men deserted from each side during the war? Complete the table.

Fleeing the Battlefield	
Union Army Desertions	
Confederate Army Desertions	

5B Why did they desert?

ESSENTIAL QUESTION

Why does conflict develop?

Scott's Great Snake

DIRECTIONS: Study the image below. Then answer the questions that follow.

EXPLORE THE CONTEXT: Winfield Scott (1786–1866), served the US Army for more than half a century. He fought in the War of 1812 and was the great hero of the war against Mexico. In that war, he led his forces to victory after victory until they captured the capital, Mexico City, thus winning the war. A national hero, he ran for president in 1852, but lost.

At the beginning of the Civil War, Scott, unlike many others, already knew the horrors of warfare. "The destruction of life and property ... would be frightful," he wrote. Instead of invading the South, Scott argued that a blockade of the Atlantic and Gulf coasts and the Mississippi River would slowly starve the Confederacy into surrender. At first, this plan was rejected as too slow. The press ridiculed it as the "Anaconda Plan." Only later, as the war progressed, was the merit of Scott's plan realized.

VOCABULARY

blockade: sealing off a place so no one can go in or get out

anaconda: large snake that wraps its coils around its prey to suffocate it

PRIMARY SOURCE: POLITICAL CARTOON

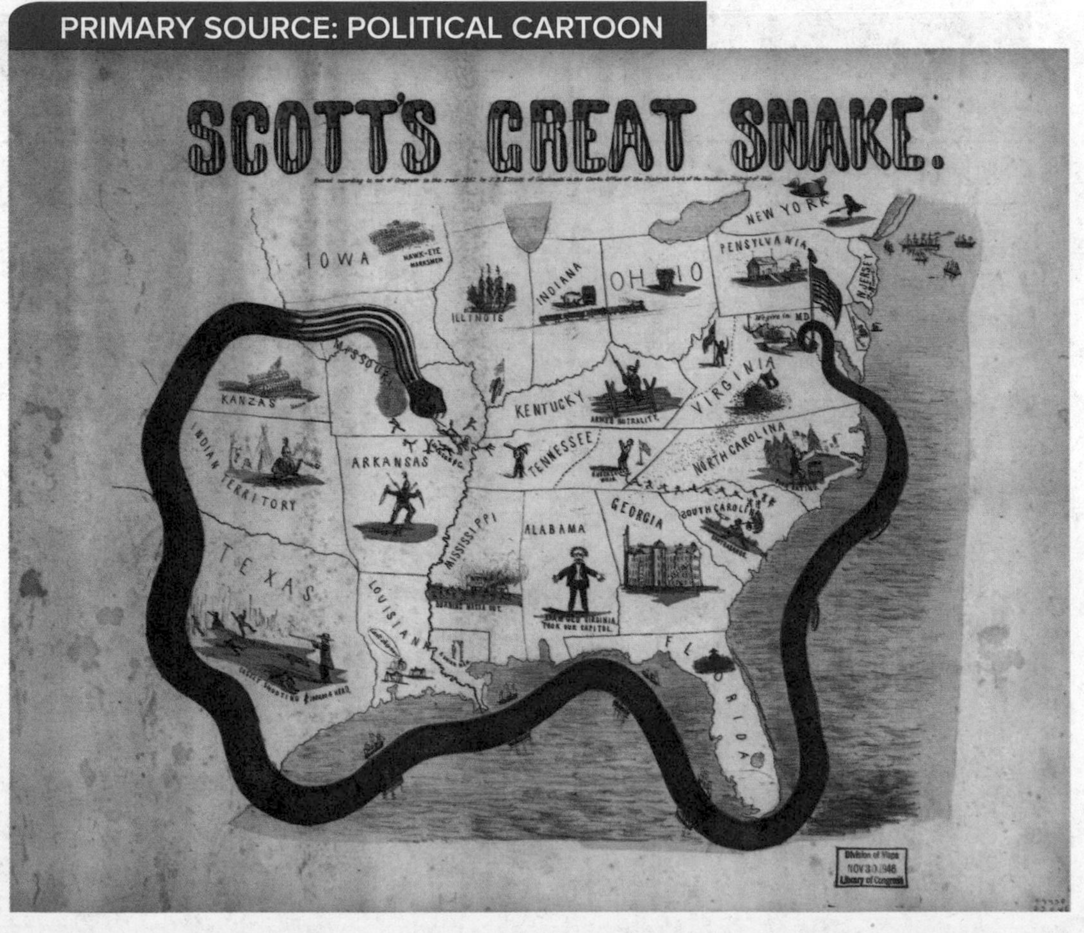

1A DETERMINING POINT OF VIEW How does this cartoon map portray Scott's plan?

____

1B What part of the image supports your answer to the previous question?

____

____

____

2 INFERRING This cartoon map was published in Cincinnati in 1861. What can you infer from this?

____

____

____

____

____

3 MAKING CONNECTIONS Why does the map focus on just the southeastern states?

____

____

____

4 ECONOMICS How was Scott's plan supposed to work? Why would blockades of Southern ports force the South to surrender?

____

____

____

____

ESSENTIAL QUESTION

Why does conflict develop?

A Girl from New York Describes the Outbreak of the Civil War

DIRECTIONS: Read the excerpt from a diary below. Then respond to the questions that follow.

EXPLORE THE CONTEXT: When the Civil War broke out, Caroline Cowles Richards (1842–1913) was 19. She lived in Canandaigua, New York, and kept a diary. In this diary entry, she relates what she saw as the people of Canandaigua prepared for war.

VOCABULARY

martial: military

square: central part of town

garments: clothes

PRIMARY SOURCE: DIARY

"*May, 1861.*—Many of the young men are going from Canandaigua and all the neighboring towns. It seems very patriotic and grand when they are singing, "It is sweet, Oh, 'tis sweet, for one's country to die," and we hear the martial music and see the flags flying and see the recruiting tents on the square and meet men in uniform at every turn and see train loads of the boys in blue going to the front, but it will not seem so grand if we hear they are dead on the battlefield, far from home.

A lot of us girls went down to the train and took flowers to the soldiers as they were passing through and they cut buttons from their coats and gave to us as souvenirs.

They work every day in one of the rooms of the court house and cut out garments and make them and scrape lint and roll up bandages. We are going to write notes and enclose them in the garments to cheer up the soldier boys."

—Caroline Cowles Richards, entry from her diary *Village Life in America, 1852-1872*

1 **DETERMINING PURPOSE** Why do you think Richards wrote down what she saw?

2A **INFERRING** What is the purpose of the "recruiting tents"?

2B Who are the "boys in blue"?

2C **INFERRING** Who might "they" who work in the courthouse be?

3 **MAKING CONNECTIONS** In the first paragraph, how does Richards contrast the description of the preparations for war versus actual war?

4 **ANALYZING POINT OF VIEW** Based on the excerpt, how would you describe Richards's attitude toward the war?

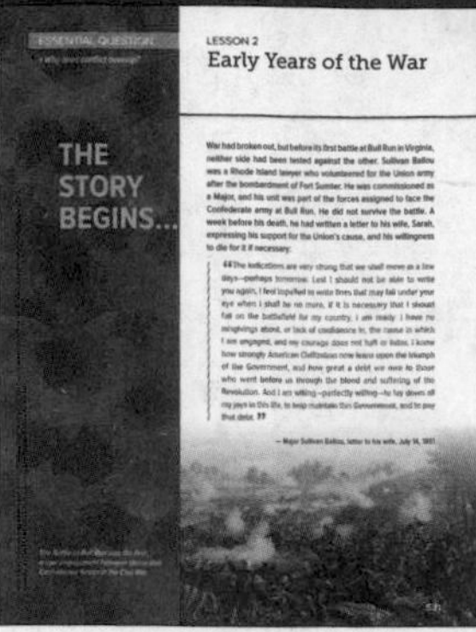

ESSENTIAL QUESTION

Why does conflict develop?

As you gather evidence to answer the Essential Question, think about

- the crucial first battles of the war.
- the South's invasion of the North.
- the Emancipation Proclamation.

My Notes

Early Years of the War

DIRECTIONS: Search for evidence in Chapter 15, Lesson 2 to help you answer the following questions.

1 DESCRIBING Complete the table.

The First Major Battle of the Civil War	
Name	
Date	
Location	
Victor	

2 EXPLAINING What was the Union's geographic goal in the West?

3 DESCRIBING Complete the table.

The Ironclads	
Definition	
Battle in Chesapeake Bay	
Union Ship	
Confederate Ship	
Results	

4 ANALYZING Why was the Battle of Shiloh important?

5 **IDENTIFYING EFFECTS** What did Farragut's capture of New Orleans for the Union mean for the Confederacy?

6 **IDENTIFYING CAUSES** Confederate victories in the East were largely the result of the military genius of two generals. Who were they?

7 **SUMMARIZING** Complete the table.

Early Confederate Victories in the East	

8 **IDENTIFYING EFFECTS** What were the results of the Battle of Antietam?

9 **IDENTIFYING CAUSES AND EFFECTS** The Emancipation Proclamation was issued in September 1862. What were some of the reasons abolitionists gave for insisting it was needed? What did it state?

10 **EXPLAINING EFFECTS** Although the immediate results of the Emancipation Proclamation were limited, what was its larger significance if the Union won the war?

ESSENTIAL QUESTION

Why does conflict develop?

Rufus Blanchard Defends the Emancipation Proclamation

DIRECTIONS: Read the excerpt from the broadside. Then answer the questions that follow.

EXPLORE THE CONTEXT: Rufus Blanchard (1821–1904) was a mapmaker, writer, printer, and outspoken advocate of the Union cause who lived in Chicago. He described Abraham Lincoln as an "American genius." Blanchard printed a broadside of the Proclamation with his personal footnote added. This is an excerpt from his footnote.

PRIMARY SOURCE: BROADSIDE

"The [Emancipation] Proclamation is an incalculable element of strength to the Union cause. It makes an alliance between the Rebels and Foreign States as impossible as it is for millions of [enslaved persons] to love Slavery better than Freedom. They [will love] our Government [more] as it becomes a free land of promise and shelter from oppression, thus saving thousands of precious lives and millions of treasure from being lost in foreign wars.

It perfects the purposes of the Declaration of Independence and impairs no constitutional rights, those whom it would affect having forfeited those rights by proving false to their country, to humanity and religion.

No real support to the Union cause will be lost by this Proclamation. ... It will be a powerful incentive to the slave to fight for the Union instead of his rebel master. ... Labor will be rewarded, justice fulfilled, and the Old Ship of State will again sail majestic o'er the unrippled waters of Liberty and Peace."

--Rufus Blanchard, from his footnote to the Emancipation Proclamation

VOCABULARY

broadside: a large sheet of paper printed on one side; similar to a flyer

incalculable: huge

treasure: money

impairs: weakens

forfeited: gave up

1 **ANALYZING TEXT** List at least five reasons that Blanchard cites for supporting the Emancipation Proclamation.

2A **INFERRING** Who are "those" who "forfeited those rights by proving false to their country, to humanity and religion"?

2B **DETERMINING MEANING** How did they prove "false to their country"?

3 **ANALYZING POINTS OF VIEW** Blanchard writes that the Emancipation Proclamation "impairs no constitutional rights." Would slaveholders agree? Why or why not?

ESSENTIAL QUESTION

Why does conflict develop?

A Female Spy Is Discovered

DIRECTIONS: Read the article. Then respond to the questions that follow.

EXPLORE THE CONTEXT: This article is about "Pauline Cushman." However, that was not the subject's real name. She was born Harriet Wood (1833–1893) and as a young woman changed her name to be an actress in New York City. Later, after being under suspicion for her Southern ties, "Cushman" was offered the chance to prove her loyalty to the Union as a spy, putting her acting skills to use for the good of the country. Here, the New York *Times* reprints a story from the Detroit *Tribune* about Cushman's bravery and cleverness in her greatest role.

VOCABULARY

narrative: story
the rebellion: the Civil War
rendered: given
Federal cause: Union cause, Northern cause
pike: turnpike, road
picket: guard or guards; lookouts
feigned: faked
ascertained: discovered
commiserate: felt sympathy for

PRIMARY SOURCE: NEWSPAPER ARTICLE

"A THRILLING NARRATIVE. Miss Maj. Pauline Cushman, the Federal Scout and Spy (From the Detroit Tribune, May 24)

Among the women of America who have made themselves famous since the opening of the rebellion, few have suffered more or rendered more service to the Federal cause than Miss Maj. PAULINE CUSHMAN, the female scout and spy. At the commencement of hostilities she resided in Cleveland, Ohio, and was quite well known as a clever actress.

From Cleveland she went to Louisville [Kentucky], where she had an engagement in Wood's Theatre. Federal authorities... asked if she would enter the secret service of the Government. She readily consented, and was at once employed to carry letters between Louisville and Nashville. She was [then] employed by Gen. ROSECRANS, and was for many months with the Army of the Cumberland. She visited the rebel lines time after time, and was thoroughly acquainted with all the country and roads in Tennessee, Northern Georgia, Alabama and Mississippi, in which sections she rendered our armies invaluable service. She was twice suspected of being a spy, and taken prisoner, but managed to escape.

At last, however, she was not so fortunate. [She] was captured on the Hardin pike.... She was placed on a horse, and in charge of two scouts, was being taken to Spring Hill, the headquarters of [Confederate General] FORREST.

1 IDENTIFYING POINT OF VIEW Which side in the conflict does the writer support? How can you tell?

. . . continued

While on the way to this place, she feigned sickness, and said she could not travel any further without falling from her horse. Her captors stopped at a house on the roadside, when it was ascertained that a Federal scouting party had passed the place an hour before. Knowing that her guards had important papers for Gen. BRAGG, the quick-witted spy seized the fact and schemed to use it to her advantage.

Seeing an old [African American man], who appeared to commiserate her unfortunate plight, she watched her opportunity and placed $10 in Tennessee money in his hand, saying: "run up the road, Uncle, and come back in a few minutes, telling us that four hundred Federals are coming down the street." [The man] obeyed the order literally, and soon came back in the greatest excitement, telling the story....

The scouts... believed his story, mounted their horses, and "skedaddled" for the woods. Miss CUSHMAN, seizing a pistol belonging to a wounded solider in the house, also mounted her horse and fled.... ”

—from "A Thrilling Narrative," an article in the Detroit *Tribune*, May 24, 1864

2 INFERRING How might Cushman's being a woman make her a more effective spy?

3 ANALYZING According to the article, federal authorities asked Cushman to work in the "secret service of the Government." Why might they choose an actress to serve as a spy?

4 DRAWING CONCLUSIONS The story suggests that Cushman must have been a very brave woman to risk being captured, put in prison, or even executed. Why would a person risk her life in such a way?

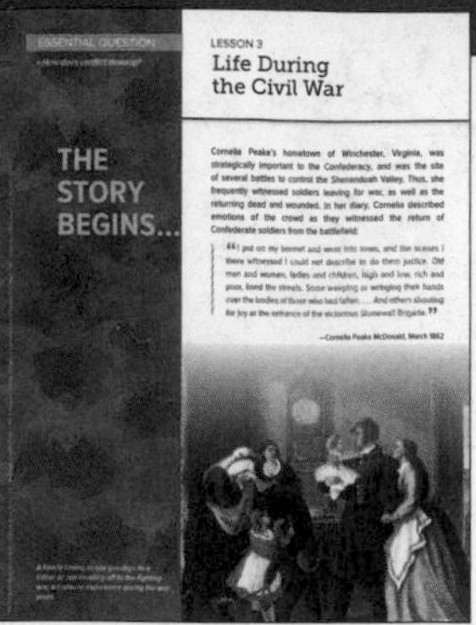

ESSENTIAL QUESTION

Why does conflict develop?

As you gather evidence to answer the Essential Question, think about

- the hardships of the Civil War.
- how the war affected women.
- the political and economic changes brought by the war.

My Notes

Life During the Civil War

DIRECTIONS: Search for evidence in Chapter 15, Lesson 3 to help you answer the following questions.

1 **ASSESSING** "Almost everyone who stayed home was touched in some way by the war." Do you think this statement is true, or an exaggeration? Explain.

2 **EXPLAINING** Why were hardships greater in the South than in the North?

3 **SUMMARIZING** Fill out the list by writing down the roles that women played during the Civil War.

Contributions of Women in the Civil War	

4 **DESCRIBING** Complete the table.

Notable Female Nurses of the Civil War	
Nurse	Accomplishments
Mary Edwards Walker	
Dorothea Dix	
Clara Barton	
Sally Tompkins	

5 **CITING TEXT EVIDENCE** What conditions did captured soldiers face in Civil War prisons?

6 **IDENTIFYING** Who were the "Copperheads"?

7 CIVICS During the war, President Lincoln suspended habeas corpus —a legal process that keeps the government from holding a person indefinitely without showing cause. How did suspending habeas corpus help the Union deal with Northerners who opposed the war?

8 **EXPLAINING** During the Civil War, people in the North and the South complained it was "a rich man's war and a poor man's fight." What did they mean?

9 **ANALYZING CAUSE AND EFFECT** What caused the draft riots?

10A **IDENTIFYING EFFECTS** What three ways did the North and the South have to pay for the war?

10B Which side felt the economic effects of the Civil War more, the North or the South? Give reasons for your answer.

ESSENTIAL QUESTION

Why does conflict develop?

A Southern Woman Describes a Bread Riot in Richmond

DIRECTIONS: Read the excerpt from the letter below. Then answer the questions that follow.

EXPLORE THE CONTEXT: One of the more heartbreaking results of the Civil War were food shortages. Most soldiers did not eat very well, but civilians suffered as well. In the South the shortages were particularly severe. "Bread riots" broke out. Bread riots were just that: starving people rioting, desperate for even a scrap of bread to eat. The one described here took place in Richmond, Virginia, the capital of the Confederacy. The rioters were women and children.

VOCABULARY

emaciated: dangerously thin
calico: printed cotton
wan: weak
read the Riot Act: a verbal warning given to a mob to disperse
disperse: separate, withdraw
dray: large flat cart
rations: portions of food

1 ANALYZING POINT OF VIEW What is the tone or overall feeling of this letter?

____

____

____

____

____

____

____

____

PRIMARY SOURCE: LETTER

"Since the weather has been so pleasant, I have been in the habit of walking in the Capitol Square before breakfast every morning. . . . Yesterday, upon arriving, I found within the gates a crowd of women and boys – several hundreds of them, standing quietly together.

I sat on a bench near, and one of the number left the rest and took the seat beside me. She was a pale, emaciated girl, not more than eighteen. . . . As she raised her hand to remove her sunbonnet and use it for a fan, her loose calico sleeve slipped up and revealed the mere skeleton of an arm. She perceived my expression as I looked at it, and hastily pulled down her sleeve with a short laugh. 'This is all that's left of me,' she said. 'It seems real funny, don't it? . . . We are starving. As soon as enough of us get together, we are going to the bakeries and each of us will take a loaf of bread. That is little enough for the government to give us after it has taken all our men.'

The girl turned to me with a wan smile, and as she rose to join the long line that had now formed and was moving, she said simply, 'Good-by! I'm going to get something to eat!'. . .

The crowd now rapidly increased, and numbered, I am sure, more than a thousand women and children. It grew and grew until it

. . . continued

reached the [size] of a mob—a bread riot. They [took] all the light carts they met, and marched along silently and in order. They marched through Cary Street and Main, visiting the stores ... and emptying them of their contents. Governor Letcher sent the mayor to read the Riot Act, and as this had no effect he threatened to fire on the crowd. The city battalion came up. The women fell back with frightened eyes, but did not obey the order to disperse.

The President [Jefferson Davis] then appeared, ascended a dray, and addressed them. It is said he was received at first with hisses from the boys, but after he had spoken some little time with great kindness and sympathy, the women moved quietly on, taking their food with them. General Elze and General Winder wished to call troops from the camps to 'suppress the women,' but [Secretary of War James] Seddon, a wise man, declined to issue the order. While I write women and children are still standing in the streets, demanding food, and the government is issuing to them rations of rice.”

— Mrs. Roger A. Pryor, from a letter dated April 4, 1863

2A **INFERRING** Why are all of the rioters women and children?

2B **ANALYZING** Why do you think the rioters did not leave, even after they were threatened with being shot?

3 **DRAWING CONCLUSIONS** Did the rioters get what they wanted? Explain.

ESSENTIAL QUESTION

Why does conflict develop?

"Don't Unchain the Tiger!"

DIRECTIONS: Read the excerpt below taken from a broadside. Then respond to the questions that follow.

EXPLORE THE CONTEXT: The worst draft riot of the Civil War occurred in New York City in July 1863 . It lasted four days. Most of the rioters were recent immigrants. Some were angry that wealthy men could avoid the draft by hiring substitutes. Others opposed the war, thinking that the end of slavery would mean freed African Americans who would work for little and take most jobs. When Irish dockworkers went on strike and were replaced by African American workers, it seemed to confirm their fears. This triggered the riot. The rioters burned the draft office, government buildings, police stations, and property owned by abolitionists, and murdered many African Americans. More than 100 people died. Federal troops were needed to suppress the violence.

The broadside excerpted here, originally in German, took a clear stand on the rioting.

PRIMARY SOURCE: BROADSIDE

"[F]or two years we have seen and suffered the consequences [of the war], written in tears, and blood, and ruin, in our once happy land; and now, when the rebellion is being nearly crushed, and Jeff. Davis is finding his plans defeated....I say to myself— Don't unchain the Tiger!

When I hear Working-Men talk about resisting the law, burning houses, killing public officers, and bursting the doors wide open for every kind of crime and disorder, it seems to me they do not think of all the cost and of all the horrors, or of widows and orphans, and their scalding tears, and I say to them, " Brothers! in the name of God— Don't unchain the Tiger!"

When I see well-dressed demagogues filling the ears of the people with lies... only to get the Working-Men aroused to deeds of crime and violence.... I wish I had the voice of a thunderer, that I might say to them—Don't unchain the Tiger!

VOCABULARY

broadside: a large sheet of paper printed on one side; similar to a flyer
demagogues: leaders who use false information and empty promises to persuade people
spurn: reject
viper: poisonous snake

. . . *continued*

Working-Men! When any man asks you to break the law, and tries to stir up your passions....you may set him down as your worst enemy. Spurn him as you would a viper. The patriotic Working-Men of the North cannot afford to spend time in killing each other. Be wise, and above all things, DON'T UNCHAIN THE TIGER! ”

—from a broadside "A Democratic Workingman," July 24, 1863

1A Who wrote this broadside?

1B **ANALYZING POINT OF VIEW** Is he for or against the rioting? How can you tell?

2 **INFERRING** What can you infer from the broadside being published in German?

3A **DETERMINING MEANING** What does the writer mean by "Don't unchain the Tiger!"?

3B Whom does the writer blame for stirring up the working-men to violent conflict?

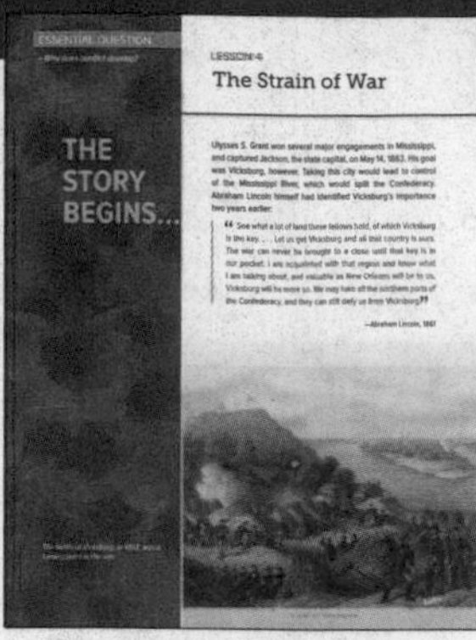

ESSENTIAL QUESTION

Why does conflict develop?

As you gather evidence to answer the Essential Question, think about

- key Southern victories during the Civil War.
- the roles African Americans played in the war.
- the significance of the battles of Gettysburg and Vicksburg.

My Notes

The Strain of War

DIRECTIONS: Search for evidence in Chapter 15, Lesson 4 to help you answer the following questions.

1 **SUMMARIZING** Complete the table.

Southern Victories	
Battle	**Key to Victory**
Fredericksburg	
Chancellorsville	

2 **CITING TEXT EVIDENCE** List in order the generals Lincoln tried.

Lincoln Searches for a General

3 **DETERMINING CENTRAL IDEAS** How did the role of African Americans in the military change during the course of the war?

4 **IDENTIFYING CAUSES** Why did Lee invade the North a second time?

5A GEOGRAPHY How did geographic factors play a part in the outcome of the Battle of Gettysburg?

5B **ANALYZING** Why was the Battle of Gettysburg important in the course of the war?

6 **DETERMINING CAUSE AND EFFECT** What was the outcome of the siege of Vicksburg and what was its ultimate result?

7 **DETERMINING POINT OF VIEW** What do you think Lincoln was attempting to do in the Gettysburg Address?

ESSENTIAL QUESTION

Why does conflict develop?

"The Beginning of the End"

DIRECTIONS: Read the excerpt below from a magazine article published at the time. Then answer the questions that follow.

EXPLORE THE CONTEXT: After the Confederate defeats at Gettysburg and Vicksburg, more and more Northerners—and Southerners—thought the end of the war was near. Six months later, the *Atlantic Monthly* gave voice to what many people felt in an article titled "The Beginning of the End."

PRIMARY SOURCE: MAGAZINE ARTICLE

"...Taken as a whole, we have but little reason to complain of results. ... Great things have been done in 1863, [placing] the military result of the war beyond all doubt, and permitting us to hope for the early restoration of peace.

...

No blow that we have received – and many blows have been dealt upon us – has been followed by any loss of territory, any decrease of the means of warfare, or any diminution of our purpose to carry on the contest. ... The enemy have taken of our men, our cannon, our stores, and our money, more than once, but not one of their victories produced any "fruit" beyond what was gleaned from the battle-field itself. Our victories, on the contrary, have been fruitful, as the position of our forces on the enemy's coast, and on much of their territory, and in many of their ports, satisfactorily proves.

...

At Gettysburg we had ample compensation for Chancellorsville. ... [We] put an end to all attempts at invasion on the part of the Rebels, while we continued to hold all that we had acquired of their territory, and soon added more of it to our previous acquisitions. ... The superior generalship of General Grant at and near Vicksburg compelled them to surrender.

....

VOCABULARY

gleaned: gathered or taken
halved: cut in half; cut into two pieces
quartered: cut into four pieces

. . . *continued*

The Mississippi [River] was placed at our control, and the enemy were deprived of those supplies, both domestic and foreign, which they had drawn in so large quantities from the River.

...

The effects of all the successes which have been mentioned are various... as General Grant's success at Vicksburg halved the Confederacy, so have his Chattanooga successes quartered it.

The Rebels are no longer one people, but are divided into a number of communities, which cannot act together. ... Of the inhabitants of the original Confederacy probably two-fifths are no longer under the control of the Richmond Government."

—"The Beginning of the End," from the *Atlantic Monthly*, January 1864

1 **RELATING EVENTS** How close to the end of the Civil War was this article written?

2 **ANALYZING POINT OF VIEW** Is this written from the point of view of a Northerner or a Southerner? How do you know?

3 **ANALYZING SOURCES** In the first paragraph, the articles states that events place "the military result of the war beyond all doubt." What does this mean?

4 **INFERRING** How does the sentence "The Rebels are no longer one people, but are divided into a number of communities, which cannot act together" shed light on why conflict develops?

ESSENTIAL QUESTION

Why does conflict develop?

Deceiving the People

DIRECTIONS: Read the excerpt from a newspaper editorial below. Then respond to the questions that follow.

EXPLORE THE CONTEXT: Today, Abraham Lincoln is a national hero. He is pictured on the penny and the five-dollar bill. He birthday is celebrated as a national holiday. His Gettysburg Address is studied by millions of students every year.

Therefore, it can be difficult to remember that Lincoln was not entirely popular for much of his presidency. His election in 1860 helped start the Civil War. When he ran for reelection in 1864, the war was still raging and he was not assured of victory. Lincoln, a Republican, faced Democratic opponent George B. McClellan—Lincoln's former general. McClellan promised to bring a swift end to the war.

The writer of this editorial, published in 1864 in a Pennsylvania newspaper, held clear opinions of how Lincoln and his colleagues had fought the war until then.

NEWS

VOCABULARY

credulity: trust
artful: tricky
duping: fooling
self-aggrandizement: working to make oneself powerful and important
deluded: misled
suppression: defeat
humbugs: people who deceive
interminable: endless

1A DETERMINING CENTRAL IDEAS Who is being attacked in this editorial?

PRIMARY SOURCE: NEWSPAPER EDITORIAL

"The [efforts] made by the leaders of the Republican Party to deceive the people are utterly inexcusable and disgraceful. The practicing of deception and fraud seems to be their trade.

Ever since the commencement of the war they have been only too successful in playing upon the credulity of the people and misleading the public mind in reference to the real condition of the country. These men, who are as bad as they are bold, and as corrupt as they are ambitious, by artful devices and ... falsehoods, have thus far been pretty successful in duping and misleading the honest, unsuspecting masses of the country, by which means they have been able to carry out their wicked schemes of personal ambition and self-aggrandizement to the almost total ruin of the country....

The announcement, by [Secretary of State] Seward, that the war would be over in sixty or ninety days, is still fresh in the memory. ... Nothing was too absurd for them to believe, or affect to believe; and no

. . . *continued*

falsehood was too great for them to attempt to palm off on the people as truth. Mr. Seward's sixty or ninety days have rolled into the past more than a dozen times since the prediction was uttered, and the war still rages with unabated fury.....

Thousands [of people] still permit themselves to be deluded ... and ... still look for the suppression of the rebellion at the end of every sixty or ninety days....

How long will the people continue to be deceived by these monstrous political quacks and humbugs? How long will they permit themselves to be deluded on to their ruin? Under the policy of the present Administration, this war *can never end!* Their *policy* precludes the possibility of such a result. It is against the law of reason, of human nature, and of God. From the very nature of the case the war must be interminable.

If the people want peace they must go back to the principles of common sense from which they have departed. They must hurl from power this imbecile, wicked and corrupt administration. They must elect Statesmen to preside over the destinies of the nation instead of buffoons. Then they may expect to obtain peace and a restored Union, and not until then. ”

—from "Dispatch from Kentucky," *The Valley Spirit,* Chambersburg, Pennsylvania, July 6, 1864

1B What are they being accused of? Why, according to the editorial, would they do this?

2 **ANALYZING** Does this editorial show why conflict develops between people?

ESSENTIAL QUESTION

Why does conflict develop?

As you gather evidence to answer the Essential Question, think about

- the role Ulysses S. Grant played in ending the Civil War.
- the effect of General William Tecumseh Sherman's March to the Sea.
- what happened at Appomattox Court House.

My Notes

The War's Final Stages

DIRECTIONS: Search for evidence in Chapter 15, Lesson 5 to help you answer the following questions.

1 **SUMMARIZING** What was General Grant's plan to end the war?

2 **EXPLAINING** Why did people in the North call General Grant a "butcher"?

3 **DESCRIBING** What was "the Wilderness"?

4A **CITING TEXT EVIDENCE** "I can't spare this man. He fights." Who wrote this?

4B Who was Lincoln referring to as the man who fights?

5 **CITING TEXT EVIDENCE** "Damn the torpedoes, full speed ahead!" Who gave this order and what was he engaged in doing?

6 **IDENTIFYING POINT OF VIEW** What was the tone of Lincoln's Second Inaugural Address?

7 **EXPLAINING** What was Sherman's March to the Sea?

8 **DESCRIBING** What is the significance of Appomattox Court House?

ESSENTIAL QUESTION

Why does conflict develop?

The Aftermath of Destruction at a Town near Washington, D.C.

DIRECTIONS: Read the excerpt from the newspaper article below. Then answer the questions that follow.

EXPLORE THE CONTEXT: The Civil War destroyed countless buildings and towns. Powerful cannons, rifles, and other weapons left their mark. In this excerpt, a Union soldier tells of the destruction he sees in the aftermath of a battle.

VOCABULARY

cavalry: horse-mounted soldiers
haversacks: small bags
tacked: nailed
fly-leaf: blank page at beginning of book
balance: rest
stand from under: take caution; beware

PRIMARY SOURCE: NEWSPAPER ARTICLE

"I proceeded north of Fort Stevens on the seventh street road half-a-mile, when I came to the ruins of the residence of Mr. Lay of the city post office, which was destroyed day before yesterday by shell from Fort Stevens to prevent the sharp shooters from occupying it. A little north ... are the ruins of the residence of Mr. Carberry, which was also destroyed by our own shell.

Near this place I came upon the new made grave of an unknown cavalry man. Still further north and a mile from Fort Stevens, I came to a fence thrown across the road, and occupied ... by the rebels the day previous. Here were marks of hard fighting; Union and rebel muskets, broken and unbroken, and thrown aside by their owners, hay piled in a heap by the way; while hats, caps, haversacks, pouches, and thousands of cartridges and bullets were scattered here and there on both sides of the rebel breastworks and among the rifle pits dug by the Union soldiers in a field near by. Every rail on the fence and the tree show well the work which has been done the last few hours in that vicinity. ...

I continued on my way, and visited the residences of Dr. S. Heath and Captain Richardson—Here was a scary picture. Hearing of the approach of the rebels on Monday morning, they removed the female members of their families to the fort, and before they could return the rebels had possession of the premises. Everything about the place is scattered in great confusion. What clothing could be made use of the

1 **INFERRING** The writer comes across the fresh grave "of an unknown cavalry man." How does he react and why do you think he reacts the way he does?

____

____

____

____

____

____

. . . continued

rebels exchanged for their less attractive suits. The building itself shows with what accuracy our artillerymen directed their shot and shell against its sides. Eight cannon balls or shells had passed through one side to the other and the doors, windows, and side boards are filled with bullet marks....

In a grove on the opposite from Mr. Blair's residence, was found a book ...tacked by a rebel, which I have brought with me, and transcribes the following inscription, while which is written on a fly-leaf:

"NEAR WASHINGTON, JULY 12, 1864

Now, Uncle Abe, you had better be quiet the balance of your administration. We only come near your town this time just to show what we could do—but if you go on in your mad career we will come again soon, and then you had better stand from under.

Yours, respectfully,

The Worst Reb you ever saw.

FIFTY-EIGHT VIRGINIA INFANTRY." ”

—from the *Baltimore Sun,* July 15, 1864

2A The writer states, "Every rail on the fence and the tree show well the work which has been done the last few hours in that vicinity." What does this mean?

2B The writer reports that in one house, "Everything about the place is scattered in great confusion." Why would this be the case?

3 **DRAWING CONCLUSIONS** What do you think was the point of the rebel's note in the book?

ESSENTIAL QUESTION

Why does conflict develop?

An Opinion: "They Have Earned It"

DIRECTIONS: Read the excerpt from the article below. Then respond to the questions that follow.

EXPLORE THE CONTEXT: At the beginning of the Civil War, there were about four million enslaved people in the United States. The war was not about slavery at first, at least not in Abraham Lincoln's mind. He sought to preserve the Union. As the war progressed, however, it became increasingly clear that the Civil War would end slavery. What, then, would the future hold for formerly enslaved people? In an article for the *Atlantic Monthly*, one writer gave his opinion on what rights should be given to those formerly enslaved.

VOCABULARY

valor: courage
freedman: formerly enslaved person
franchise: the rights of citizenship, especially voting
recompense: reward
in its train: behind it
benefactor: someone who helps others

PRIMARY SOURCE: MAGAZINE ARTICLE

"The [African American] men of Richmond, of Charleston, of Savannah, of all the South, have been and are now the true Union men of the seceded States. When or where have they raised their hands against the Union? They have fought for the flag of the Union, and have earned by their patriotism and valor a name and a place in history. Citizenship is theirs by natural right; besides, they have earned it. Make the freedman a voter, a land-owner, a tax-payer, ... give him in every respect free franchise, and the recompense will be security, peace, and prosperity. Anything less than absolute right will sooner or later bring trouble in its train. Now, in this day of settlement, this reconstruction of the nation, this renewal of life, it is the privilege of America to become the world's great teacher and benefactor."

—"Late Scenes in Richmond," from the *Atlantic Monthly*, June 1865

1A DETERMINING CENTRAL IDEAS What is the main point the writer is making?

1B What are the reasons given for this position? Identify at least four.

2 EXPLAINING What does the writer mean by "day of settlement"?

3 CIVICS Does this source suggest a way to avoid conflict developing in the future? What is it?

4 ANALYZING TEXT Why does the writer say the African American men of "all the South, have been and are now the true Union men of the seceded States"?

5 SUMMARIZING Could this writer's opinion be summarized in one sentence from the excerpt?

ESSENTIAL QUESTION

Why does conflict develop?

1 Think About It

Review the supporting questions that you developed at the beginning of the chapter. Review the evidence that you gathered in Chapter 15. Were you able to answer each supporting question? If there was not enough evidence to answer your supporting questions, what additional evidence do you think you need to include?

2 Organize Your Evidence

Think about organizing what you have learned into reasons that conflict develops. For example, the Civil War developed for many reasons. One was the conflict over slavery, which can be considered a moral reason. Another reason the Civil War developed was disagreements amount how the national government should deal with cheap imports. That was an economic reason. Use the graphic organizer below to organize what you have learned. The first one is filled in for you. You can use any conflicts, both big and small, including wars, disagreements with friends, and problems at school.

Why Conflicts Develop		
Source of Conflict	Describe the Conflict	Examples of Conflict
Slavery	Moral conflict	Civil War

❸ Write About It

How do conflicts develop? Are there ways to prevent them, or are they inevitable? Write your ideas in a paragraph, giving reasons to support your answers.

❹ Talk About It

Get together with a partner or small group and discuss the reasons that conflicts develop. Which type or types seem most common? What can your group learn from this?

❺ Connect to the Essential Question

Choose what you think is the most important type of reason from your graphic organizer in question 2 above. Write an argumentative essay explaining why you think that type of reason is the key to understanding why conflict develops.

CITIZENSHIP

TAKE ACTION

The horror of the Civil War showed Americans that armed conflict should be avoided whenever possible.

Nevertheless, armed conflict is part of life in the United States today. US forces are engaged in conflict in several places in the world. Many US citizens volunteer to join the armed services: the Army, Navy, Air Force, Coast Guard, and Marines.

In small groups, make a list of any veterans of the armed forces that people in the group know. Does the list include anyone you talk to regularly?

Start by asking those who know a veteran to reach out and learn more about their stories of service. Have them ask if the person would be willing to come and talk to your class. Be sure the veterans know that they are coming to talk about their experiences and to help the class learn more about the Essential Question: *Why does conflict develop?*

Work with your teacher to arrange a day for some of the veterans to come and speak to the class about their service.

Before the veterans arrive, work with your group to create questions about conflict and about military service. Be sure your teacher has reviewed and approved your questions before the veterans arrive.

The Reconstruction Era

ESSENTIAL QUESTION

How do new ideas change the way people live?

Think about how this question would relate to people emerging from a civil war.

TALK ABOUT IT

Discuss with a partner what type of information you would need in order to understand the changes brought by new ideas after the Civil War. How did the changes affect the way ordinary people lived their lives?

DIRECTIONS: Now write down three additional questions that will help you explain how new ideas emerged during Reconstruction and changed the way Americans lived their lives. For example, you might ask "What were some new ideas that people were forced to deal with?

MY RESEARCH QUESTIONS

Supporting Question 1:

Supporting Question 2:

Supporting Question 3:

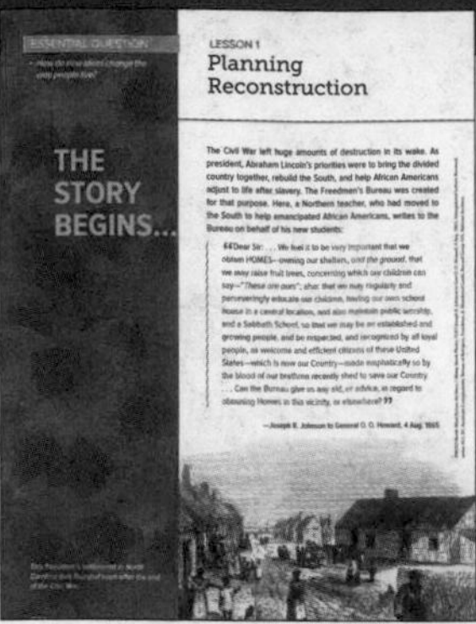

ESSENTIAL QUESTION

How do new ideas change the way people live?

As you gather evidence to answer the Essential Question, think about

- how government leaders implement new ideas.
- what happens when government leaders disagree about how a country should change.
- why people sometimes want to change or improve the way they live.

My Notes

Planning Reconstruction

DIRECTIONS: Search for evidence in Chapter 16, Lesson 1 to help you answer the following questions.

1 **EXPLAINING** What were the various plans for Reconstruction after the Civil War?

2 **DRAWING CONCLUSIONS** What were the advantages and the drawbacks of Lincoln's plan?

3 **INFERRING** What does Johnson's plan, in comparison to Lincoln's, tell you about the social and political climate of the country during Reconstruction?

4 **IDENTIFYING PROBLEMS AND SOLUTIONS** What problems did Congress face after the Civil War? How did they go about trying to solve those problems?

5 Complete the following chart.

Three Plans for Reconstruction

Plan	Description

6 **EXPLAINING** Why was the Freedmen's Bureau founded and what did it do?

ESSENTIAL QUESTION

How do new ideas change the way people live?

"When Lilacs Last in the Dooryard Bloom'd"

DIRECTIONS: Use the excerpt from the poem to answer the questions.

EXPLORE THE CONTEXT: Walt Whitman (1819–1892) was an American poet often referred to as "the father of free verse." In most of his poetry he broke with traditional poetic structures of rhyme and meter and wrote in longer, fluid sentences. This new idea about how to express oneself poetically changed poetry forever. In the following poem, Whitman is writing about witnessing the funeral train of President Abraham Lincoln carrying his body from Washington, D.C., to Springfield, Illinois. This train, draped in black fabric, stopped at cities along the way, where citizens gathered to pay tribute to their fallen president.

1 DETERMINING MEANING After reading the Introduction, what might the "star" represent in section 2 of the poem? What clues might indicate this?

____

____

____

____

____

____

____

____

____

____

____

____

PRIMARY SOURCE: POEM

"1

When lilacs last in the dooryard bloom'd,
And the great star early droop'd in the western sky in the night,
I mourn'd, and yet shall mourn with ever-returning spring.
Ever-returning spring, trinity sure to me you bring,
Lilac blooming perennial and drooping star in the west,
And thought of him I love.

2

O powerful western fallen star!
O shades of night—O moody, tearful night!
O great star disappear'd—O the black murk that hides the star!
O cruel hands that hold me powerless—O helpless soul of me!
O harsh surrounding cloud that will not free my soul.

3

In the dooryard fronting an old farm-house near the
white-wash'd palings,
Stands the lilac-bush tall-growing with heart-shaped
leaves of rich green,
With many a pointed blossom rising delicate,
with the perfume strong I love,
With every leaf a miracle—and from this bush in the dooryard,
With delicate-color'd blossoms and heart-shaped leaves of rich
green,
A sprig with its flower I break.

VOCABULARY

trinity: group of three
perennial: yearly
murk: darkness, gloom
palings: pickets for a picket fence
recesses: inner areas
thrush: a bird with a beautiful song
crape: archaic spelling of *crepe* – a light, thin wrinkled fabric, black bands of which were worn as a token of mourning
flambeau: torch
inloop'd: formed or draped in loops
sombre: sad, serious
dirge: a funeral song

. . . continued

4

In the swamp in secluded recesses,
A shy and hidden bird is warbling a song.

Solitary the thrush,
The hermit withdrawn to himself, avoiding the settlements,
Sings by himself a song.

Song of the bleeding throat,
Death's outlet song of life, (for well dear brother I know,
If thou wast not granted to sing thou would'st surely die.)

...

6

Coffin that passes through lanes and streets,
Through day and night with the great cloud darkening the land,
With the pomp of the inloop'd flags with the cities draped in black,
With the show of the States themselves as of
crape-veil'd women standing,
With processions long and winding and the flambeaus of the night,
With the countless torches lit, with the silent
sea of faces and the unbared heads,
With the waiting depot, the arriving coffin,
and the sombre faces,
With dirges through the night, with the thousand
voices rising strong and solemn,
With all the mournful voices of the dirges pour'd around the coffin,
The dim-lit churches and the shuddering
organs—where amid these you journey,
With the tolling tolling bells' perpetual clang,
Here, coffin that slowly passes,
I give you my sprig of lilac. . . . ”

—Walt Whitman, from "When Lilacs Last in the Dooryard Bloom'd," 1865

2 DRAWING CONCLUSIONS What conclusions can you draw in Section 4 about how the speaker feels toward the solitary thrush?

3 MAKE CONNECTIONS In what ways is Whitman's new style of poetry well suited for a poem about grief?

ESSENTIAL QUESTION

How do new ideas change the way people live?

A Southern Newspaper Reports "Glorious News"

DIRECTIONS: Use the excerpt from the article to answer the questions.

EXPLORE THE CONTEXT: William H. Seward (1801–1872) was secretary of state during Lincoln's presidency. Lewis Powell, part of the plot to kill Lincoln, seriously wounded Seward in his home on the day of Lincoln's assassination. At the same time, Confederate generals, including Robert E. Lee, had surrendered. The Civil War was coming to an end. However, communication of the news was sometimes faulty, as seen in the excerpt below.

PRIMARY SOURCE: NEWSPAPER ARTICLE

"GLORIOUS NEWS.
Lincoln and Seward Assassinated!
LEE DEFEATS GRANT.
Andy Johnson Inaugurated President.

We have been favored with the following private dispatch, which we hasten to lay before our readers, with the hope that it may prove true:

Demopolis, April 18, 1865—To Col. Garner:—Sir—The operator at Meridian has just telegraphed me that Memphis papers state, over the signature of Secretary [of War Edwin] Stanton, that Lincoln and Seward were both assassinated the same night at Washington City. Lincoln was shot through the head in the theatre; Seward slain while sick in bed.

Andy Johnson was inaugurated as President of the United States on the 15th.

This is said to be true without a doubt.

I inquired particularly from the operator as to whether there was anything more in regard to Lee's capitulation, and he said nothing at all from Northern papers.

A gentleman just in from Selma says it is believed in Selma that Lee and [General Joseph] Johnston had effected a junction and whipped Grant soundly. Passengers, wounded soldiers and officers can confirm this. This is given on the authority of the operator at Meridian.

JOHN W. HENLEY, Operator."

—*from the Demopolis, Alabama Herald*, April 18, 1865

VOCABULARY

dispatch: official communication sent by messenger
capitulation: surrender
junction: a coordinated effort, a joining together

1A DETERMINING MEANING What, according to this article, happened to William H. Seward?

1B What, according to the Introduction above, actually happened to Seward?

2 INTERPRETING INFORMATION Why do you think a newspaper in a Southern town would print this report?

3A INTERPRETING INFORMATION What do the headlines tell you about how Southerners felt when they learned about President Lincoln's assassination?

3B Why do you think Southerners felt this way?

4 MAKING CONNECTIONS How is news communicated today? Do you think it is more accurate? Why or why not?

The Radicals Take Control

DIRECTIONS: Search for evidence in Chapter 16, Lesson 2 to help you answer the following questions.

ESSENTIAL QUESTION

How do new ideas change the way people live?

As you gather evidence to answer the Essential Question, think about

- how government leaders implement new ideas.
- what happens when government leaders disagree about how a country should change.
- why people sometimes want to change or improve the way they live.

My Notes

1. **IDENTIFYING CAUSE AND EFFECT** What was the effect of Congress's disagreement with President Johnson?

2. **INFERRING** What made Radical Reconstruction and the Radical Republicans so "radical"?

3. **IDENTIFYING PROBLEM AND SOLUTION** How did the black codes and the rising racial tensions in the South affect Congress? How did Congress decide to approach that problem?

4. **EVALUATING** Do you think the Fifteenth Amendment was an effective solution to racial problems in the South? Why or why not?

5 **IDENTIFYING CAUSE AND EFFECT** Fill in the chart with steps in the Impeachment of President Andrew Johnson.

ESSENTIAL QUESTION

How do new ideas change the way people live?

Two New Amendments

DIRECTIONS: Use the documents below to answer the questions.

EXPLORE THE CONTEXT: The Thirteenth, Fourteenth, and Fifteenth Amendments to the U.S. Constitution are called the Civil War Amendments. They are called this because they were ratified in the aftermath of, and because of, the Civil War. The amendments are of great historical importance: these actions expressed new ideas that dramatically changed the way millions of people live. Below are excerpts from the Thirteenth and the Fifteenth Amendments that show their most important points.

PRIMARY SOURCE: U.S. CONSTITUTION

"THIRTEENTH AMENDMENT

Section 1

Neither slavery nor involuntary servitude, except as a punishment for crime whereof the party shall have been duly convicted, shall exist within the United States, or any place subject to their jurisdiction.

Section 2

Congress shall have power to enforce this article by appropriate legislation.

Passed by Congress January 31, 1865. Ratified December 6, 1865."

"FIFTEENTH AMENDMENT

Section 1

The right of citizens of the United States to vote shall not be denied or abridged by the United States or by any State on account of race, color, or previous condition of servitude.

Section 2

The Congress shall have the power to enforce this article by appropriate legislation.

Passed by Congress February 26, 1869. Ratified February 3, 1870."

— The Constitution of the United States of America

VOCABULARY

involuntary servitude: being forced to work for another person
duly: appropriately
jurisdiction: area of control
ratified: officially approved
abridged: lessened

1A IDENTIFYING CENTRAL IDEAS What is the basic purpose of the Thirteenth Amendment?

1B Was this considered a new idea at the time? Explain your answer.

2A ANALYZING SOURCES What is the basic purpose of the Fifteenth Amendment?

2B DETERMINING MEANING What does "previous condition of servitude" mean?

2C Was what this amendment accomplished considered a new idea at the time? Explain your answer.

3 Whose lives were changed by the ideas made into law through these amendments?

ESSENTIAL QUESTION

How do new ideas change the way people live?

An Interview with a Formerly Enslaved Person

DIRECTIONS: Use the excerpt from the interview to answer the questions.

EXPLORE THE CONTEXT: In the 1930s, the federal government launched a program to record the memories of formerly enslaved African Americans. Their recollections are a fascinating glimpse of life during and after slavery. Here, A. J. Mitchell recalls voting. Mitchell was 78 at the time of the interview. He was born at about the time the Civil War began.

PRIMARY SOURCE: INTERVIEW

“I've cast a many a vote. Not a bit of trouble in the world. Hope elect most all the old officers here in town.... Well of course, Miss, I don't think it's right when they disfranchised the colored people. I tell you, Miss, I read the Bible and the Bible says every man has his rights — the poor and the free and the bound. I got good sense from the time I leaped in this world. I 'member well I used to go and cast my vote just that quick but they got so they wouldn't let you vote unless you could read.

I've had 'em to offer me money to vote the Democrat ticket. I told him, no. I didn't think that was principle. The colored man ain't got no representive now. Colored men used to be elected to the legislature and they'd go and sell out. Some of 'em used to vote the Democrat ticket. God wants every man to have his birthright.”

—from an interview with A.J. Mitchell, a formerly enslaved man, in the late 1930s

VOCABULARY

Hope: Helped
disfranchised: took away the right to vote from
was principle: was right or ethical
representive: representative
birthright: natural right held by all people

1. **EXPLAINING** Who are the "bound" that Mitchell refers to along with the free and the poor?

2. **ANALYZING TEXT** What words does Mitchell use to state that he has a right to vote?

3. **INTERPRETING** What is Mitchell complaining about in the second paragraph?

4. **MAKING CONNECTIONS** How might Mitchell's voting have changed his life?

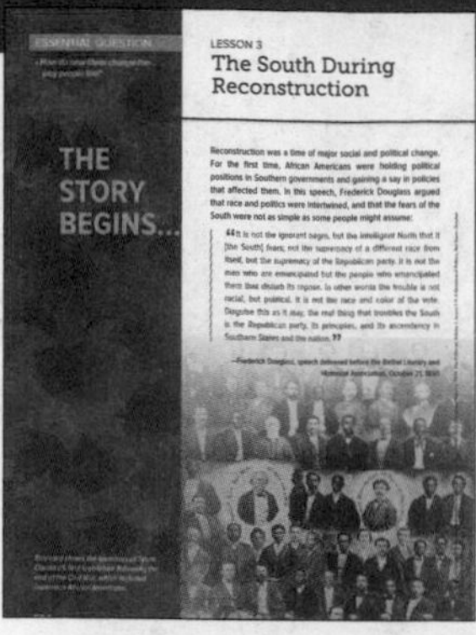

ESSENTIAL QUESTION

How do new ideas change the way people live?

As you gather evidence to answer the Essential Question, think about

- how government leaders implement new ideas.
- what happens when government leaders disagree about how a country should change.
- why do people sometimes want to change or improve the way they live.

My Notes

The South During Reconstruction

DIRECTIONS: Search for evidence in Chapter 16, Lesson 3 to help you answer the following questions.

1 **EXPLAINING** What did Frederick Douglass mean when he said, "It is not the race and color of the vote" that Southerners feared?

2 **CITING TEXT EVIDENCE** Were African Americans included in the new governments set up after the war?

3 **DETERMINING MEANING** Who were "scalawags" and "carpetbaggers"?

4 EXPLAINING What were some of the ways white Southerners resisted Reconstruction?

5 IDENTIFYING EFFECTS

Fill in the boxes with disadvantages of the sharecropping system.

ESSENTIAL QUESTION

How do new ideas change the way people live?

A Ku Klux Klan Threat

DIRECTIONS: Use the excerpt from the letter below to answer the questions that follow.

EXPLORE THE CONTEXT: The African American man who received this letter, Davie Jeems, had been elected to the Sheriff's Office of the County of Lincoln, Georgia. Similar threats to other Republican officials prevented them from assuming their positions.

PRIMARY SOURCE: LETTER

"NOTICE

To Jeems, Davie. you. must. be, a good boy. and. Quit. hunting on Sunday and shooting your gun in the night. you keep people from sleeping. I live in a big rock above the Ford of the f Creek. I went from Lincoln County during the War I was Killed at Manassus in 1861 I am here now as a Locust in the day Time and. at night I am a Ku Klux sent here to look after you and all the rest of the radicals and make you know your place. I have got my eye on you every day, I am at the Ford of the creek every evening From Sundown till dark I want to meet you there next Saturday tell platt Madison we have, a Box. For him and you. We nail all, radicals up in Boxes and send them away to KKK - there is. 200 000 ded men retured to this country to make you and all the rest of the radicals good Democrats and vote right with the white people you have got it to do or leave this country. . . . Take heed and govern yourself accordingly and give all your Friends timely warning.

Ku, Ku, Klux, Klan"

—from a letter by a member of the Ku Klux Klan, c. 1868

VOCABULARY

Manassus: the first Battle of Manassas; also called the First Battle of Bull Run

ford: shallow part of creek where people and animals cross

200 000 ded men: 200,000 dead Confederate soldiers

1A **DETERMINING MEANING** What does the letter-writer mean by "I was Killed at Manassus in 1861" and "I am here now as a Locust"?

1B **INFERRING** Why does he do this?

1C What does the writer threaten Jeems with?

1D What does the letter writer want Jeems to do?

2 **INFERRING** What can you infer about the letter writer?

3 **MAKING CONNECTIONS** What does this letter tell you about how people sometimes react to new ideas?

ESSENTIAL QUESTION

How do new ideas change the way people live?

Remembering the Ku Klux Klan

DIRECTIONS: Use the excerpt from the interview below to answer the questions that follow.

EXPLORE THE CONTEXT: The Ku Klux Klan arose during Reconstruction. Klansmen terrorized African Americans to prevent them from exercising their new rights as free people. Waters McIntosh was born in Sumter County, South Carolina, in 1862. After Reconstruction, he moved to Arkansas and attended college, becoming a minister. Later, he also studied and practiced law. Below is an excerpt from an interview with McIntosh, who had witnessed Klan activities firsthand as a young boy.

PRIMARY SOURCE: INTERVIEW

“Whenever there was a man of influence, [Klansmen] terrorized him. They were at their height about the time of [President Grant's election in 1868]. Many a time my mother and I have watched them pass our door. They wore gowns and some kind of helmet. They would be going to catch some leading Negro and whip him. There was scarcely a night they couldn't take a leading Negro out and whip him if they would catch him alone. On that account, the Negro men did not stay at home in Sumter County, South Carolina at night. They left home and stayed together. The Ku Klux very seldom interfered with a woman or a child. ...

They often scared colored people by drinking large quantities of water. They had something that held a lot of water, and when they would raise the bucket to their mouths to drink, they would slip the water into it.”

—from an interview with Waters McIntosh, a formerly enslaved man, in the late 1930s

1A **ANALYZING TEXT** Where did the events McIntosh describes take place?

1B When did the events McIntosh describes take place?

2 **EXPLAINING** In what ways did Klansmen terrorize the people they targeted?

3 **MAKING CONNECTIONS** What were the new ideas that entered the lives of the Klansmen and African Americans that led to the sort of violence McIntosh witnessed?

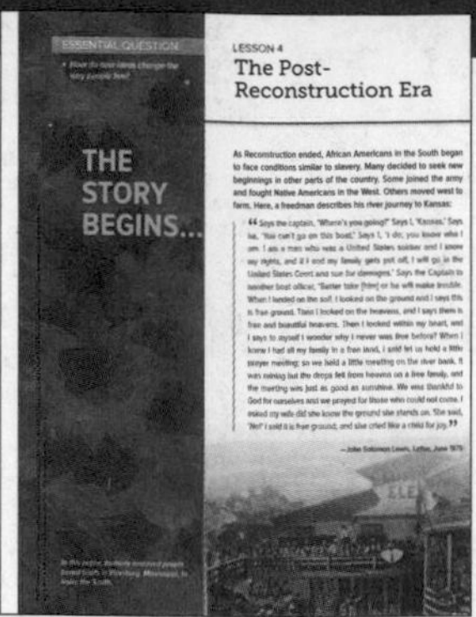

ESSENTIAL QUESTION

How do new ideas change the way people live?

As you gather evidence to answer the Essential Question, think about

- how government leaders implement new ideas.
- what happens when government leaders disagree about how a country should change.
- why people sometimes want to change or improve the way they live.

My Notes

The Post-Reconstruction Era

DIRECTIONS: Search for evidence in Chapter 16, Lesson 4 to help you answer the following questions.

1 **IDENTIFYING EFFECTS** How did President Grant's lack of experience affect the Republican Party?

2 **DRAWING CONCLUSIONS** What implications did the Republican Party losing the majority in Congress have for African Americans?

3 **SUMMARIZING** In the election of 1876, what concession did Republicans make in order to have President Hayes take office?

4 **IDENTIFYING** What changes characterized the "New South"?

5 Fill in the chart with obstacles to voting that African Americans faced in the South.

Obstacles to Voting Facing Southern African Americans	

6 **IDENTIFYING PROBLEMS AND SOLUTIONS** What problems did African Americans face after Reconstruction? How did they seek to solve those problems?

ESSENTIAL QUESTION

How do new ideas change the way people live?

Buffalo Soldier

DIRECTIONS: Use the photograph to answer the following questions.

EXPLORE THE CONTEXT: "Buffalo soldiers" was the name Native Americans gave to the African American soldiers of the U.S. 10th Cavalry. Eventually, all African American regiments were known as Buffalo Soldiers. The Buffalo Soldier regiments were created in 1866 and served in many capacities. Some fought in the Indian Wars, and some were responsible for protecting travelers in stagecoaches and on trains. Others helped build roads and military installations.

PRIMARY SOURCE: PHOTOGRAPH

Buffalo Soldier, 25th Infantry, Company J, c. 1884–1890

1 DESCRIBING What is your first impression of this photograph?

2 DRAWING CONCLUSIONS What conclusions might you draw about this man from the expression on his face, his clothing, and his body language?

3 HISTORY Looking back at Lesson 4 in your textbook, what aspects of this photograph confirm what is said there about the Buffalo Soldiers?

4 MAKING CONNECTIONS How is becoming a Buffalo Soldier evidence of how new ideas change the way people live?

ESSENTIAL QUESTION

How do new ideas change the way people live?

The "Jim Crow" Car

DIRECTIONS: Use the poem below to answer the questions.

EXPLORE THE CONTEXT: "Jim Crow" was the system of laws and practices that segregated, or separated, whites and African Americans from the 1880s to the 1960s. During this time, African Americans and whites went to separate schools, sat in different sections of theaters, and even had to use separate restrooms. The Jim Crow car was a separate train car for African Americans. The name "Jim Crow" comes from a character in a song that was popular before the Civil War.

Reverend Walter Henderson Brooks (1851–1945) was an ordained Baptist minister and an accomplished poet, orator, and reformer. He was also an African American. In this poem, he describes his experience on a train in the South during the Jim Crow era.

PRIMARY SOURCE: POEM

"This too is done to crush me,
But naught can keep us back;
'My place.' forsooth, a section.
'Twixt smoker, front and back,
While others ride in coaches
Full large and filled with light,
And this our Southern Christians
Insist is just and right.

There Yellow man from China,
And Red man from the plain,
Are seated with the White man,
But I could not remain.
However clean my person,
My linen and my life,
They snarl: "Your k-yar ahead, Jim,
Go thar and take your wife."

We're singled out from others,
A mark for shafts of scorn,
Here huddled, like tamed cattle,

VOCABULARY

naught: nothing
forsooth: indeed
'twixt: between
smoker: train car where smoking was allowed
k-yar: another way to pronounce "car"
thar: there
shafts: arrows
gird: put on in preparation

. . . continued

From early night til morn;
The golden rule's rejected,
Who cares for such a thing?
Do they whose prejudice o'er race
Inflict this bitter sting?

This insult almost kills me—
God, help me bear the wrong,
Well, mine's the story of the weak
Who falls before the strong ;
Who fall—to rise in triumph,
When God his sword shall gird.
And the proudest evil doer
Shall tremble at His word. ”

—Reverend Walter Henderson Brooks, a poem in *The Richmond Planet,* Richmond, Virginia, September 15, 1900

1 **INFERRING** How does the experience of Asian Americans and Native Americans compare to that of African Americans in this poem?

2 **EXPLAINING** What gives comfort to the writer of this poem?

3 **ANALYZING TEXT** Do you think the writer has any "new ideas" about Jim Crow?

ESSENTIAL QUESTION

How do new ideas change the way people live?

1 Think About It

Review the supporting questions that you developed at the beginning of the chapter. Review the evidence that you gathered in Chapter 16. Were you able to answer each supporting question? If there was not enough evidence to answer your supporting questions, what additional evidence do you think you need to include?

2 Organize Your Evidence

Use the graphic organizer below to list what you have learned about how new ideas change the way people live.

Source	Effects of New Ideas
"When Lilacs Last in the Dooryard Bloom'd"	
Glorious News!	
Fifteenth Amendment	
Interview with a Formerly Enslaved Person	
Ku Klux Klan letter	
Remembering the Klan	
Photograph of a Buffalo Soldier	
"The 'Jim Crow 'Car"	

3 Talk About It

Work in a small group. Discuss the effects of new ideas you included in the graphic organizer you completed for step 2. Did everyone jot down the same basic ideas, or were your classmates' responses different from your own? Discuss any differences in what you wrote down. Take notes so that you can create a new graphic organizer that includes the best ideas of your group.

4 Write About It

Write about a way that conflict led you to have a new idea. Consider the evidence you and your group organized in steps 2 and 3 and see if you can apply what you have learned to your own experience.

5 Connect to the Essential Question

Using your work from step 2 above, work with your group to create a skit that connects what you have learned to the ESSENTIAL QUESTION: ***How do new ideas change the way people live?*** Be sure you provide multiple answers to the Essential Question, bringing them to life for your classmates in a classroom performance.

CITIZENSHIP
TAKING ACTION

After the Civil War, the Southern states had to rejoin the Union. For a period of time, citizens in the former Confederacy did not enjoy the same rights of citizenship as the areas that were in the Union. You might be surprised to learn that there are still places that are part of the United States but which do not enjoy all the rights and privileges of full citizenship that other regions do.

Get together with a partner and use the Internet to research Puerto Rico or Washington, D.C. Both of these places are part of the United States, but citizens living in those places do not have equal rights with other Americans.

How many of these places does the United States control? What rights do they have, and what rights do they lack? Do people in those places tend to like it that way, or do they fight against it? Choose Washington, D.C., Puerto Rico, or another territory of the United States and find out more about the rights of American citizens who live there.

What can you do to educate others in your community about these "less equal" parts of the United States? Working with your partner, decide what message you want to spread. Do you think it is a good thing that the United States controls parts of the world without granting those areas the full benefits of citizenship? What advantages does the United States gain from this arrangement? Do these areas gain advantages from this relationship?

Take action to educate other students and people in your community about these places that are part of the United States. Choose just one "big message" to tell people. Then choose a method of telling them: making a website, posting on social media, executing a poster campaign, designing a slogan for a T-shirt, writing an article for the newspaper, recording a podcast, or anything else you can think of. It's your choice how you tell people about this issue, but be sure that you have a message and get it out there!

Opening the West

ESSENTIAL QUESTION

How does geography influence the way people live?

Think about how this question relates to the opening of the American West.

TALK ABOUT IT

Discuss with a partner what type of information you would need to know to answer this question. For example, one question might be: Is the West all the same geographically, or does it vary from place to place?

DIRECTIONS: Now write down three additional questions that you need to answer to explain how geography influences the way people live.

MY RESEARCH QUESTIONS

Supporting Question 1:

____

____

Supporting Question 2:

____

____

Supporting Question 3:

____

____

ESSENTIAL QUESTION

How does geography influence the way people live?

As you gather evidence to answer the Essential Question, think about

- how what was found in the ground drew so many people west.
- what life in boomtowns was like.
- what role railroads played in the late 1800s.

My Notes

Mining and Railroads in the West

DIRECTIONS: Search for evidence in Chapter 17, Lesson 1 to help you answer the following questions.

1 **IDENTIFYING CAUSES** Why had about 50,000 newcomers arrived in Colorado by 1859?

2 **EXPLAINING** What is ore? Why does it make mining difficult?

3 **DESCRIBE** What was the Comstock Lode? When and where was it discovered?

4 **DESCRIBE** What is a boomtown? What was life like there?

5 ANALYZING Complete the table below to show why railroads were vital for westward growth.

The Importance of Railroads	
For People in the West	For People in the East

6 EXPLAINING How was the transcontinental railroad paid for?

7 DESCRIBING EFFECTS Complete the table below with the effects of the expansion of railroads across the United States.

Effects of Railroad Expansion

ESSENTIAL QUESTION

How does geography influence the way people live?

"Mining on the Comstock"

DIRECTIONS: Study the image below. Then provide answers to the questions that follow.

EXPLORE THE CONTEXT: Named for prospector Henry Comstock, the Comstock Lode was an enormous silver deposit. Gold was found there as well. Mines on the Comstock Lode were productive from 1859 to 1865. Later, more ore was found, and mines were productive again from 1873 to 1882. Virginia City, in Nevada, was the Comstock Lode's boomtown.

VOCABULARY

lithograph: image printed using lithography, in which a hard surface is treated to repel ink except where it is used to form an image

lode: a rich vein of ore

PRIMARY SOURCE: LITHOGRAPH

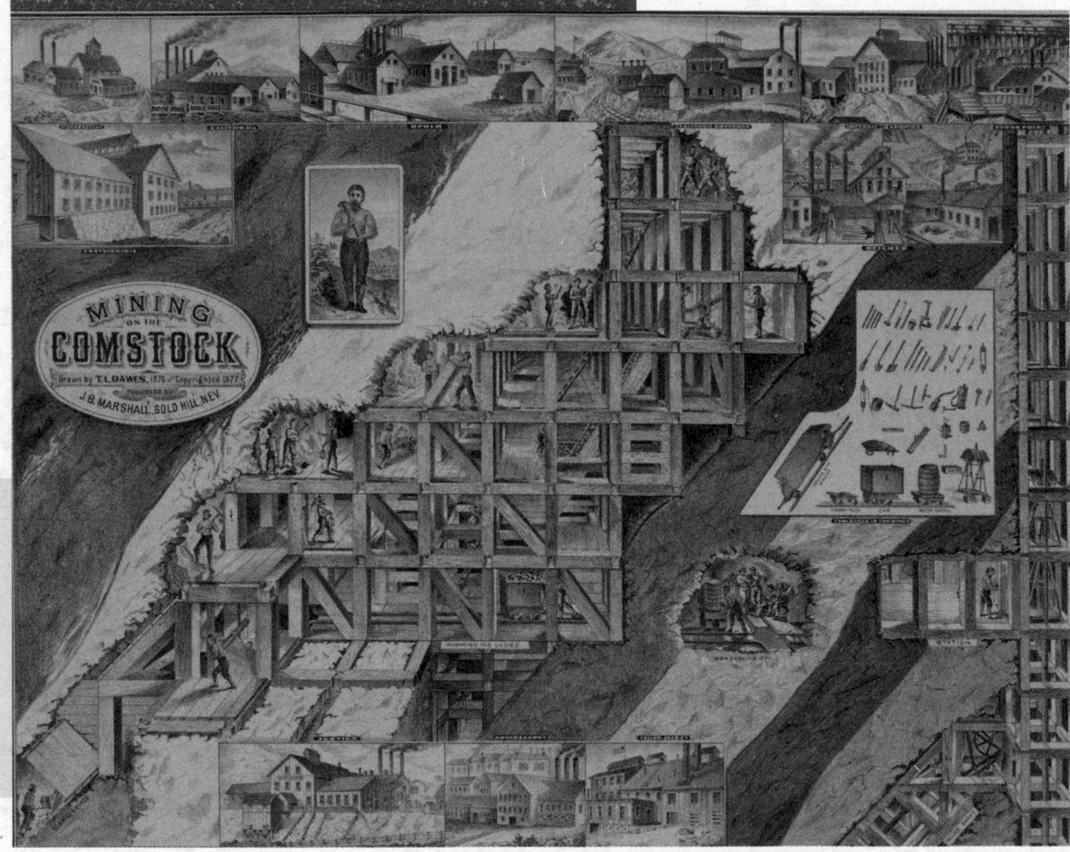

Mining on the Comstock, lithograph, 1876

1A ANALYZING SOURCES Looking at the lithograph, do you think it was difficult to build the mine? Why or why not?

1B ANALYZING SOURCES What might you infer from this?

2 EXPLAINING What do you think is the purpose of the lithograph?

3 INFERRING What do you think is the purpose of the above-ground buildings when the mining takes place underground?

4 GEOGRAPHY Does this lithograph support the idea that geography influences the way people live? Explain.

ESSENTIAL QUESTION

How does geography influence the way people live?

"Our New West"

DIRECTIONS: Read the passage below. Then respond to the questions that follow.

EXPLORE THE CONTEXT: Samuel Bowles (1826–1878) was a journalist from Massachusetts. He and others rode the new railroads out west during the summers of 1865 and 1866. Fascinated by what he saw, he told the people of the East about America's "New West" in a book. In the excerpt below, Bowles describes some of the things he observed.

PRIMARY SOURCE: BOOK

"We witnessed ... the fabulous speed with which the Railroad was built. Through the two or three hundred miles beyond were scattered ten to fifteen thousand men in great gangs preparing the road bed; plows, scrapers, shovels, picks and carts; and, among the rocks, drills and powder were doing the grading as rapidly as men could stand and move with their tools. Long trains brought up to the end of the completed track loads of ties and rails; the former were transferred to teams, sent one or two miles ahead, and put in place upon the grade. Then rails and spikes were reloaded on platform cars, these pushed up to the last previously laid rail, and with an automatic movement and a celerity that were wonderful, practiced hands dropped the fresh rails one after another on the ties exactly in line, huge sledges sent the spikes home, the car rolled on, and the operation was repeated; while every few minutes the long heavy train behind sent out a puff from its locomotive, and caught up with its load of material the advancing work. The only limit, inside of eight miles in twenty-four hours, to the rapidity with which the track could thus be laid, was the power of the road behind to bring forward the materials.

As the Railroad marched thus rapidly across the broad Continent of plain and mountain, there was improvised a rough and temporary town at its every public stopping-place. As this was changed every

VOCABULARY

powder: gunpowder, used for blasting through rocks
grading: leveling
garments: clothes
ties: pieces of wood that support the railroad track
rails: metal track
spikes: very large metal nails used to attach the track to the ties
celerity: speed
sledges: sledgehammers
shanties: shacks
hovels: small, unpleasant dwellings
aught: anything
desperadoes: criminals

. . . continued

thirty or forty days, these settlements were of the most perishable materials,—canvas tents, plain board shanties, and turf-hovels, —pulled down and sent forward for a new career, or deserted as worthless, at every grand movement of the Railroad company. Only a small proportion of their populations had aught to do with the [rail]road, or any legitimate occupation. Most were the hangers-on ... restaurant and saloon keepers, gamblers, desperadoes of every grade.... ”

—Samuel Bowles, from *Our New West: Records of Travel between the Mississippi River and the Pacific Ocean,* 1869

1 **DETERMINING PURPOSE** Who was the intended audience for Bowles's writing?

2A **INFERRING** What railroad do you think the author is writing about?

2B What evidence is there for this?

3 GEOGRAPHY Does this document support the idea that geography influences the way people live? Explain.

Ranchers and Farmers

DIRECTIONS: Search for evidence in Chapter 17, Lesson 2 to help you answer the following questions.

1 EXPLAINING Where did the wild longhorn cattle of the Texas Plains come from?

2A EXPLAINING What were "long drives"?

2B What was their purpose?

3 ANALYZING Think about the settlers who decided to live on the Great Plains. Complete the table by describing how each factor helped them to settle these new areas.

Factors That Encouraged Settlement of the Great Plains	
Factor	How It Encouraged Settlement
railroads	
Homestead Act	
new technology	

ESSENTIAL QUESTION

How does geography influence the way people live?

As you gather evidence to answer the Essential Question, think about

- how the cattle business developed in the West.
- what drew people to the Great Plains.
- how the farmers on the Great Plains lived.

My Notes

4 **DESCRIBING** What was life like on the Great Plains?

5 GEOGRAPHY How did farmers grow crops in the drier regions of the Great Plains?

ESSENTIAL QUESTION

How does geography influence the way people live?

Bronc Busters: The Story of Two Texas Cowboys

DIRECTIONS: Read the excerpt from the interview below. Then answer the questions that follow.

EXPLORE THE CONTEXT: Elvira Hobbs Law was born in Tennessee and moved with her family to Texas in 1890. After marrying a cowboy, she lived on a Texas cattle ranch in the late 1890s. Here, she gives an eyewitness account of the life of a cowboy.

PRIMARY SOURCE: INTERVIEW

"My brother, John Hobbs, had the same love of horses I did, and got a job on the Upchurch [Ranch] in the Sulphur River Bottoms. The Upchurch Ranch ran 8,000 head of cattle on about 12,000 acres. His brand was an '8' on the animal's right hip. John liked to work with horses, and got Upchurch to let him wrangle the horse herd. He done just that, and that was where John got his training to be a bronc buster. One season with that herd, and he never done anything else but bust horses as long as he worked around ranches. He used to go to the different ranches and take contracts for busting their horses. ... That looked to me like the hardest way in the world to make a living, but John seemed to get along at it. It finally done him up in the end, though, because every step he takes today pains him....

John broke both them horses from wild horses, but there was another horse he broke for himself. She was a race mare he named 'Daisy,' because she was such a pretty thing....

It seemed like the cowboys didn't like the Rusk Ranch, or were drifters, because they kept drifting in and then out. Among the best riders that ever came there were Harvey Rawlings, John Lewis, and Bob Roden.

Bob Roden's riding days were finished on that place. One day, his horse shied at a sand rattler, and started pitching. Bob was pitched

VOCABULARY

wrangle: manage

bronc buster: person who broke and trained broncs, a name for wild horses

bust horses: train wild horses

skittish: nervous, jumpy

sand rattler: a kind of snake

pitching: bucking to throw off a rider

drug: dragged

. . . *continued*

off, but his left foot hung in the stirrup. His horse ran round and round a clump of cedars, and drug Bob all the way.... Bob lay between death and life for a long time before he rallied, then he left the range a broken man.

You can't hardly realize just how dangerous a cowboy's work is 'til you've seen the narrow escapes they have. Besides riding broncs and wild horses, there's stampedes to put up with. A stampeding herd is something to be really reckoned with, because it runs over anything it can't knock down if it doesn't look too big.... After a herd has got sort of skittish, any kind of a sudden noise will start it off like an airplane. Just roaring along with the noise of a freight train at full speed.”

—from an Interview with Elvira Hobbs Law

1. **ANALYZING TEXT** Law says the Upchurch Ranch included about 12,000 acres. What does this tell you about the geography of the Great Plains?

2. **GEOGRAPHY** How did the geography of the Great Plains influence John Hobbs's choice of career?

3. **IDENTIFY CAUSES** Why does Law say of John that "every step he takes today pains him"?

4. **DESCRIBING** How would you describe the life of a cowboy?

ESSENTIAL QUESTION

How does geography influence the way people live?

A Sod House on the Great Plains

DIRECTIONS: Study the photograph below. Then respond to the questions that follow.

EXPLORE THE CONTEXT: Americans have long called the Great Plains the "Great American Desert." It was a vast grassland with very few trees. No trees meant no lumber. Settlers had to improvise with other materials to build homes and other structures. The photograph below shows what they used.

PRIMARY SOURCE: PHOTOGRAPH

A family in front of their sod house in Custer County, Nebraska, 1890

VOCABULARY

sod: top layer of soil with grass growing on it

soddie: a house made of layers of sod

1 INFERRING What can you infer about the geography of Custer County, Nebraska, based on this photograph?

2A ANALYZING SOURCES What is the structure in the photograph?

2B INFERRING How was the home heated? How do you know?

3 EXPLAINING What kinds of animals are in the photograph? What do you think they were used for?

ESSENTIAL QUESTION

How does geography influence the way people live?

As you gather evidence to answer the Essential Question, think about

- how Native Americans survived on the Great Plains.
- why there were conflicts between Native Americans and settlers.
- how Native American culture changed.

My Notes

Native American Struggles

DIRECTIONS: Search for evidence in Chapter 17, Lesson 3 to help you answer the following questions.

1. **CITING TEXT EVIDENCE** Which groups were in conflict on the Great Plains? What did they compete for?

2. **ANALYZING** How was the buffalo key to the survival of Native Americans on the Great Plains?

3. **IDENTIFYING CENTRAL IDEAS** What did the Treaty of Fort Laramie promise? Was the promise kept?

4. **ANALYZING TEXT** Which words attributed to Chief Joseph reveal how he feels about surrendering?

5 Complete the chart to show aims and features of the Dawes Act.

The Dawes Act

ESSENTIAL QUESTION

How does geography influence the way people live?

General Custer's *My Life on the Plains*

DIRECTIONS: Study the excerpt below. Then respond to the questions that follow.

EXPLORE THE CONTEXT: George Armstrong Custer is one of the most famous people in American history. Many people know him for his defeat at the Battle of Little Bighorn. However, earlier in his career, he was so successful as a soldier for the Union during the Civil War that he was made a general at the young age of 23. After the war, stationed on the Great Plains, Custer was a keen observer of geography, as seen in the passage below.

PRIMARY SOURCE: BOOK

"The favorite range of the buffalo is contained in a belt of country running north and south, about two hundred miles wide, and extending from the Platte river on the north to the valley of the Upper Canadian on the south. In migrating, if not grazing or alarmed, the buffalo invariably moves in single file, the column generally being headed by a patriarch of the herd, who is not only familiar with the topography of the county, but is the leader of his herd. He maintains this leadership only so long as his strength and courage enable him to remain the successful champion in the innumerable contests which he is called upon to maintain. The buffalo trails are always objects of interest and inquiry to the sight-seer on the Plains. These trails made by the herds in their migrating movements are so regular in their construction and course as to well excite curiosity. They vary but little from eight to ten inches in width, and are usually from two to four inches in depth; their course is almost as unvarying as that of the [compass] needle, running north and south. . . .

Wherever water is found on the Plains, particularly if it is standing, innumerable gadflies and mosquitoes generally abound. To such an

VOCABULARY

invariably: every time
patriarch: male head of a group
innumerable: many
sanguinary: bloodthirsty
myriads: countless numbers

. . . *continued*

extent do these pests to the animal kingdom exist, that to our thinly-coated animals, such as the horse and mule, grazing is almost an impossibility, while the buffalo with his huge shaggy coat can browse undisturbed. The most sanguinary and determined of these troublesome insects are the 'buffalo flies'; they move in myriads, and so violent and painful are their assaults upon horses that a herd of the latter has been known to stampede as the result of an attack from a swarm of these flies.”

—General George Armstrong Custer, from *My Life on the Plains*, 1874

1 **INFERRING** For whom was Custer writing? How do you know?

2 **IDENTIFYING POINT OF VIEW** How would you describe Custer's attitude toward buffalo?

3 **IDENTIFYING CAUSE** What does Custer say causes the horses to stampede?

ESSENTIAL QUESTION

How does geography influence the way people live?

1 IDENTIFYING CENTRAL IDEAS What is Custer being ordered to do?

2A INFERRING What are the Rosebud, Little Bighorn, Tongue, and Little Horn?

2B Why are they mentioned?

VOCABULARY

regiment: a large group of soldiers

zeal: passion

supply-steamer: steamboat carrying supplies

Custer's Last Orders

DIRECTIONS: Study the excerpt below. Then respond to the questions that follow.

EXPLORE THE CONTEXT: General George Armstrong Custer's defeat at Little Bighorn is legendary. It is one of the most studied battles in history. At the time, Custer was known as a brilliant commander, and his defeat seemed unthinkable. Below are the last orders Custer received.

PRIMARY SOURCE: MILITARY ORDERS

"Headquarters of the Department of Dakota (In the Field)
Camp at Mouth of Rosebud River, Montana Territory June 22nd, 1876

Lieutenant-Colonel Custer,
7th Calvary

Colonel: The Brigadier-General Commanding directs that, as soon as your regiment can be made ready for the march, you will proceed up the Rosebud in pursuit of the Indians whose trail was discovered by Major Reno a few days since. It is impossible to give you any definite instructions in regard to this movement, and were it not impossible to do so the Department Commander places too much confidence in your zeal, energy, and ability to wish to impose upon you precise orders which might hamper your action when nearly in contact with the enemy. He will, however, indicate to you his own views of what your action should be, and he desires that you should conform to them unless you shall see sufficient reason for departing from them. He thinks that you should proceed up the Rosebud until you ascertain definitely the direction in which the trail above spoken of leads. Should it be found (as it appears almost certain that it will be found) to turn towards the Little Bighorn, he thinks that you should still proceed southward, perhaps as far as the headwaters of the Tongue, and then turn toward the Little Horn, feeling constantly, however, to your left, so as to preclude the escape of the Indians passing around your left flank.

. . . continued

The column of Colonel Gibbon is now in motion for the mouth of the Big Horn. As soon as it reaches that point it will cross the Yellowstone and move up at least as far as the forks of the Big and Little Horns. Of course its future movements must be controlled by circumstances as they arise, but it is hoped that the Indians, if upon the Little Horn, may be so nearly inclosed by the two columns that their escape will be impossible. The Department Commander desires that on your way up the Rosebud you should thoroughly examine the upper part of Tullock's Creek, and that you should endeavor to send a scout through to Colonel Gibbon's command.

The supply-steamer will be pushed up the Big Horn as far as the forks of the river is found to be navigable for that distance, and the Department Commander, who will accompany the column of Colonel Gibbon, desires you to report to him there not later than the expiration of the time for which your troops are rationed, unless in the mean time you receive further orders.”

Very respectfully, Your obedient servant,
E. W. Smith, Captain, 18th Infantry A. A. J. G.

3 **EXPLAINING** Rewrite this sentence in simpler language: “The supply-steamer will be pushed up the Big Horn as far as the forks of the river is found to be navigable for that distance.”

4 **DETERMINING POINT OF VIEW** What are some words you could use to describe the tone of this letter?

hESSENTIAL QUESTION

How does geography influence the way people live?

As you gather evidence to answer the Essential Question, think about

- what problems confronted farmers in the late 1800s.
- why the National Grange was formed.
- what new political party appeared.

My Notes

Farmers—A New Political Force

DIRECTIONS: Search for evidence in Chapter 17, Lesson 4 to help you answer the following questions.

1. **EXPLAINING** What hardships faced American farmers in the late 1800s? Complete the table.

Life on the Farm Gets More Difficult	
Factor	**What It Did**
supply	
demand	
prices	
railroad companies	
banks	

2 **IDENTIFYING CAUSES** How did farming on the Great Plains cause the price of crops to fall?

3 **IDENTIFYING EFFECTS** What network did farmers form in response to economic hardships?

4 **RELATING EVENTS** Complete the flow chart.

From Farmers to Political Force

Farmers Alliance	became	

5 **EXPLAINING** Why did the Populists support free silver?

ESSENTIAL QUESTION

How does geography influence the way people live?

"I Feed You All!"

DIRECTIONS: Study the lithograph below. Then respond to the questions that follow.

EXPLORE THE CONTEXT: In the late 1800s, more Americans lived in rural areas than in urban areas. The National Grange was a reflection of the newfound pride and power of the American farmer, as seen below.

VOCABULARY

lithograph: image printed using lithography, in which a hard surface is treated to repel ink except where it is used to form an image

physic: treat medically

PRIMARY SOURCE: LITHOGRAPH

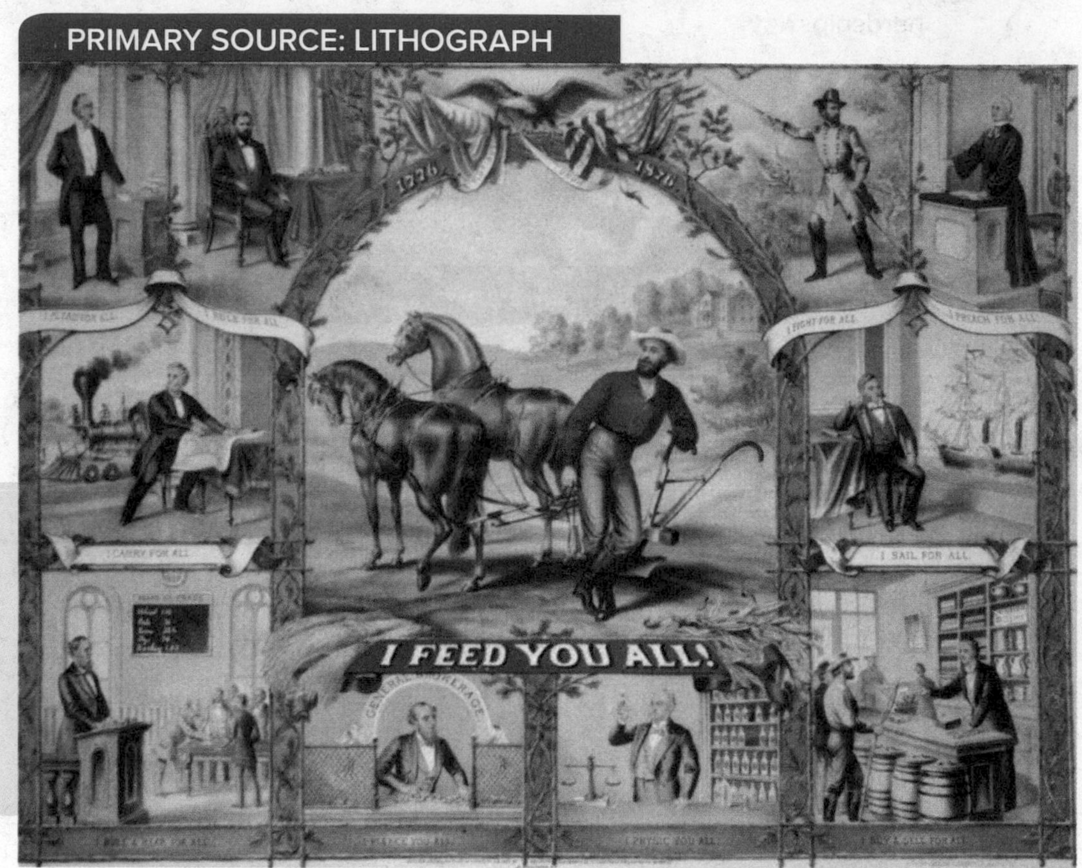

In this c. 1875 lithograph, the central image is surrounded many smaller ones. The smaller ones are: a lawyer ("I Plead for All"); President Ulysses S. Grant ("I Rule for All"); an officer leading a charge ("I Fight for All"); a clergyman ("I Preach for All"); a ship owner watching his ship ("I Sail for All"); a shopkeeper in a general store ("I Buy & Sell for All"); a doctor ("I Physic You All"); a broker at his window ("I Fleece You All"); a trader ("I Bull & Bear for All"); and a railroad owner watching his locomotive ("I Carry for All").

1A ANALYZING SOURCES Who is the "I" in the central image?

1B What does his position in the lithograph indicate?

2 IDENTIFYING CENTRAL IDEAS How does this lithograph reflect the idea of the National Grange?

3 INFERRING Who would be the audience for this lithograph? Explain.

4 EXPLAINING What relationships between geography and occupation are shown in the lithograph?

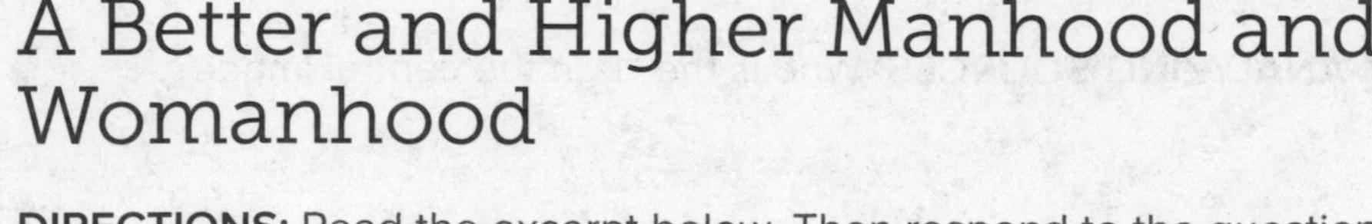

A Better and Higher Manhood and Womanhood

DIRECTIONS: Read the excerpt below. Then respond to the questions that follow.

EXPLORE THE CONTEXT: The National Grange was an economic movement and a political movement, but it was also a social movement, as the National Grange sought to connect farmers and abide by high principles of living. The National Grange set out its many purposes in a document, excerpted below.

PRIMARY SOURCE: DECLARATION OF PURPOSES

"We shall endeavor to advance our cause by laboring to accomplish the following objects:

To develop a better and higher manhood and womanhood among ourselves;

to enhance the comforts and attractions of our homes, and strengthen our attachments to our pursuits;

to foster mutual understanding and cooperation;

to maintain unbroken our laws, and to emulate each other in labor, to hasten the good time coming;

to reduce our expenses, both individual and corporate;

to buy less and produce more, in order to make our farms self-sustaining;

to diversify our crops ...;

to condense the weight of our exports,....;

to systematize our work, and calculate intelligently on probabilities; to discountenance the credit system, the mortgage system, the fashion system, and every other system tending to prodigality and bankruptcy.

We propose meeting together, talking together, working together, buying together, selling together, and, in general, acting together for our mutual protection and advancement. ... We shall constantly strive to secure entire harmony, good will, vital brotherhood among ourselves, and to make our Order perpetual. We shall earnestly endeavor to suppress

VOCABULARY

endeavor: try
emulate: imitate, copy
discountenance: avoid
prodigality: reckless spending
perpetual: everlasting

. . . *continued*

personal, local, sectional, and national prejudices, all unhealthy rivalry, all selfish ambition. Faithful adherence to these principles will insure our mental, moral, social and material advancement. ”

—from *Declaration of Purposes of the National Grange*, February 11, 1874

1 INFERRING What can you infer from the line "To develop a better and higher manhood and womanhood among ourselves"?

2 ANALYZING SOURCES The National Grange served economic, political, and social purposes. Are the purposes cited here economic, political, or social?

3 IDENTIFYING CENTRAL IDEAS What is the central idea of this declaration?

4 ANALYZING TEXT What do the writers of the declaration believe will happen if Grange members abide by all these principles?

ESSENTIAL QUESTION

How does geography influence the way people live?

1 Think About It

Review the supporting questions that you developed at the beginning of the chapter. Review the evidence that you gathered in Chapter 17. Were you able to answer each supporting question? If there was not enough evidence to answer your supporting questions, what additional evidence do you think you need to include?

2 Organize Your Evidence

Think about organizing what you have learned about how geography influences the way people live. Consider the groups of people listed in the table below. For each, identify at least one way geography influences the way they lived in the late 1800s.

How Does Geography Influence the Way People Live?	
Group of People	**How Geography Influenced Them**
Western miners	
railroad owners and workers	
Easterners using the railroad	
Westerners using the railroad	
Texas ranchers	
Great Plains farmers	
Native Americans	

3 Talk About It

Get together with a partner or small group and discuss the different groups above. Which group holds the most interest for you? Why? Focus on that group and list additional ways geography affected how they lived.

4 Connect to the Essential Question

Choose one of the groups of people from your graphic organizer in question 2 above. Draw a picture of an individual or a smaller group from that group. Add text boxes to your picture to show how geography influenced the way that person or persons lived.

CITIZENSHIP

TAKE ACTION

Many of the places you have been reading about have been preserved. For example, the site of the Battle of Little Bighorn is preserved as a National Monument. Virginia City, Nevada, home of the Comstock Lode, preserves a historic district. In fact, there are thousands of historic sites that tell the great story of the opening of the American West. All of these places are related to geography. They are located in places with geographic features that influenced the way the people there lived.

Despite their importance to our country's history, a lot of these places receive few visitors. Why is that? One reason is some of them are in remote locations. But a more important reason is that not as many people know about them as should.

You can help change that!

With a partner or small group, work to publicize a historic place in California that was important during the late 1800s. Research the Internet to choose a place.

Jot down your notes here.

____

____

____

____

Make a Publicity Poster

Make a poster that tells about your chosen California historic site. Make sure your poster identifies the place, tells how geography influenced the people who lived there, and explains why people should visit. If possible, work with other students to create a whole group of posters and display them in your school's halls.

The Industrial Age

ESSENTIAL QUESTION

How does technology change the way people live and work?

Think about how this question relates to the dramatic changes of the Industrial Age.

TALK ABOUT IT

Discuss with a partner what type of information you would need to know to answer this question. For example, one question might be: How did industry change the lives of workers?

DIRECTIONS: Now write down three additional questions that you need to answer to be able to explain how technology changes the way people live and work.

MY RESEARCH QUESTIONS

Supporting Question 1:

___

___

Supporting Question 2:

___

___

Supporting Question 3:

___

___

ESSENTIAL QUESTION

How does technology change the way people live and work?

As you gather evidence to answer the Essential Question, think about

- how railroads grew during the last half of the 1800s.
- how railroads affected the economy.
- how railroads affected American life.

My Notes

Railroads Lead the Way

DIRECTIONS: Search for evidence in Chapter 18, Lesson 1 to help you answer the following questions.

1A How many miles of railroad track were there in the United States in 1900?

1B How many miles of railroad track were there in the United States in 1860?

1C **DRAWING CONCLUSIONS** What might you conclude from these two facts alone?

2 **EXPLAINING** Why was standard gauge an important technological advance?

3 **DESCRIBING** Fill in the table to show how railroads helped other industries.

Railroads Help Other Industries	
Industry	**How Railroads Helped**
iron	
coal	
timber	
manufacturers	
farmers	
steel	

4 **CITING TEXT EVIDENCE** Complete the table of inventors by describing their inventions.

Inventors of New Railroad Technology	
Name	**Contribution**
George Westinghouse	
Eli H. Janney	
Gustavus Swift	
George Pullman	

5 **IDENTIFYING EFFECTS** How did railroads change where people lived and worked?

ESSENTIAL QUESTION

How does technology change the way people live and work?

John Henry, Steel Driving Man

DIRECTIONS: Read the lyrics, the words to the song. Then respond to the questions that follow.

EXPLORE THE CONTEXT: John Henry was a real person. He worked on the railroad in West Virginia in the 1870s. His job was to use a large hammer to pound a steel rod into rock. The rod was then removed, leaving a long narrow hole. Workers put explosives in the hole to blast holes in the rock to make a railroad tunnel. An inventor brought a steam-powered drill to the building site. He claimed it could make the holes much faster than men could. John Henry raced the machine and won. He died shortly thereafter, probably from a cave-in.

VOCABULARY

captain: boss
hammer: a very large, long-handled hammer like a sledgehammer

1A DETERMINING CENTRAL IDEAS What makes Henry a "steel driving man"?

____

____

1B Who or what does he compete against?

____

PRIMARY SOURCE: SONG LYRICS

"JOHN HENRY, STEEL DRIVING MAN

John Henry was a railroad man,
He worked from six till five,
'Raise 'em up bullies and let 'em drop down,
I'll beat you to the bottom or die.'
John Henry said to his captain:
'You are nothing but a common man,
Before that steam drill shall beat me down,
I'll die with my hammer in my hand.'
John Henry said to the Shakers:
'You must listen to my call,
Before that steam drill shall beat me down,
I'll jar these mountains till they fall.'
John Henry's captain said to him:
'I believe these mountains are caving in.'
John Henry said to his captain: 'Oh, Lord!
'That's my hammer you hear in the wind.'
John Henry he said to his captain:
'Your money is getting mighty slim,
When I hammer through this old mountain,
Oh Captain will you walk in?'
John Henry's captain came to him
With fifty dollars in his hand,

He laid his hand on his shoulder and said:

'This belongs to a steel driving man.'

John Henry was hammering on the right side,

The big steam drill on the left,

Before that steam drill could beat him down,

He hammered his fool self to death.

. . .

John Henry was lying on his death bed,

He turned over on his side,

And these were the last words John Henry said

'Bring me a cool drink of water before I die.'

John Henry had a little woman,

Her name was Pollie Ann,

He hugged and kissed her just before he died,

Saying, 'Pollie, do the very best you can.'

John Henry's woman heard he was dead,

She could not rest on her bed,

She got up at midnight, caught that No. 4 train,

'I am going where John Henry fell dead.'

They carried John Henry to that new burying ground

His wife all dressed in blue,

She laid her hand on John Henry's cold face,

'John Henry I've been true to you.' ”

—"John Henry, Steel Driving Man," traditional folk song

2 DRAWING CONCLUSIONS What is the outcome of the competition?

____

3 DETERMINING MEANING What is the message of the song? Explain.

____

____

____

____

4 ANALYZING ISSUES How did technology affect workers like John Henry?

____

____

____

____

"A First Class Steel Rail Road"

ESSENTIAL QUESTION

How does technology change the way people live and work?

DIRECTIONS: Read the excerpt from the letter. Then respond to the questions that follow.

EXPLORE THE CONTEXT: This letter was written by General William Tecumseh Sherman to General David. D. Colton. Colton held the rank of general in the California militia. His many investments made him extremely wealthy. This letter was written when he was serving as a vice president of the Southern Pacific Railroad.

VOCABULARY

Great Desert: now called the Chihuahuan and Sonoran deserts, located in modern-day Arizona, New Mexico, Texas, California, and Mexico

Arizonia: a misspelling of Arizona

garrison: are assigned to defend

great civilizer: something that advances a group of people

1A DETERMINING POINT OF VIEW What is Sherman's opinion of Colton's railroad?

____

1B What is the purpose of this letter?

____

____

____

PRIMARY SOURCE: LETTER

"[From]

Palace Hotel San Francisco Cal.

September 26th 1878.

[To]

General David. D. Colton

Vice President, Southern Pacific R.R.

My dear Sir:

Having just arrived from the East ... I cannot honestly neglect the opportunity to thank you and your associates personally and officially for having built a first class Steel Rail Road across the Great Desert, to the Colorado River. The public convenience is so great Especially to the troops who garrison the Arizonia posts, that I as their head venture to offer you thanks....

I take it for granted that you have made full investigation of the natural resources of Arizonia, and that you are well advised of the progress of the two Rail Roads approaching New Mexico from the East, one, or both of which seems destined to meet you in your progress Eastward, making another TransContinental Railway.

To the Military Authorities it makes little difference with which of these two roads you ultimately make connection, but meantime Every mile of rail road you build Eastward, is of great importance to us; saves the

costly and difficult transportation of stones by wagons, and the infinitely more tedious and painful marching of men over dusty roads, at long intervals without water and with scanty food.

A Railroad East and West through Arizonia, apart from its importance as a Commercial Route from the Pacific to the Atlantic, is a "great civilizer" and will Enable the Military Authorities to maintain peace and order among Indians, as well as the Equally dangerous class of Robbers who of late have so much increased in members and boldness....

With Great respect & c
W. T. Sherman
General."

—General William Tecumseh Sherman, from a letter to General David D. Colton, September 26, 1878

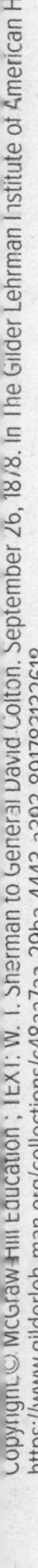

2A IDENTIFYING EFFECTS How does Sherman say the railroad will affect the army?

2B What does Sherman mean by calling the railroad a "great civilizer"?

3 INFERRING According to General Sherman, which groups of people will have their lives affected by the railroad?

Inventions Change Society

DIRECTIONS: Search for evidence in Chapter 18, Lesson 2 to help you answer the following questions.

1A EXPLAINING What technology did Samuel Morse develop?

1B What "language" was used with this device?

1C What was a telegram?

2 What did Cyrus Field accomplish?

3 Who invented the telephone?

4A SUMMARIZING Complete the table.

Great Inventions		
Inventor	Invention	Year
Christopher Sholes		
William Burroughs		
George Eastman		
John Thurman		

ESSENTIAL QUESTION

How does technology change the way people live and work?

As you gather evidence to answer the Essential Question, think about

- how technology changed communications in the late 1800s.
- the many inventions of this time period.
- how technology changed American society.

My Notes

4B Complete the table.

A Great Inventor
Thomas Edison Invented the...

4C Who invented the transformer, and what was it used for?

5 ECONOMICS What was Henry Ford's vision for the Model T?

ESSENTIAL QUESTION

How does technology change the way people live and work?

"A Free Land of Promise"

DIRECTIONS: Read the excerpt from the interview. Then answer the questions that follow.

EXPLORE THE CONTEXT: Historians often say that Samuel F. B. Morse "developed" the telegraph instead of "invented" the telegraph. Morse worked with others in creating it. Later in life, Morse faced legal disputes about who owned the patent to the telegraph. In this source, a prominent Philadelphia resident recalls a ship voyage with Morse during which Morse discussed the idea of the telegraph.

PRIMARY SOURCE: INTERVIEW

"In the fall of the year 1832 I returned from Europe as a passenger with Mr. Morse, in the ship *Sully*...; during the voyage the subject of an electric telegraph was one of frequent conversation.

Mr. Morse was most constant in pursuing it, and alone the one who seemed disposed to [put] it to a practical test; and I recollect that for this purpose he devised a system of signs for letters, to be indicated and marked by a quick succession of strokes, or shocks of the [electric] current; and I am sure of the fact that it was deemed by Mr. Morse perfectly competent...;

I did not suppose that any other person on board the ship claimed any merit in the invention, or was in fact interested to pursue it to maturity, as Mr. Morse then seemed to be; nor have I been able since that time to recall any fact or circumstance to justify the claim of any person other than Mr. Morse to the invention."

—from an interview with J. Francis Fisher, Esq., quoted in *The Life of Samuel F.B. Morse*

VOCABULARY

disposed: wanting
deemed: judged
competent: workable

1 DETERMINING CENTRAL IDEAS What is the main idea that Fisher is expressing?

2A ANALYZING TEXT What does Fisher mean when he says, "Mr. Morse was most constant in pursuing" the development of the telegraph?

2B Morse was granted a patent for the telegraph in 1840. The excerpt discusses a sea voyage in 1832. What might you conclude about technology from these two dates?

3 DRAWING CONCLUSIONS "[H]e devised a system of signs for letters, to be indicated and marked by a quick succession of strokes, or shocks of the [electric] current." What was this system later called?

4 ANALYZING SOURCES Why do you think this letter was important to Morse's claim that he alone invented the telegraph?

ESSENTIAL QUESTION

How does technology change the way people live and work?

"The Real McCoy"

DIRECTIONS: Read the excerpt below. Then answer the questions that follow.

EXPLORE THE CONTEXT: Have you ever heard the expression "the real McCoy"? It means "the real thing," or the original invention. The expression has been around for more than a century. It may have come from a man named Elijah McCoy (1844?–1929). McCoy was born in Canada, the son of a couple who had escaped slavery. He worked as an oilman on the railroads. An oilman lubricated (oiled) the moving parts on a train. The train had to be stopped to do this. But then McCoy invented the lubricator cup. This device lubricated moving parts in a machine as the machine operated. The machine no longer had to be stopped to lubricate it. Below is an excerpt from McCoy's application for a patent on his invention that he submitted to the U.S. Patent Office.

PRIMARY SOURCE: PATENT APPLICATION

"LUBRICATOR.

SPECIFICATION forming part of Letters Patent No. 470,163, dated March 1, 1892.

Application filed August 15, 1890. Serial No. 362,064. (No model.)

To all whom it may concern:

Be it known that I, ELIJAH MCCOY, a citizen of the United States, residing at Detroit, county of Wayne, State of Michigan, have invented a certain new and useful improvement in Lubricators, and declare the following to be a full, clear, and exact description of the invention, such as will enable others skilled in the art to which it appertains, to make and use the same, reference being had to the accompanying drawings, which form a part of this specification.

My invention has for its object certain new and useful improvements in lubricators, and is more particularly designed to provide a lubricator adapted to more efficiently feed heavy oils and for lubricating double and triple expansion engines.

VOCABULARY

patent: a license issued by the government that gives someone the right to make, use, and sell an invention without others copying it

It consists of the combinations of devices and appliances hereinafter specified and claimed, and illustrated in the accompanying drawings...”

—Elijah McCoy, application for a patent for a steam engine lubricator, filed with the U.S. Patent Office, 1892

1 **IDENTIFYING** What did McCoy call his invention?

____

2 **ANALYZING TEXT** What does McCoy say is the purpose of his new invention?

____

____

____

____

3A **IDENTIFYING EFFECTS** McCoy's lubricator made it unnecessary for trains to stop for lubrication. What would be the effects of this change?

____

____

____

3B What might the effects on oilmen be?

____

____

4 **ANALYZING ISSUES** How did McCoy's invention change the way railroads were run?

____

____

____

ESSENTIAL QUESTION

How does technology change the way people live and work?

As you gather evidence to answer the Essential Question, think about:

- what the factors of production are.
- how corporations are organized.
- how the oil and steel industries grew.

My Notes

An Age of Big Business

DIRECTIONS: Search for evidence in Chapter 18, Lesson 3 to help you answer the following questions.

1 **CITING TEXT EVIDENCE** How did the petroleum industry first start?

2 **SUMMARIZING** Complete the table by naming and describing the three factors of production.

The Factors of Production	
Factor	Definition/Examples

3 **SUMMARIZING** Complete the table by filling in the definition for each term.

Corporations Sell Shares to Raise Money (Capital) to Grow the Business	
Term	**Meaning**
stock	
shareholders	
dividends	

4 **SUMMARIZING** Complete the table to include accomplishments of these two men.

Two Industrialists		
	John D. Rockefeller	**Andrew Carnegie**
industry		
company		
philanthropic activity		

ESSENTIAL QUESTION

How does technology change the way people live and work?

"Wealth"

DIRECTIONS: Read the excerpt below. Then respond to the questions that follow.

EXPLORE THE CONTEXT: Andrew Carnegie was one of the richest people in U.S. history. In fact, he was worth so much money that it is hard to even picture it. In today's dollars, Carnegie was worth about $100 billion. He made most of his money through iron and steel mills, providing these materials to people who built railroads, bridges, and buildings. Below, he lays out some of his ideas about wealth.

VOCABULARY

gospel: a set of principles
unostentatious: simple; not showy or fancy
surplus revenues: money left over after obligations are met

PRIMARY SOURCE: JOURNAL ARTICLE

"The problem of our age is the proper administration of wealth, so that the ties of brotherhood may still bind together the rich and poor in harmonious relationship....

This, then, is held to be the duty of the man of Wealth: First, to set an example of modest, unostentatious living, shunning display or extravagance; to provide moderately for the legitimate wants of those dependent upon him; and after doing so to consider all surplus revenues which come to him simply as trust funds, which he is called upon to administer, and strictly bound as a matter of duty to administer in the manner which, in his judgment, is best calculated to produce the most beneficial results for the community....

[The] best means of benefiting the community is to place within its reach the ladders upon which the aspiring can rise—parks, and means of recreation, by which men are helped in body and minds; works of art, certain to give pleasure and improve the public taste; and public institutions of various kinds, which will improve the general condition of the people—in this manner returning their surplus wealth to the mass of their fellows in the forms best calculated to do them lasting good....

Individualism will continue, but the millionaire will be but a trustee for the poor; entrusted for a season with a great part of the increased

1A DETERMINING CENTRAL IDEAS What problem does Carnegie hope to solve with his "gospel"?

____
____
____
____
____
____
____
____

. . . *continued*

wealth of the community, but administering it for the community far better than it could or would have done for itself....

Such, in my opinion, is the true Gospel concerning Wealth, obedience to which is destined some day to solve the problem of the Rich and the Poor, and to bring "Peace on earth, among men Good-Will. ”

—Andrew Carnegie, from a journal article "Wealth," June 1889

1B How does he propose to do this?

1C **CITING TEXT EVIDENCE** What are some specific things Carnegie suggests spending money on?

2 **DETERMINING POINT OF VIEW** What is Carnegie's view of "the Poor"?

3 **ANALYZING** In Carnegie's time, do you think technology helped or hindered the relationship between the rich and the poor? Give reasons for your answer.

ESSENTIAL QUESTION

How does technology change the way people live and work?

A Generous Gift

DIRECTIONS: Read the letter below. Then respond to the questions that follow.

EXPLORE THE CONTEXT: Andrew Carnegie made his money in steel and railroads and was worth about $100 billion in today's dollars. John D. Rockefeller made his money in oil and was worth *four times as much.* He was the richest person in modern history. Rockefeller wrote the following letter to the Rockefeller Foundation, a charity he founded in 1913.

PRIMARY SOURCE: LETTER

"March 6, 1914

The Rockefeller Foundation

26 Broadway, New York City

Gentlemen:

I hereby give you, less the interest accrued and the dividends declared thereon to date, the securities shown in the accompanying statement, of a total value at the market price of March 1, 1914, of Sixty-five million, five hundred sixty-nine thousand, five hundred sixty-nine dollars, forty-six cents. ($69,569,569.46), making with the amounts heretofore given by me to the Rockefeller Foundation, One hundred million dollars. ($100,000,000).

Very truly,

John D. Rockefeller"

—John D. Rockefeller, letter to the Rockefeller Foundation, March 6, 1914

VOCABULARY

interest: a percentage of money borrowed that must be paid to the lender as a fee

accrued: accumulated; gathered

dividend: a share of profits

heretofore: up to this time

1 **INFERRING** What could you infer about Rockefeller from the letter even if you didn't know anything about him already?

2 **ANALYZING SOURCES** Rockefeller wrote this letter more than 100 years ago. Why would a person or business keep this letter for so long?

3 **ANALYZING TEXT** Why do you suppose Rockefeller spelled out the dollar amount of his gifts but used numbers as well?

4 **IDENTIFYING CENTRAL IDEAS** What is the central idea of this letter?

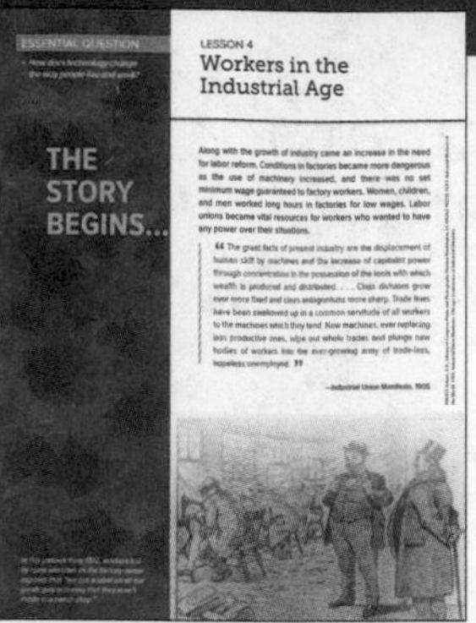

Workers in the Industrial Age

DIRECTIONS: Search for evidence in Chapter 18, Lesson 4 to help you answer the following questions.

ESSENTIAL QUESTION

How does technology change the way people live and work?

As you gather evidence to answer the Essential Question, think about

- working conditions in factories and sweatshops.
- why labor unions grew.
- what labor unions fought for.

My Notes

1 DESCRIBING How did working conditions change during the Industrial Age?

2 IDENTIFYING CAUSES Complete the table.

Why Workers Organized Labor Unions
1.
2.

3 SUMMARIZING Fill in the table with information about two early unions.

Two Unions		
Union	Leader	Membership
Knights of Labor		
American Federation of Labor		

4 **IDENTIFYING EFFECTS** What was one major effect of the tragic deaths in the Triangle Shirtwaist Company fire?

5 **SUMMARIZING** Complete the table to describe three major strikes of the period and whether or not they helped the cause of the striking workers.

Three Strikes			
Strike	**Year**	**Result**	**Success or Failure?**
Haymarket Square	1886		
Homestead	1892		
Pullman	1894		

ESSENTIAL QUESTION

How does technology change the way people live and work?

"Too Much Blood Has Been Spilled"

DIRECTIONS: Read the excerpt from the speech below. Then respond to the questions that follow.

EXPLORE THE CONTEXT: The Triangle Shirtwaist Factory fire was one of the deadliest industrial disasters in U.S. history. Of the 146 people who lost their lives, 70 were teenagers. The youngest victims were 14. The average age was 21. Here, Rose Schneiderman speaks out in the aftermath of the tragedy. At the time, Schneiderman was vice president of the Women's Trade Union League.

PRIMARY SOURCE: SPEECH

"We have tried you good people of the public and found you wanting....

We have tried you, citizens! We are trying you now and you have a couple dollars for the sorrowing mothers and brothers and sisters.... But every time the workers come out [on strike]...to protest against conditions which are unbearable, the strong hand of the law is allowed to press down heavily upon us.

Public officials only have words of warning for us—warning us that we must be intensely orderly and must be intensely peaceable, and they have the workhouse just back of all their warnings. The strong hand of the law beats us back when we rise—back into the conditions that make life unbearable.

I can't talk fellowship to you who are gathered here. Too much blood has been spilled. I know from experience that it is up to the working people to save themselves. And the only way to is through a strong working-class movement."

—Rose Schneiderman, from a speech at the Metropolitan Opera House meeting, April 2, 1911

VOCABULARY

wanting: lacking, falling short
sorrowing: grieving
unbearable: agonizing, intolerable
workhouse: a prison in which inmates have to work
just back of: to back up

1A **DETERMINING POINT OF VIEW** What tone or attitude does Schneiderman have?

1B What is her attitude toward the public?

1C Why does she feel this way toward them?

2 **EXPLAINING** What does Schneiderman mean by "the strong hand of the law beats us back"?

3 How did factory conditions like those in the Triangle Shirtwaist Factory fire lead to the call for workers to rise up?

ESSENTIAL QUESTION

How does technology change the way people live and work?

"To Help Lift Up the Whole Human Family"

DIRECTIONS: Read the passage below. Then respond to the questions that follow.

EXPLORE THE CONTEXT: Samuel Gompers (1850–1924) was the first president of the American Federation of Labor. From 1886 until his death in 1924, he continued to serve as president (except for one year). Gompers believed that workers should stand together to collectively bargain, but that they should stand independently of any government bodies. Below, Gompers was speaking at a meeting in Lynn, Masssachusetts, in support of the 9 hour workday for machinists.

PRIMARY SOURCE: SPEECH

"This is an earnest and a serious movement. It is aggressive, but yet peaceful. ... Our members strive to secure better social and industrial conditions. When secured these conditions apply to every man, woman and child.

How can employees, in the face of combinations of capital, act as individuals? How can the employers ask them to do so? There is greater danger from industrial imperialism than from any other form of imperialism. All workers must unite for the industrial emancipation of the world. ...

Show me a country in which there are no strikes and I'll show you that country in which there is no liberty. The State, when it has interfered with industrial affairs, has become the greatest tyrant in the world. The labor movement is not fantastic or visionary. The object of the movement is to help lift up the whole human family."

—Samuel Gompers, from a speech to a meeting of machinists in Lynn, Massachusetts, April 15, 1901

VOCABULARY

earnest: sincere
secure: get
imperialism: domination; taking over
emancipation: freeing
the State: government
fantastic: just a fantasy
collectively: involving all members of a group

1A INFERRING What "movement" does Gompers refer to in the first line?

1B When he refers to "members," to whom is he referring?

2 EXPLAINING How does the second paragraph relate to the idea of collective bargaining?

3 ANALYZING TEXT What does Gompers mean when he says, "The object of the movement is to help lift up the whole human family"?

ESSENTIAL QUESTION

How does technology change the way people live and work?

As you gather evidence to answer the Essential Question, think about

- expansionism and imperialism.
- how the United States expanded.
- the role of the U.S. Navy.

My Notes

Becoming a World Power

DIRECTIONS: Search for evidence in Chapter 18, Lesson 5 to help you answer the following questions.

1A ECONOMIC REASONING What is imperialism?

1B What drove imperialism?

2 **MAKING CONNECTIONS** What did Captain Alfred Thayer Mahan mean when he said, "Sea power is essential to the greatness of every splendid people"?

3 **SUMMARIZING** Complete the table.

New Technology for the Navy		
	Old	New
hull construction		
power		

4 **IDENTIFYING CAUSES** Why did the United States forcefully annex Hawaii?

5 **IDENTIFYING EFFECTS** What effect did the Spanish-American War have on America's role in the world?

6 **EXPLAINING** How did the opening of the Panama Canal affect the United States?

ESSENTIAL QUESTION

How does technology change the way people live and work?

"War Plans and Preparations"

DIRECTIONS: Read the excerpt below. Then respond to the questions that follow.

EXPLORE THE CONTEXT: After the Civil War, U.S. Navy authorities realized that the navy desperately needed to upgrade its fleet of ships. The navy scrambled to build new ships, and by the time the Spanish-American War broke out in 1898, the fleet was significantly improved.

SECONDARY SOURCE: ACADEMIC PAPER

"The U.S. Navy had in commission over 600 vessels at the close of the American Civil War. Nearly all of the new ships were wartime purchases, hasty constructions, or made from unseasoned timber. After the war, most were sold off or destroyed. ... Naval technology had stagnated in the U.S., illustrated by the fact that there was not a single high-power, long-range rifled gun in the entire fleet. In 1884 the U.S. Navy's newest ships were wooden-hulled steam sloops built in the previous decade.

Modernization began during the administration of President Chester Arthur in the early 1880s. ... Congress continued the process [in the late 1890s] by approving additional steel warships, including the ... first armored ships, USS Texas and USS Maine. ...

Along with the battleship *Iowa,* authorized in 1892, [three battleships later named *Indiana, Oregon,* and *Massachusetts*] formed the core of a new fleet willing to challenge European navies for control of the waters in the Western Hemisphere."

— Mark L. Hayes, from an academic paper "War Plans and Preparations and Their Impact on U.S. Naval Operations in the Spanish-American War"

VOCABULARY

sloop: a kind of sailing ship
stagnated: stopped moving or growing
unseasoned: wood that is not as strong as seasoned wood and therefore not as good for building

1 **INFERRING** What can you infer from the fact that the Civil War–era ships were "sold off or destroyed" after the war?

2 **IDENTIFYING CENTRAL IDEAS** What is the central idea of this excerpt?

3 **EXPLAINING** How was the navy's fleet improved by the late 1890s?

ESSENTIAL QUESTION

How does technology change the way people live and work?

"They Form the Center of a Large Circle"

DIRECTIONS: Read the document below. Then respond to the questions that follow.

EXPLORE THE CONTEXT: During the 1800s, most sailing ships gave way to a new technology: steamships. Steamships were powered by steam engines that drove propellers. To create steam, the ships boiled water in huge tanks. To heat the water, steamships relied on coal—hundreds of tons of it.

The range of steamships was limited by how much coal they could carry. They required "coaling stations"—or ports—where they could refill their coal. The idea is similar to going to a gas station to refill a car. One of the greatest maritime strategists in history, Admiral Alfred Mahan of the U.S. Navy, in 1893 commented on how ideally suited for this purpose the Sandwich Islands would be.

VOCABULARY

Sandwich Islands: Hawaiian Islands
impediment: obstacle
immense: huge
well-nigh prohibitive: almost impossible
imperative: necessary or important

PRIMARY SOURCE: CONGRESSIONAL REPORT

"Anyone viewing a map ...of the Pacific Ocean... will see at a glance that the Sandwich Islands stand by themselves...amid a vast expanse of sea; and, again, that they form the center of a large circle, whose radius is approximately...the distance from Honolulu to San Francisco. From San Francisco to Honolulu, 2,500 miles easy steaming distance, is substantially the same as from Honolulu to the Gilbert, Marshall. Samoan, Society and Marquesas groups (the nearest inhabited islands), all under European control....

Too much stress cannot be laid upon the immense disadvantages to us of any maritime enemy having a coaling station well within 2,500 miles of every point of our coast line [on the Pacific Ocean]....

Shut out from the Sandwich Islands as a coal base, an enemy is thrown back for supplies of fuel to distances of 3,500 or 4,000 miles, or between 7,000 and 8,000 going and coming—an impediment to sustained maritime operations well-nigh prohibitive. It is rarely that

. . . continued

so important a factor in the attack or defense of a coast line...is concentrated in a single position, and the circumstances renders it doubly imperative upon us to secure it, if we righteously can ”

—Admiral Alfred Thayer Mahan, quoted in a report to Congress by the Committee on Naval Affairs, March 1908

1 **CITING TEXT EVIDENCE** Where does Mahan say the Sandwich Islands are located?

2 **DETERMINING CENTRAL IDEAS** Why does Mahan say that it is so important for America to control the Sandwich Islands?

3 **ANALYZING ISSUES** How does technology affect Mahan's thinking?

4 **INFERRING** Do you think the United States established its own coaling stations on the Sandwich Islands? Why?

ESSENTIAL QUESTION

How does technology change the way people live and work?

1 Think About It

Review the supporting questions that you developed at the beginning of the chapter. Review the evidence that you gathered in Chapter 18. Were you able to answer each supporting question? If there was not enough evidence to answer your supporting questions, what additional evidence do you think you need to include?

____

____

____

____

2 Organize Your Evidence

Change can be good or bad. Also, the same change can be good for some people and bad for others. Think about the many examples of the ways technology changed the way people lived and worked that you have been reading about. Were they mostly good changes? Bad? Or were they both, or neither? Use the graphic organizer below to organize what you have learned.

Technology Leads to Change		
Technology	Change(s) It Led To	Good or Bad

3 Talk About It

Get together with a partner or small group and discuss your work in Step 2. What are some conclusions you can draw about technology and change?

____

____

____

____

____

____

4 Connect to the Essential Question

Choose one example of a change that could be viewed as both good and bad. Write about it in an exploratory essay.

CITIZENSHIP

TAKE ACTION

You read in your textbook that "the late 1800s saw a burst of inventiveness in the United States." "Bursts of inventiveness" still happen today. Just think of all the new pieces of technology that have been developed in only the past few years, such as self-driving cars and virtual reality headsets. It is truly amazing.

You know that technology changes the way people live and work. You also know that the changes brought by technology can be good for some and bad for others.

Think About It

Today, more and more jobs are being automated. That means they are being taken over by machines. These machines can be robots, computers, mechanical crop pickers, and so on. The more jobs that are done by technology, the fewer jobs there are for humans to do.

Talk About It

Gather a group of other students and appropriate adults. Discuss what automation is doing to the workforce in California, especially agricultural workers. Write your notes in the space provided below.

____

____

____

____

____

____

Express Your Opinion

Do you think increasing automation is a good change or a bad change brought by technology? Express your opinion—and the reasons for it—in a blog post.

A Changing Society

ESSENTIAL QUESTION

How do new ideas change the way people live?

Think about how this question would relate to people after the Industrial Age.

TALK ABOUT IT

Discuss with a partner what type of information you would need in order to understand what ideas significantly changed the way people lived in the decades following the Industrial Age.

DIRECTIONS: Now write down three additional questions that you need to answer to explain why major changes in education, business, and politics occurred. For instance, you might ask, "How did changes in politics affect education?"

MY RESEARCH QUESTIONS

Supporting Question 1:

Supporting Question 2:

Supporting Question 3:

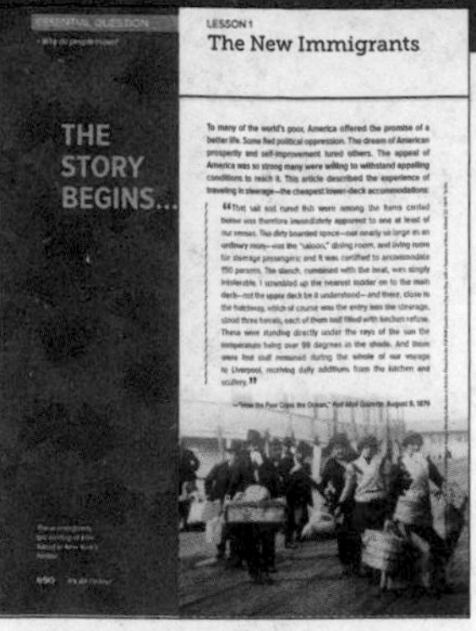

ESSENTIAL QUESTION

How do new ideas change the way people live?

As you gather evidence to answer the Essential Question, think about

- what causes changes to a culture.
- how migration influences the physical and cultural geography of a place.
- how people respond to major changes in culture, economy, and politics.

My Notes

The New Immigrants

DIRECTIONS: Search for evidence in Chapter 19, Lesson 1 to help you answer the following questions.

1A EXPLAINING CAUSE AND EFFECT What were some of the "push" factors that prompted immigrants to leave their native countries?

1B EXPLAINING CAUSE AND EFFECT What were some of the "pull" factors that drew new immigrants to the United States?

2 EXPLAINING Use the graphic organizer to show the various obstacles that immigrants faced during their journey toward making a home in the United States.

Before Immigrating	Upon Arrival	After Immigrating

3 DRAWING CONCLUSIONS Why did some new immigrants strive to assimilate to mainstream American culture?

4 DESCRIBING HISTORY What was life like for new immigrants?

5 IDENTIFYING CAUSE AND EFFECT Using the graphic organizer, identify three of the effects of new immigrants on American culture, life, and politics.

CAUSE	EFFECTS
Arrival of New Immigrants	

ESSENTIAL QUESTION

How do new ideas change the way people live?

Illiteracy and Immigration

DIRECTIONS: Use the image to answer the questions that follow.

EXPLORE THE CONTEXT: The Immigration Restriction League was founded in 1894 by three American-born graduates of Harvard University. They believed a literacy requirement would limit the steady flow of immigrants coming into the United States. The league believed in assimilation, that all immigrants should be incorporated into the existing American society and abandon their native cultures. They hoped that certain rules would slow the flood of immigrants and allow the government and various groups to work with new immigrants on assimilation.

VOCABULARY

Figures: statistics
Fiscal: having to do with money
debarred: prevented from doing something
illiterates: those who are unable to read and write
manifests: documents that list all the passengers on a ship

PRIMARY SOURCE: STATISTICS

lgat. div

PUBLICATIONS OF THE IMMIGRATION RESTRICTION LEAGUE No. 38.

Immigration Figures for 1903.

(From data furnished by the Commissioner-General of Immigration.)

Comparison of the Fiscal Years ending June 30, 1902 and 1903.

	1902.	1903.
Total immigration	648,743	857,046
Percentage of increase over 1902		32
Percentage of increase over 1901	33	76
Percentage of increase over 1899	108	175
Percentage of increase over 1898	183	274
Number debarred from entrance and returned within one year after landing	5,429	9,316
Per cent. debarred and returned	0.8	1.1
Number of illiterates over 14 years of age. [*See Note 1.*]	165,105	189,008
Per cent. of illiterate in total immigration over 14 years of age	28.7	25.0
Immigration from countries of Northern and Western Europe. [*See Note 2.*]	138,700	203,689
Per cent. of total immigration	21.4	23.8
Immigration from countries of Southern and Eastern Europe. [*See Note 2.*]	480,331	610,813
Per cent. of total immigration	74.0	71.3
Immigration from Asia	22,271	29,966
Per cent. of total immigration	3.4	3.5
Average money brought, in dollars	16	19
Per cent. of immigrants who have been in the United States before	9.5	8.9
Per cent. of total immigration having no occupation, including women and children	23.6	23.3
Per cent. of total immigration who were farm-laborers, laborers, or servants	60.6	57.3
Per cent. of total immigration destined for the four States of Ill., Mass., N.Y., and Pa.	67.8	65.4

NOTE 1.—Although the percentage of illiteracy shows an improvement this year over last, it should be remembered that these figures are based upon the manifests, which in turn are made up from the statements of the immigrants. One test recently made at New York showed that 175

10

1 **ANALYZING SOURCES** Did immigration increase, decrease, or stay the same from 1898 through 1903?

2 **CITING TEXT EVIDENCE** What does this document tell you about who was immigrating to the United States in 1902 and 1903?

3 **DRAWING CONCLUSIONS** What ideas do you think influenced the Immigration Restriction League to create this document?

4 **SUMMARIZING** What do you think the Immigration Restriction League meant when it said, "Although the percentage of illiteracy shows an improvement this year over last, it should be remembered that these figures are based upon the manifests, which are in turn made up from the statements of immigrants."

5A HISTORY What percentage of immigrants from 1903 were from Asia?

5B Why is this number so low in comparison to the amount of immigrants coming from Europe?

ESSENTIAL QUESTION

How do new ideas change the way people live?

The Other Half

DIRECTIONS: Read the excerpt and answer the questions that follow.

EXPLORE THE CONTEXT: Jacob Riis was a writer and photographer in the late 1800s. He used his camera and his writing skills to document the harsh lives of people who lived in New York City's tenements. His book *How the Other Half Lives* was an eye-opener for many readers. When his book was released, Theodore Roosevelt, who was the New York Police Commissioner at the time, agreed to walk the streets with Riis to learn more about the difficult circumstances in which people lived. As a result of Riis's book, the police force and political officials enacted reforms to improve people's living conditions in New York City.

PRIMARY SOURCE: NONFICTION BOOK

"The nearer the river and the great workshops the more numerous the tenements. The kind of work carried on in any locality to a large extent determines their character. ... Gas-houses, slaughter-houses and the docks, that attract the roughest crowds and support the vilest saloons, invariably form slum-centres. . . .

It is true that they tell only one side of the story; that there is another to tell. A story of thousands of devoted lives, laboring earnestly to make the most of their scant opportunities for good; of heroic men and women striving patiently against fearful odds and by their very courage coming off victors in the battle with the tenement; of womanhood pure and undefiled. That it should blossom in such an atmosphere is one of the unfathomable mysteries of life. And yet it is not an uncommon thing to find sweet and innocent girls, singularly untouched by the evil around them, true wives and faithful mothers, ... "like jewels in a swine's snout," in the worst of the infamous barracks. It is the experience of all who have intelligently observed this side of life in a great city, not to be explained—unless on the theory of my friend, the priest in the Mulberry Street Bend, that inherent purity revolts instinctively from the naked brutality of vice as

VOCABULARY

barracks: plain, simple housing for groups of people
tenement: run-down, overcrowded apartment building housing impoverished people
vilest: most disgusting
earnestly: sincerely
striving: working hard
unfathomable: not understandable
inherent: a permanent attribute

. . . *continued*

seen in the slums—but to be thankfully accepted as the one gleam of hope in an otherwise hopeless desert.”

—Jacob Riis, from *How the Other Half Lives,* 1890

1 **ANALYZING SOURCES** What does Riis mean when he says, “The kind of work carried on in any locality to a large extent determines their character”?

2A **DETERMINING POINT OF VIEW** How does Riis feel about the immigrants who live in the tenements?

2B What words does Riis use to demonstrate his feelings?

3 **CITING TEXT EVIDENCE** What sentence in this excerpt indicates Riis is drawing conclusions the reader may not expect?

4 **IDENTIFYING PERSPECTIVES** Who do you think would disagree with Riis's observations about tenement life?

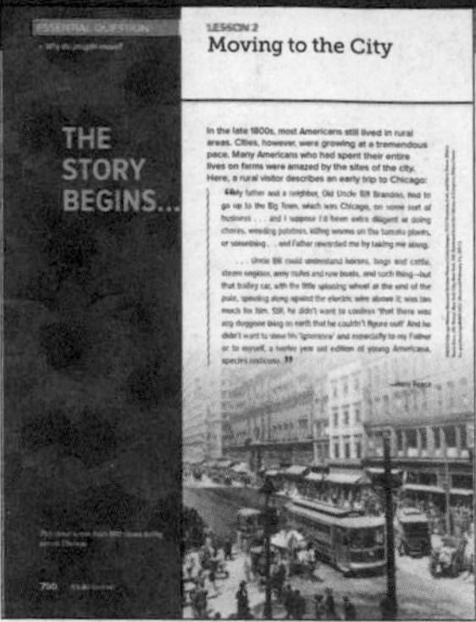

ESSENTIAL QUESTION

How do new ideas change the way people live?

As you gather evidence to answer the Essential Question, think about

- what causes changes to culture.
- how migration influences the physical and cultural geography of a place.
- how people respond to major changes in culture, economy, and politics.

My Notes

Moving to the City

DIRECTIONS: Search for evidence in Chapter 19, Lesson 2 to help you answer the following questions.

1 IDENTIFYING CAUSE AND EFFECT Use the graphic organizer below to show the causes of the growth of cities.

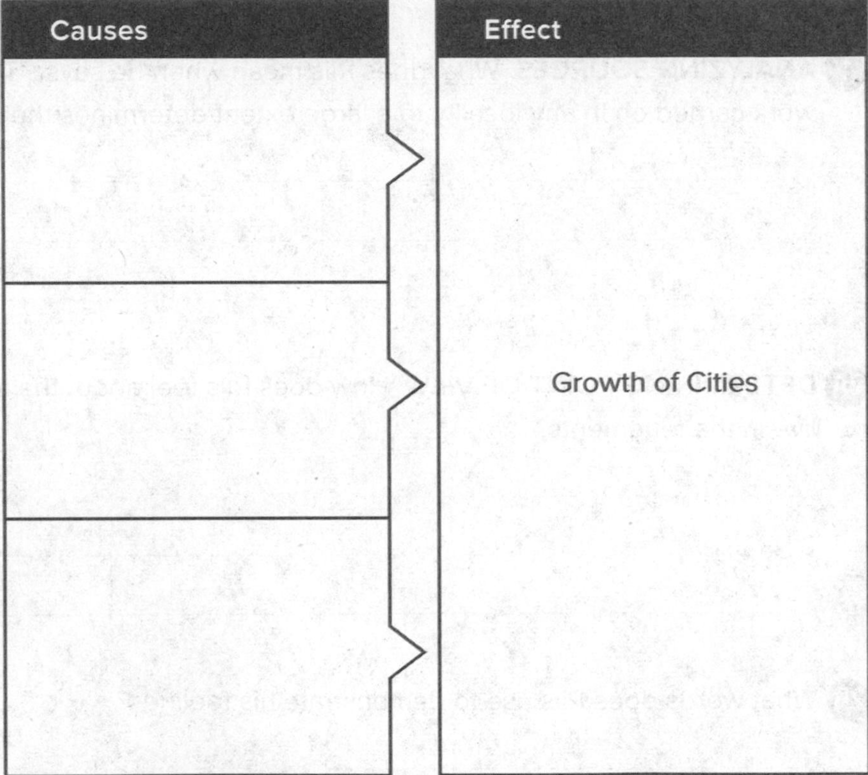

2 SUMMARIZING What ideas contributed to the development during this era of economic classes?

3 **IDENTIFYING PERSPECTIVES** How did life for those living in tenements compare to life in the suburbs?

4 HISTORY **DESCRIBING** How did architecture change in the late 1800s?

5A **INFERRING** Why was the "City Beautiful" movement so important?

5B What idea or principle guided the "City Beautiful" movement?

ESSENTIAL QUESTION

How do new ideas change the way people live?

The Woolworth Building

DIRECTIONS: Use the image below to answer the questions.

EXPLORE THE CONTEXT: Construction on the Woolworth Building occurred from 1910 to 1912. It is in the neo-gothic style and was designed by Cass Gilbert. The building was supposed to be only 40 stories at first, but the architect and building owner Frank Woolworth decided to expand it to 60 stories. The architectural style is reminiscent of cathedrals. For this reason, the building was nicknamed "The Cathedral of Commerce." It was the tallest building in the world until 1930, when other skyscrapers surpassed it; it is still one of the 30 tallest buildings in New York City.

PRIMARY SOURCE: PHOTO

The Woolworth Building under construction, c. 1911

1 **DRAWING CONCLUSIONS** Why did architects and business owners like Frank Woolworth decide to build skyscrapers?

2 **IDENTIFYING POINT OF VIEW** How do you think New Yorkers felt about the Woolworth Building when it was completed?

3 **GEOGRAPHY** Based on the image, what do you think the rest of New York City was like? Give specific reasons for your answer.

4 **COMPARING** How does this image of New York City compare to one from the 21st century?

5 **INFERRING** How do you think the introduction of skyscrapers to the city changed life in New York?

ESSENTIAL QUESTION

How do new ideas change the way people live?

Carnegie's Hall

DIRECTIONS: Use the excerpt below to answer the questions.

EXPLORE THE CONTEXT: Andrew Carnegie was a self-made billionaire who expanded the steel industry during the Industrial Age. One of the richest Americans in history, he is also known for donating millions of dollars to charities and foundations. He asked other wealthy people to put their money toward philanthropy as well. Carnegie funded construction of Carnegie Hall, a concert hall in New York City that opened in 1891 and is now considered a historic landmark. Hiram Hitchcock was an entrepreneur and the owner of the Fifth Avenue Hotel. In this letter, Carnegie asks if he is ready to start the project.

PRIMARY SOURCE: LETTER

"Jany 31/89

5 West Fifty-First Street,

New York

My Dear Mr. Hitchcock

Yours rec'd — We must begin at once if Hall is to be ready for next winter.

Please let it be understood between us that if upon my return from the South say February 15th you have not succeeded that we consider the idea given up. We have property in view & quite ready to go on & build the Hall Capital all ready—although we will wait on you until Feby 15th

If we build it will be much farther up town—not below 56th. Would not build upon Madison Square if we have to invest beyond the last 50,000 ft I agreed to take [illegible]. Perhaps if your people leased us ground & agreed that our investment for Hall should bear [*crossed out*: up to illegible] interest upon cost and first net receipts, before ground rent was payable We might consider it—in that case you

VOCABULARY

Jany: January

Invest: to use money to make a profit

Interest: extra fees that accumulate over time, as with a loan

Mortgage: a loan for property

lease: a contract for renting land or property

. . . *continued*

would have to clear a part from Mortgage & lease to us: but [illegible] increase your investment.

Yours

Andrew Carnegie

We will organize Feby 15th unless we hear from you. AC"

—Andrew Carnegie, from a letter to Hiram Hitchcock, January 31, 1889

1. **SUMMARIZING** What message is Carnegie sending to Hitchcock?

2. **INFERRING** At what point in the construction process did Carnegie send this letter?

3. **PREDICTING** How do you think Hitchcock might have responded to this message?

4. **CITING TEXT EVIDENCE** How would you describe Carnegie's tone? Choose specific words from the text to support your answer.

ESSENTIAL QUESTION

How do new ideas change the way people live?

As you gather evidence to answer the Essential Question, think about

- what causes changes to culture.
- how migration influences the physical and cultural geography of a place.
- how people respond to major changes in culture, economy, and politics.

My Notes

A Changing Culture

DIRECTIONS: Search for evidence in Chapter 19, Lesson 3 to help you answer the following questions.

1. **SUMMARIZING** How did education change in the late 1800s and early 1900s?

2. **INFERRING** What ideas contributed to the changes in education in the late 1800s and early 1900s?

3. **SUMMARIZING** In literature, how is realism connected to regionalism?

4 **INFERRING** Why was yellow journalism so popular?

5 **SUMMARIZING** Complete the table.

Yellow Journalism		
Publisher	**Newspaper**	**City**
	World	
	Morning Journal	

6 **DRAWING CONCLUSIONS** What does the rise of sports and movies say about the culture of this time?

ESSENTIAL QUESTION

How do new ideas change the way people live?

Glazier and the Glamor of the City

DIRECTIONS: Use the book excerpt to answer the questions.

EXPLORE THE CONTEXT: Willard Glazier (1841–1905) was a teacher from New York farm country who served in the Union cavalry during the Civil War and afterward traveled throughout the United States, writing extensively about his observations. *Peculiarities of American Cities* is the book in which he summarized what he saw. It was originally published in 1883. The excerpt is from "Chapter 1: Albany."

VOCABULARY

Adams House: an old inn in Monroe County, New York
commodious: spacious, roomy
din: loud noise
disclosed: revealed
dim: unclear, hard to see
manifold: having many parts

PRIMARY SOURCE: BOOK

"The traveler now entering Albany from the east crosses the Hudson on a beautiful iron railroad bridge, which, in the steady march of improvements, has succeeded the old-time ferry boat. He is landed at the commodious stone building of the New York Central and Hudson River Railroad, which is conveniently sandwiched between the Delavan House and Stanwix Hall, two large, well known and well conducted hotels.

My first night in a city and a hotel was spent here, at the old Adams House, located at that time on Broadway just opposite the Delavan. I was awakened in the morning by the roll and rattle of vehicles, and the usual din and confusion of a city street. The contrast to my quiet home in the Valley of the St. Lawrence was so marked, I can never forget the impression I then received, and as I walked up State street toward the old Capitol, I almost fancied that such a street might be a fit road to Paradise. Albany was the gate through which I entered the world, and to my boyish vision the view it disclosed was very wide, and the grand possibilities that lay in the dim distance seemed manifold."

— Willard Glazier, from *Peculiarities of American Cities*, 1886

1 GEOGRAPHY **COMPARING** How does Albany compare to Glazier's home?

2 **INFERRING** Why did Glazier and other writers explore the country during the late 1800s?

3 **DRAWING CONCLUSIONS** Why do you think Glazier wrote down and published his observations?

4 **CITING TEXT EVIDENCE** How does Glazier feel about Albany? What sentences indicate his feelings?

5 **DRAWING CONCLUSIONS** Based on Glazier's conclusions about Albany, what ideas do you think influenced his perspective?

ESSENTIAL QUESTION

How do new ideas change the way people live?

Emily Faithfull's Journey West

DIRECTIONS: Use the book excerpt to answer the questions.

EXPLORE THE CONTEXT: Emily Faithfull was a British women's rights activist who visited the United States. She lectured in several American cities in 1872 and 1882. In this excerpt from "Chapter IV. Railroads, drawing-room cars, sleepers, and hotel cars," she writes about her travel by train from New York to Chicago.

VOCABULARY

feat: achievement
garden city: Chicago
Dr. Watts's sun: a steam-driven invention
want: lack
stifles: causes a suffocating feeling
venture: to take a risk
remonstrates: scolds
natives: people who live in a certain area, in this case Americans
upholstery: fabric and padding that covers furniture

PRIMARY SOURCE: BOOK

"The journey from the Atlantic seaboard to Chicago gave me my first experience in American railroad travelling. I thought then I had performed a great feat, as I left New York on Monday morning and did not reach the "garden city" till Wednesday, though my train, like Dr. Watts's sun, "never tired or stopped to rest." Subsequent journeys over the Rocky Mountains, across the plains to California, through Arizona and Texas, taught me afterwards to regard this as quite "an easy run." The stations are called depôts, the carriages are "cars," the line is known as the "track," the engine is spoken of as a "locomotive," the guards as conductors, the luggage is "freight," and the signal for starting is the cry of "All aboard." The ordinary cars hold about forty persons, and the utter want of ventilation almost stifles you. No one will allow you to open a window. If you venture on such an indiscretion, the conductor remonstrates "most politely" against an innovation so singular that it at once betrays your nationality and ignorance of the ways and manners of the natives. If you persist, he ends the argument by closing the window himself, quietly remarking, "I guess we can't afford to warm the prairies as we pass." Fortunately, though the great Republic acknowledges no first or second class, most of the trains are provided with drawing-room cars, in which, for a few extra dollars, you enjoy plenty of space and better air, magnificent upholstery, dressing-rooms, iced water, grand mirrors, etc., while comfortable arm-chairs are ranged on either side

. . . continued

of the avenue down the middle, through which people are always passing "back and forth" as they term it, and boys ply a brisk trade in papers, books, figs, and candies.”

—Emily Faithfull, from *Three Visits to America*, 1884

1 **DETERMINING MEANING** What are some of the train-related words that Faithfull mentions?

2 **COMPARING** What differences does Faithfull point out between British and American culture?

3 HISTORY **DESCRIBING** What was riding on a train like in the late 1800s?

4 **INFERRING** What does Faithfull's account of the train say about class in the United States?

The Rise of Progressivism

DIRECTIONS: Search for evidence in Chapter 19, Lesson 4 to help you answer the following questions.

1 DETERMINING MEANING What were "political machines"?

____

____

____

2 IDENTIFYING CAUSE AND EFFECT In the graphic organizer below, describe the events and ideas that caused the rise of the socialist and progressive movements.

Causes	Effect
	Rise of socialist and progressive movements

ESSENTIAL QUESTION

How do new ideas change the way people live?

As you gather evidence to answer the Essential Question, think about

- what causes changes to culture.
- how migration influences the physical and cultural geography of a place.
- how people respond to major changes in culture, economy and politics.

My Notes

____

____

____

____

____

____

____

____

____

3 **DRAWING CONCLUSIONS** Why were muckrakers important?

4 CIVICS **INFERRING** What principles likely guided muckrakers?

5 **EXPLAINING** Why did reform movements and muckrakers emerge?

6 **EXPLAINING** Why did women fight for suffrage?

ESSENTIAL QUESTION

How do new ideas change the way people live?

A Child Laments Alcoholism

DIRECTIONS: Study the song below to answer the questions.

EXPLORE THE CONTEXT: *Temperance* refers to the movement in the 1800s that urged people to stop drinking alcohol. Prohibition, during which alcohol was illegal in the United States, became the law in 1919. Women were at the forefront of this movement, as they were considered "guardians of the home" and also involved with social activism. The song "The Child's Lament" is told from the perspective of an anonymous child.

PRIMARY SOURCE: SONG

"Why do you cry so much mamma?
Why are your hands so thin?
Why do you sigh and shiver so
As if you'd done a sin?
Oh! Everything is now so changed
And you have grown so sad;
There's nothing I can say or do
That seems to make you glad.

CHORUS

If your father was a temp'rance man,
He'd be so kind and mild,
And happiness again would find
The drunkard's little child

Then, too, when baby brother died,
And went beneath the sod,
Why did you say that dreadful thing?
Mamma, you said, thank God.
We did not used to be so poor,
I once had pretty toys,
And papa stayed at home with us
And shared in all our joys.

VOCABULARY

lament: cry of woe
drunkard: someone who drinks a lot
dreadful: terrible
sod: the ground covered with grass
drink: alcoholic beverages

1 **CITING TEXT EVIDENCE** What lines from the song show you whether it is for or against alcohol?

. . . *continued*

CHORUS

But now you're up so late at night,
And papa stays away;
He is away so very much,
Sometimes all night, you say.
I am afraid of him mamma,
He acts so strange and queer,
He buys me no more pretty things,
He never calls me "dear."

CHORUS

We have no fire now, mamma,
Our clothes are thin and old,
My little shoes are quite worn out,
And I am very cold.
I've heard you tell of temp'rance men,
And all the good they've done;
Oh! let us kneel and pray to God,
To make my father one.

CHORUS

Some day my child, you'll understand,
The sorrow drink can bring;
You'll think of all your childish griefs
Nor wonder at their sting,
And now when you kneel down to night,
Remember if you can,
to pray your father may become
A good, true temp'rance man. ”

—from "The Child's Lament," lyrics by Florence Brightly, 1872

2 **SUMMARIZING** According to the song, what are the effects of alcohol?

3 **DETERMINING POINT OF VIEW** Whose point of view is the song told from? Cite specific lines to support your conclusion.

4 CIVICS How would this song assist the temperance movement?

5 **DRAWING CONCLUSIONS** What does this song suggest about the reform movements of the late 1800s?

ESSENTIAL QUESTION

How do new ideas change the way people live?

Gillam's Industry Protectors

DIRECTIONS: Study the image below and answer the questions.

EXPLORE THE CONTEXT: "The Protectors of Our Industries" was drawn by Bernhard Gillam and published in *Puck*, a humor magazine, in 1883. Gillam was born in England and moved to the United States with his parents when he was ten years old. He is known for his political cartoons. The four men seated on bags of money at the top of the cartoon are: Cyrus West Field, a paper manufacturer and telegraph owner; Jay Gould, a railroad developer; Cornelius Vanderbilt, railroad and shipping entrepreneur; and Russell Sage, a railroad executive. The small signs over each working person's head are their weekly wages. An ironworker, for instance, earned $7 a week.

PRIMARY SOURCE: POLITICAL CARTOON

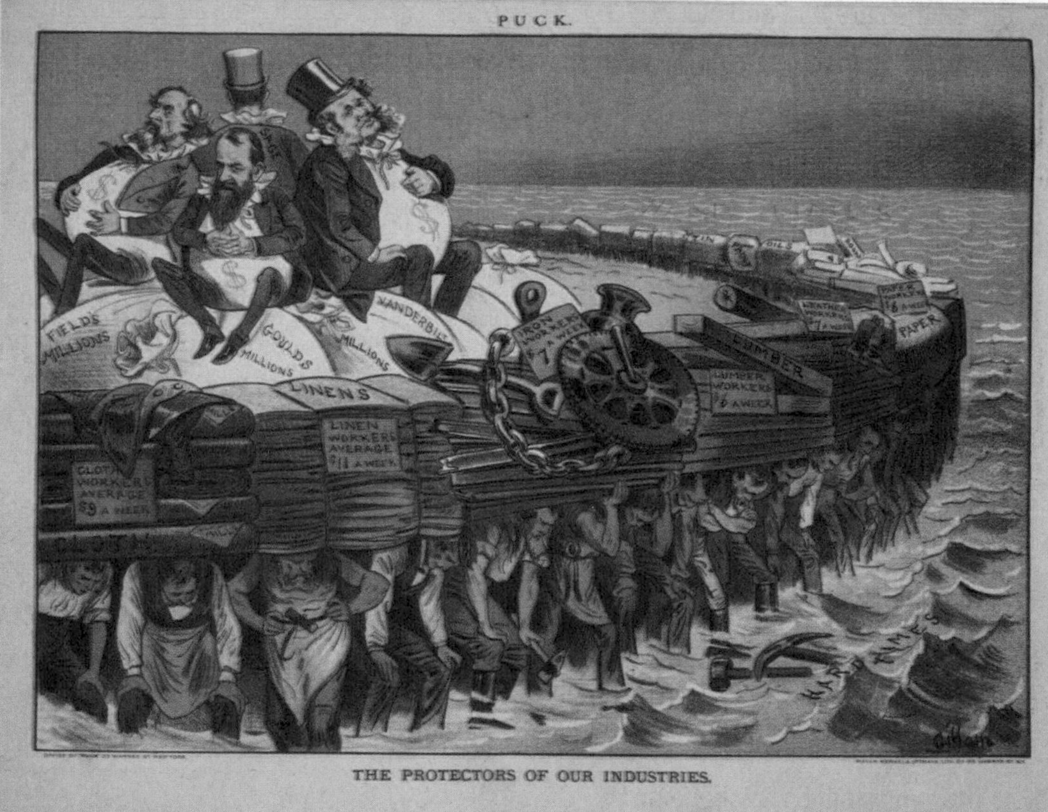

"The Protectors of Our Industries," lithograph by Bernhard Gillam in *Puck* magazine, February 7, 1883

1 **CITING TEXT EVIDENCE** Who are "The Protectors of Our Industries" in this cartoon?

2 **INTERPRETING POINTS OF VIEW** What message is the artist trying to convey with this cartoon?

3 **EXPLAINING** Why did the artist put the average weekly wage for each kind of worker in the cartoon?

4 CIVICS **DRAWING CONCLUSIONS** What do you think the artist hoped would happen as a result of this cartoon?

Progressive Achievements

DIRECTIONS: Search for evidence in Chapter 19, Lesson 5 to help you answer the following questions.

1 COMPARING How was Theodore Roosevelt's labor policy different from those of previous presidents?

2 DRAWING CONCLUSIONS How did Roosevelt's actions connect to the reform movements of the late 1800s and early 1900s?

3 INFERRING Why did Roosevelt fight to conserve natural parts of the country?

ESSENTIAL QUESTION

How do new ideas change the way people live?

As you gather evidence to answer the Essential Question, think about

- what causes changes to culture.
- how migration influences the physical and cultural geography of a place.
- how people respond to major changes in culture, economy and politics.

My Notes

4 SUMMARIZING Fill in the graphic organizer below with the purposes of the 16th, 17th, and 19th amendments.

16th AMENDMENT	17th AMENDMENT	19th AMENDMENT

5 DRAWING CONCLUSIONS How did discrimination and prejudice affect society?

____

____

____

____

Rules Governing Child Labor

ESSENTIAL QUESTION

How do new ideas change the way people live?

DIRECTIONS: Use the document below to answer the questions.

EXPLORE THE CONTEXT: In 1908, Lewis Hine took photographs for the National Child Labor Committee of some of the two million children who were working in mills, mines, factories, and stores across the United States. These photos sparked social reformists to end (or regulate) child labor. The Keating-Owen Act was the first to regulate child labor. Even though Congress and President Woodrow Wilson deemed it appropriate, the Supreme Court decided it was unconstitutional in 1918.

VOCABULARY

manufacturer: someone who produces an item to sell
interstate: between two or more states
commerce: an exchange of goods and services
commodity: an item that is sold
prosecution: being tried for a crime
conviction: being found guilty of a crime
bar: obstacle
postmeridian: after noon, i.e., p.m.
antemeridian: before noon, i.e., a.m.

PRIMARY SOURCE: GOVERNMENT DOCUMENT

"AN ACT To prevent interstate commerce in the products of child labor, and for other purposes

Be it enacted by the Senate and House of Representatives of the United States of America in Congress assembled, That no producer, manufacturer, or dealer shall ship or deliver for shipment in interstate or foreign commerce, any article or commodity the product of any mine or quarry situated in the United States, in which within thirty days prior to the time of the removal of such product therefrom children under the age of sixteen years have been employed or permitted to work, or any article or commodity the product of any mill, cannery, workshop, factory, or manufacturing establishment, situated in the United States, in which within thirty days prior to the removal of such product therefrom children under the age of fourteen years have been employed or permitted to work, or children between the ages of fourteen years and sixteen years have been employed or permitted to work more than eight hours in any day, or more than six days in any week, or after the hour of seven o'clock postmeridian, or before the hour of six o'clock antemeridian: *Provided*, That a prosecution and conviction of a defendant for the shipment or delivery for shipment of any article or commodity under the conditions herein prohibited shall be a bar to any further prosecution

. . . continued

against the same defendant for shipments or deliveries for shipment of any such article or commodity before the beginning of said prosecution.

Approved, September 1, 1916 ”

—from the Keating-Owen Child Labor Act of 1916

1 HISTORY **SUMMARIZING** What rules did the Keating-Owen Child Labor Act of 1916 put in place?

2 **IDENTIFYING CAUSE AND EFFECT** What might have contributed to the creation and enactment of the Keating-Owen Child Labor Act?

3 MULTIPLE PERSPECTIVES **IDENTIFYING POINT OF VIEW** Who do you think might have opposed the Keating-Owen Child Labor Act?

4 **INFERRING** How do you think this law changed the lives of children?

ESSENTIAL QUESTION

How do new ideas change the way people live?

A Trustbusting Law

DIRECTIONS: Use the document below to answer the questions.

EXPLORE THE CONTEXT: The Sherman Anti-Trust Act of 1890 was the first law to prohibit trusts. There were no other laws in place to limit trusts for business that crossed state lines. Trusts were considered unfair because they prevented competing businesses from arising. Without competition, industries in the hands of trusts could raise prices or lower quality without anyone to stop them. Congress found later that the act was not worded effectively, and businesses found many loopholes.

PRIMARY SOURCE: GOVERNMENT DOCUMENT

"An act to protect trade and commerce against unlawful restraints and monopolies.

Be it enacted by the Senate and House of Representatives of the United States of America in Congress assembled,

Sec. 1. Every contract, combination in the form of trust or other-wise, or conspiracy, in restraint of trade or commerce among the several States, or with foreign nations, is hereby declared to be illegal. ...

Sec. 2. Every person who shall monopolize, or attempt to monopolize, or combine or conspire with any other person or persons, to monopolize any part of the trade or commerce among the several States, or with foreign nations, shall be deemed guilty of a misdemeanor, ...

Sec. 3. Every contract, combination in form of trust or otherwise, or conspiracy, in restraint of trade or commerce in any Territory of the United States or of the District of Columbia, or in restraint of trade or commerce between any such Territory and another, or between any such Territory or Territories and any State or States or the District of Columbia, or with foreign nations, or between the District of Columbia and any State or States or foreign nations, is hereby declared illegal. ..."

— from the Sherman Anti-Trust Act, 1890

VOCABULARY

commerce: the exchange of goods and services
monopolies: when one company dominates an industry or industries, preventing competition
enacted: put into place
trust: when stockholders in several companies give all their stock to one set of trustees, preventing competition
deemed: considered
misdemeanor: a minor crime, less serious than a felony

1 **SUMMARIZING** What does the Sherman Anti-Trust Act prevent?

2 **DRAWING CONCLUSIONS** Why is the Sherman Anti-Trust Act important?

3 **ANALYZING THE SOURCE** The Supreme Court took issue with the Sherman Anti-Trust Act because it was too vague. What important words does Congress fail to define?

4 CIVICS How is the Sherman Anti-Trust Act different from state laws that prevent trusts?

5 **INFERRING** What ideas or principles may have inspired Congress to pass the Sherman Anti-Trust Act?

ESSENTIAL QUESTION

How do new ideas change the way people live?

1 Think About It

Review the supporting questions that you developed at the beginning of the chapter. Review the evidence that you gathered in Chapter 19.

Were you able to answer each supporting question? If there was not enough evidence to answer your supporting questions, what additional evidence do you think you need to include?

____

____

____

____

2 Organize Your Evidence

Use the graphic organizer below to list what you have learned about how new ideas change the way people live.

Source	Specific Evidence from Source to Cite	Effects of New Ideas
Illiteracy and Immigration		
The Other Half		
The Woolworth Building		
Carnegie's Hall		
Glazier and the Glamor of the City		
Emily Faithfull's Journey West		

3 Write About It

A position statement should show your opinion about a subject. Write a position statement in response to the Essential Question: ***How do new ideas change the way people live?***

4 Talk About It

In a small group, share the position you wrote in #3. Do you all have the same position? Talk about how your ideas are similar and different. How does the evidence you found in #2 connect to your position? Discuss this in your group.

5 Connect to the Essential Question

Using your work from steps #2 and #3, build a slideshow with captions in response to what you have learned about the Essential Question: ***How do new ideas change the way people live?*** Your goal is to show the different ways new ideas can change people, so be sure the pictures you choose illustrate this.

CITIZENSHIP
TAKING ACTION

The world is still changing, often because of progress in technology. The invention of the Internet, for example, dramatically changed the way people live their lives today.

Research It

Get together with a partner and research the mid-1990s when the Internet began to play a major role in American life. Create a chart with two columns. As you do your research, use the first column to write down things about daily life that are now different because of the Internet. In the second column, write down the thing that was made possible by the Internet. For example, people used to use a book called "The Yellow Pages" that had the phone numbers to businesses in their area. Today, people use the Internet to find the phone numbers of businesses.

Think About It

Now that you have researched some of the major changes that the Internet has brought to daily life in today's world, you might have a new perspective on how important the Internet is today. Not all communities in America have access to the Internet, usually due to poverty but also to failing infrastructure. Infrastructure is the wires, pipes, towers, and satellites that are all necessary for making the Internet function. Research (on the Internet) the percentage of homes in the United States that do not have Internet access. Find out if there are communities near you where many people are still not connected to the Internet.

Reach Out

With your partner, create a poster showing how many homes in the United States lack Internet access. A circle graph would be a good way to illustrate this. On your poster, include reasons why it's important for people to have Internet access today.